THE
SUPERFOOD
BIBLE

*150 superfood recipes to inspire
health & happiness*

This edition published by Parragon Books Ltd in 2016
LOVE FOOD is an imprint of Parragon Books Ltd

Parragon Books Ltd
Chartist House
15–17 Trim Street
Bath BA1 1HA, UK
www.parragon.com/lovefood

ISBN 978-1-4748-3806-1

Printed in China

Project managed by Annabel Hampshire
Additional text by Judith Wills
Cover photography by Max and Liz Haarala Hamilton
Designed by Karli Skelton

NOTES FOR THE READER

This book uses both metric and imperial measurements. Follow
the same units of measurement throughout; do not mix metric and
imperial. All spoon measurements are level: teaspoons are assumed
to be 5 ml, and tablespoons are assumed to be 15 ml. Unless
otherwise stated, milk is assumed to be full fat, eggs and individual
fruits and vegetables are medium, pepper is freshly ground black
pepper and salt is table salt. A pinch of salt is calculated as 1/16 of
a teaspoon. Unless otherwise stated, all root vegetables should be
peeled prior to using.

The times given are an approximate guide only. Preparation times
differ according to the techniques used by different people and the
cooking times may also vary from those given.

Please note that any ingredients stated as being optional are not
included in the nutritional values provided. The nutritional values
given are approximate and provided as a guideline only, they do not
account for individual cooks, scales and portion sizes. The nutritional
values provided are per serving or per item.

While the publisher of the book and the original author(s) of the
recipes and other text have made all reasonable efforts to ensure
that the information contained in this book is accurate and up to
date at the time of publication, anyone reading this book should note
the following important points: -

Medical and pharmaceutical knowledge is constantly changing and
the author(s) and the publisher cannot and do not guarantee the
accuracy or appropriateness of the contents of this book;
In any event, this book is not intended to be, and should not be
relied upon, as a substitute for appropriate, tailored professional
advice. Both the author(s) and the publisher strongly recommend
that a doctor or other healthcare professional is consulted before
embarking on major dietary changes;

For the reasons set out above, and to the fullest extent permitted
by law, the author(s) and publisher: (i) cannot and do not accept
any legal duty of care or responsibility in relation to the accuracy or
appropriateness of the contents of this book, even where expressed
as 'advice' or using other words to this effect; and (ii) disclaim any
liability, loss, damage or risk that may be claimed or incurred as a
consequence – directly or indirectly – of the use and/or application of
any of the contents of this book.

For best results, use a food thermometer when cooking meat. Check
the latest government guidelines for current advice.

CONTENTS

INTRODUCTION

We all want to live a long and healthy life – and one of the major keys to that is to eat well. Picking up bits of information here and there can be complicated and time-consuming but help is at hand. This is the only reference you need for choosing the foods and ingredients that will help you achieve your goal.

Eating well can help you in so many ways. A healthy diet can give you protection against all the major diseases including cardiovascular diseases, cancers, diabetes, arthritis and dementia, as well as offering protection against health problems including asthma, eczema, tiredness, insomnia, gum disease and very many more. It can also boost your general sense of wellbeing – helping you feel more alert and aiding your concentration and memory, for example, and can make you look better too, improving your skin, hair, eyes. Lastly, a healthy diet also gives you the best chance of maintaining a healthy bodyweight and avoiding weight gain and obesity throughout your life.

WHAT IS A HEALTHY DIET?

The classic definition of a healthy diet is one that provides you with all the major nutrients – carbohydrates, fats and protein – that your body needs to function well, in a good balance. It also provides the right number of calories to give you energy and maintain a suitable weight, as well as dietary fibre and fluids to keep your digestive system working well. And it also provides all the micronutrients – vitamins and minerals needed in tiny amounts but which are vital for health and wellbeing.

A healthy diet also means choosing mostly natural, unprocessed or minimally processed foods and drinks – a 'wholefood' diet. In recent years scientists have found that to be truly healthy our bodies also need a range of chemicals and compounds found in high quantities in this type of whole, natural food diet. From flavonoids to anthocyanins there are thousands of these that help keep us in optimum health. We also need a regular supply of different types of bacteria, not only for digestive health but for a host of other benefits, scientists are now discovering, and a natural diet is key to obtaining these bacteria.

WHAT IS A SUPERFOOD?

The foods that can give you the best amount or range of the major, macro and new chemicals and bacteria most likely to be in shortfall in the average diet are often called 'superfoods'. No one food on its own can give you everything you need from food for a perfect diet, so it is important to eat a range of foods to get everything you need for the healthiest possible diet for you. For example, one food may be a particularly good source of vitamin C, plant chemicals and antioxidants, while another may be especially rich in soluble fibre and vitamin B and known to promote beneficial bacteria. So superfoods work together to make a 'super' diet. In this book we've gathered together 150 of the foods that are probably most deserving of the label 'superfoods'.

OUR RECIPES

The ideal plan is to enjoy meals and recipes which include a variety of the superfoods and other staple healthy foods so that you easily get everything your body needs for good health. What you'll find within this book, as well as detailed descriptions of the superfoods and what they can do for you, are hundreds of tips for their use as well as 150 exciting recipes using each superfood – plus a wide range of other healthy foods – which together will give you a diet that can keep you healthy for life.

FRUIT

BLUEBERRIES

These berries are the richest of all fruits in antioxidant compounds, which
protect us from cancers and several other diseases.

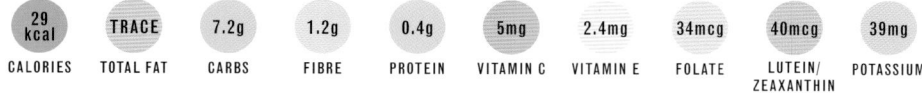

29 kcal	TRACE	7.2g	1.2g	0.4g	5mg	2.4mg	34mcg	40mcg	39mg
CALORIES	TOTAL FAT	CARBS	FIBRE	PROTEIN	VITAMIN C	VITAMIN E	FOLATE	LUTEIN/ ZEAXANTHIN	POTASSIUM

The wild blueberry has become one of the most popular berries.
They are the third highest plant food on the ORAC scale, so just a
handful of berries a day can offer protection from some diseases.
The compound pterostilbene, which is found in the fruit, could be as
effective as commercial drugs in lowering cholesterol, and may also help
prevent diabetes and some cancers. Blueberries are a good source of
anthocyanins, which can help prevent heart disease and memory loss.
They are high in vitamin C and fibre and also appear to help fight urinary
tract infections.

- Contain a cholesterol-lowering compound.
- Can help prevent coronary heart disease, diabetes and cancers.
- Help beat urinary tract infections.
- Appear to help protect against intestinal upsets, including food poisoning.
- Their carotene, in the form of lutein and zeaxanthin, helps keep eyes healthy.

DID YOU KNOW?

*Blueberries should be stored in a
non-metallic container – contact
with metal can discolour them.*

PRACTICAL TIPS

Blueberries are quite sweet so can be eaten raw, which helps to preserve
their vitamin C content. They can also be lightly cooked in a small amount
of water and eaten with the juices. Blueberries can boost the nutrient
content of muffins, cakes, crumbles, pies and fruit salads. The berries
freeze well and lose few of their nutrients.

AÇAI POWER BOWL

This is a great way to make quick, healthy dairy-free ice cream. You could even eat this for breakfast, it's so healthy! Açai berries are high in vitamin A, calcium, fibre and iron.

SERVES 4 • PREP TIME: 8 MINS, PLUS FREEZING & COOLING • COOK TIME: 8–10 MINS

PER SERVING:	279 kcal	4.5g	0.9g	58g	25.9g	10.1g	5.6g	TRACE
	CALORIES	FAT	SAT FAT	CARBS	SUGAR	FIBRE	PROTEIN	SALT

INGREDIENTS

2 bananas, sliced
300 g/10½ oz raspberries
100 g/3½ oz rolled oats
2 tbsp dried cranberries
1 tbsp sunflower seeds
3 tbsp maple syrup
100 ml/3½ fl oz non-dairy milk
1 tbsp açai powder
100 g/3½ oz blueberries

1. Place the banana slices and 200 g/7 oz of the raspberries in a single layer on a tray and freeze for at least 2 hours.

2. Preheat a grill to medium–hot. Mix the oats, cranberries, sunflower seeds and maple syrup together and spread over a baking sheet.

3. Cook under the preheated grill for 8–10 minutes, turning frequently, until golden (watch them carefully as they can suddenly burn). Leave to cool.

4. Meanwhile, place half the frozen banana in a food processor with half the frozen raspberries and half the milk. Process until broken down. With the machine running slowly add the açai powder and the remaining banana, raspberries and milk, adding enough milk to produce an ice cream consistency.

5. Divide the ice cream between four bowls, top with the blueberries and sprinkle with the maple-toasted oats.

HINT

Almond, coconut, soya, oat and rice milk are all fantastic non-dairy milks that would work well here.

AVOCADOS

The avocado is a rich source of monounsaturated fats for
heart health and is packed with important nutrients.

MAJOR NUTRIENTS PER AVERAGE-SIZED AVOCADO

240 kcal	3g	12.8g	5g	22g	9mg	3mg	728 mg
CALORIES	TOTAL FAT	CARBS	FIBRE	PROTEIN	VITAMIN C	VITAMIN E	POTASSIUM

Avocados are very high in fat, but this fat is mostly monounsaturated.
The oleic acid contained in monounsaturates can lower the risk of breast
cancer, and monounsaturates can help to reduce 'bad' blood cholesterol
levels. Avocados also have a large range of nutrients, including vitamins
C, E and B6, folate, iron, magnesium and potassium, and antioxidant plant
chemicals beta-sitosterol, which can also help lower blood cholesterol, and
glutathione, which protects against cancer.

- High vitamin E content boosts the immune system, keeps skin healthy
  and helps prevent heart disease.
- Lutein content helps protect against eye cataracts and
  macular degeneration.
- High monounsaturated fat content helps lower cholesterol.
- Good source of magnesium for a healthy heart.

DID YOU KNOW?

*Extra virgin avocado oil is now
widely available – use it for
roasting or drizzling over salads,
or serve as a dip with crusty bread.*

PRACTICAL TIPS

Choose avocados that have unblemished skins without soft spots, which
suggest bruising. They're ready to eat if the flesh yields slightly when
pressed with the thumb. To hasten ripening, put them in a paper bag
with a banana. To prepare, cut lengthways down to the stone and twist to
separate the two halves. Pierce the stone with the tip of a knife, then pull it
out. Use lemon juice, vinegar or vinaigrette to prevent discoloration.

AVOCADO CHOCOLATE MOUSSE

Avocados add creaminess and richness to this delicious mousse, while chocolate is decadent and flavoursome – wonderful!

SERVES 4 • PREP TIME: 10 MINS • COOK TIME: NONE

PER SERVING:	151 kcal	11.8g	2.1g	15.0g	2.7g	7.5g	3.0g	0.4g
	CALORIES	FAT	SAT FAT	CARBS	SUGAR	FIBRE	PROTEIN	SALT

INGREDIENTS

2 ripe avocados, peeled, stoned and roughly chopped
35 g/1¼ oz cocoa powder
2 tbsp rice malt syrup
1 tsp vanilla extract
small pinch of sea salt
2 tbsp unsweetened almond milk

1. Put all the ingredients in a blender or food processor and process until combined. Scrape down the sides and process for a further minute, or until the mousse is airy. If it is still too thick, add a splash more almond milk and process again briefly.

2. Spoon the mousse into small teacups or serving bowls and serve immediately, or cover and chill in the refrigerator for up to 4 hours.

STRAWBERRIES

Extremely rich in vitamin C, strawberries boost the immune system
and contain chemicals that offer cancer protection.

MAJOR NUTRIENTS PER 100 G/3½ OZ STRAWBERRIES

32 kcal	0.3g	7.7g	2g	0.7g	59mg	24 mcg	26 mcg	153mg
CALORIES	TOTAL FAT	CARBS	FIBRE	PROTEIN	VITAMIN C	FOLATE	LUTEIN/ZEAXANTHIN	POTASSIUM

Strawberries rank very high in antioxidant activity. They are extremely rich in vitamin C (an average portion contains the entire recommended daily amount for an adult) and this helps to boost the immune system and aid wound healing, prevent arterial damage, promote iron absorption, and strengthen blood vessel walls. They also contain other antioxidant phenolic plant chemicals such as anthocyanins and ellagic acid, which can block cancer cells and help prevent some cancers. Lastly, they contain good amounts of fibre, folate and potassium.

- Excellent source of vitamin C.
- Contain ellagic acid, a compound with anti-cancer and antioxidant properties.
- Contain anthocyanins, which can help lower 'bad' blood cholesterol.
- Useful source of fibre and soluble fibre, potassium and folate, and zeaxanthin for healthy eyes.

DID YOU KNOW?
Once washed, strawberries will spoil quickly – don't wash them until immediately before serving.

PRACTICAL TIPS

Choose strawberries that look plump and glossy; dull ones are usually past their best. Smaller strawberries tend to have higher levels of ellagic acid, concentrated in the outer layer, and have more flavour. Store in a container with air holes, in a refrigerator, for up to three days, but bring them to room temperature before using.

LAYERED AVOCADO & STRAWBERRY SOUP

Chilled soups are wonderfully refreshing. This creamy avocado and watercress version is lightly cooked and puréed, then layered with raw puréed strawberries.

SERVES 4 • PREP TIME: 20 MINS, PLUS COOLING & CHILLING • COOK TIME: 10 MINS

PER SERVING:	196 kcal	14.4g	2.3g	18.8g	7.2g	8.1g	3.2g	1.1g
	CALORIES	FAT	SAT FAT	CARBS	SUGAR	FIBRE	PROTEIN	SALT

INGREDIENTS

1 tsp avocado oil
4 spring onions, sliced
30 g/1 oz watercress
250 ml/8½ fl oz vegetable stock
1 avocado, halved, stoned and flesh scooped out
225 g/8 oz strawberries, hulled and halved
juice of ½ lemon

1. Heat the oil in a saucepan, add the spring onions and cook over a medium heat, stirring, for 2 minutes until soft. Add the watercress and stock and bring to the boil, stirring. Cover and simmer for 3–4 minutes until the watercress has just wilted. Leave to cool, then chill well.

2. Purée the chilled watercress mixture with the avocado in a blender or food processor until smooth, then pour into a jug. Rinse the blender goblet, then purée the strawberries and mix with the lemon juice. Press through a sieve into a jug.

3. Spoon half the avocado soup into the base of four small glass tumblers, spoon over half the strawberry mixture to give two different coloured layers, then repeat.

4. Serve immediately or chill for up to 45 minutes.

VARIATION

If you can't get watercress and want that peppery flavour that complements the strawberries, replace the watercress with rocket.

WATERMELON

Watermelon has beneficial effects on the body's fluid balance, helping prevent water retention and promoting well-hydrated skin.

MAJOR NUTRIENTS PER 100 G/3½ OZ WATERMELON

30 kcal	0.15g	7.55g	0.4g	0.61g	8.1mg	303 mcg	4532 mcg	112mg
CALORIES	TOTAL FAT	CARBS	FIBRE	PROTEIN	VITAMIN C	BETA-CAROTENE	LYCOPENE	POTASSIUM

Watermelon has long been used in tropical countries to quench thirst, with the supporting effect of helping the body to shed excess fluid, which is often held in the face, hands, ankles and feet and causes bloating and puffiness. As the watermelon is 92 per cent water, its 6 per cent of sugar stays well diluted, and does not negatively affect blood sugar levels, but instead helps to pull water into the cells. This action keeps skin and organs well hydrated, which is crucial to retaining youthfulness. The bright red colour of the flesh is due to the watermelon's high levels of the carotenoid antioxidants beta-carotene and lycopene, which help protect skin from the damage caused by the sun's UV rays.

- Diuretic effect helps clean out the kidneys, thus supporting revitalizing detoxification.
- The amino acid arginine takes sugars out of the bloodstream for use as energy, helping to regulate weight.
- Excellent source of vitamin C for healing all body tissues and keeping skin plump and free of age spots.

DID YOU KNOW?

Cubic watermelons, grown in glass boxes, have been developed in Japan because they are easier to stack and store than the natural, spherical fruit.

PRACTICAL TIPS

Choose watermelons with skin that looks smooth and dull. They should sound hollow when tapped, then reveal strong red-coloured flesh inside with no white streaks, and dark brown or black seeds. Eat slices of watermelon to cool down on a hot day, or make juice by scooping out the seeds and blending the flesh.

WATERMELON SUNDAES

Colourful and tempting, this refreshing breakfast is a perfect
start to the day when you feel like something light.

SERVES 4 • PREP TIME: 10 MINS • COOK TIME: NONE

PER SERVING:

172 kcal	8.3g	1.3g	14.2g	10g	2.1g	12g	0.2g
CALORIES	FAT	SAT FAT	CARBS	SUGAR	FIBRE	PROTEIN	SALT

INGREDIENTS
200 g/7 oz low-fat bio yogurt
200 g/7 oz low-fat soft cheese
1 tsp stevia granules
30 g/1 oz pistachio nuts, roughly chopped
30 g/1 oz toasted flaked almonds
200 g/7 oz watermelon chunks
30 g/1 oz pomegranate seeds

1. In a mixing bowl, thoroughly combine the yogurt, soft cheese and stevia granules.

2. Stir in half the pistachio nuts and flaked almonds.

3. Divide the watermelon chunks between four serving glasses and spoon a quarter of the yogurt mixture over the top of each.

4. Sprinkle with the remaining nuts, followed by the pomegranate seeds, and serve the sundaes immediately.

APPLES

In recent years, scientific evidence has shown that the old proverb,
'An apple a day keeps the doctor away', may be correct.

MAJOR NUTRIENTS PER AVERAGE-SIZED APPLE

60 kcal	TRACE	16g	2.8g	TRACE	5mg	123mg
CALORIES	TOTAL FAT	CARBS	FIBRE	PROTEIN	VITAMIN C	POTASSIUM

Although apples don't, with the exception of potassium, contain any particular high levels of vitamins or minerals, they do contain high levels of various plant chemicals, including the flavonoid quercetin, which has anti-cancer and anti-inflammatory action. They are also a valuable source of pectin, a soluble fibre that can help lower 'bad' cholesterol and help prevent colon cancer. Research has found that adults who eat apples have smaller waistlines, less abdominal fat and lower blood pressure than those who don't – apples may also prevent asthma in children. Apples are also virtually fat free.

- Rich in flavonoids for healthy heart and lungs.
- Ideal snack for dieters as they are low in calories, low on the glycaemic index and can keep hunger at bay.
- Fibre content is rich in pectin, which can improve the blood lipids profile and reduce 'bad' cholesterol.
- A good source of potassium, which can prevent fluid retention.

DID YOU KNOW?

Research has found a link between quercetin – found in apples – and protection against Alzheimer's disease.

PRACTICAL TIPS

Don't keep your apples in a light, hot room as they will rapidly lose their vitamin C content. Instead, keep them in a polythene bag with air holes in the refrigerator, or in a cool, dark cupboard. Try to eat the skin as it contains up to five times as many plant chemicals as the flesh. When preparing apples, put the cut slices into a bowl of water with 1–2 tablespoons of lemon juice to prevent discoloration.

CHEDDAR & APPLE-STUFFED CHICKEN BREASTS

Apples are seen as a natural companion for pork, but they're also delicious with chicken and any type of hard cheese. This recipe makes the most of this pairing.

SERVES 4 • PREP TIME: 15 MINS • COOK TIME: 25–30 MINS

PER SERVING:

 329 kcal — CALORIES
 17g — FAT
6.8g — SAT FAT
 8g — CARBS
 5.2g — SUGAR
1.5g — FIBRE
 35g — PROTEIN
2.1g — SALT

INGREDIENTS

1 tbsp sunflower oil, for oiling
4 thick boneless, skinless chicken breasts, about 200 g/7 oz each
1 tbsp sunflower oil
1 small onion, finely chopped
1 celery stick, finely chopped
¼ tsp dried sage
1 eating apple, cored and diced
85 g/3 oz mature Cheddar cheese, coarsely grated
2 tbsp finely chopped parsley
6 slices Parma ham
salt and pepper (optional)
300 g/10½ oz cooked green vegetables, to serve

1. Preheat the oven to 190°C/375°F/Gas Mark 5 and lightly oil a small roasting tin.

2. Put a chicken breast on a chopping board, rounded side up. Use a small, sharp knife to cut a pocket along the length of the breast, cutting as deep as you can without cutting through to the other side or the ends. Repeat with the remaining chicken breasts, then set aside.

3. To make the stuffing, heat the oil in a frying pan, add the onion, celery and sage and fry, stirring, for 3–5 minutes until soft. Stir in the apple and fry for a further 2 minutes until it is soft but not falling apart. Stir in the cheese and most of the parsley and season with salt and pepper, if using.

4. Divide the stuffing between the breast pockets. Wrap 1½ slices of ham around each breast, then rub the tops with a little oil.

5. Transfer to the prepared tin and roast in the preheated oven for 20–25 minutes, or until the chicken is cooked through and the juices run clear when a skewer is inserted into the thickest part of the meat. Remove from the oven, cover with foil and leave to stand for 3–5 minutes before serving with green vegetables. Garnish with the remaining parsley.

CRANBERRIES

These small red fruits have a variety of health benefits
and help to boost the work of the kidneys.

PER 100 G/3½ OZ RAW CRANBERRIES

46 kcal	TRACE	12.2g	4.6g	0.4g	13mg	1.2mg	91 mcg
CALORIES	TOTAL FAT	CARBS	FIBRE	PROTEIN	VITAMIN C	VITAMIN E	LUTEIN/ ZEAXANTHIN

Fresh cranberries are too sour and acidic to eat raw, but they have been used for many years as a sauce to serve with turkey. However, since their health-giving properties were discovered, they are now widely found sweetened and dried, as a juice drink and in baked desserts and preserves. Their best-known benefit is that they can help to prevent, or alleviate, urinary tract infections. This is partly because they contain quinic acid, which increases the acidity of the urine, and partly because of the tannins they contain, which are antibacterial. The same compounds may also help protect against stomach ulcers and heart disease.

- High soluble fibre content may help reduce 'bad' cholesterol.
- May protect against heart disease.
- Help prevent and alleviate urinary tract infections.
- Help prevent digestive disorders and stomach ulcers.

DID YOU KNOW?

People taking warfarin should avoid eating cranberries or drinking cranberry juice – the berry can raise blood levels of this anticoagulant drug to a very high, possibly fatal, degree.

PRACTICAL TIPS

Fresh cranberries should have a smooth, bright skin. It is said that one way to test their freshness is to drop one – if it bounces, it is fresh! Cranberries are rich in pectin, and make a valuable addition to jams made with low-pectin fruit, such as strawberries, to help them set. The sugar content of most cranberry products, such as drinks and dried fruit, means that they are relatively high in calories and so may not be suitable for people on a low-calorie or low-sugar diet.

CRIMSON VITALITY SMOOTHIE

This drink combines cranberries, beetroot, apples and ginger for a healthy burst of goodness that can be enjoyed any time of day.

SERVES 1 • PREP TIME: 10–15 MINS • COOK TIME: NONE

PER SERVING:

287 kcal	0.9g	0.1g	74.1g	49.5g	3.9g	3g	0.2g
CALORIES	FAT	SAT FAT	CARBS	SUGAR	FIBRE	PROTEIN	SALT

INGREDIENTS

1 beetroot, halved
115 g/4 oz cranberries
1-cm/½-inch piece fresh ginger, peeled
2 apples, quartered
small handful of crushed ice (optional)
chilled water, to taste

1. Feed the beetroot, then the cranberries and ginger, then the apples through a juicer.

2. Half-fill a glass with crushed ice, if using, pour in the juice, top up with water to taste and serve immediately.

HINT

If your beetroot has fresh, vibrant leaves rather than tired, limp-looking ones, add them to the juicer too.

BANANAS

The banana is the ultimate energy snack because it provides quick,
quality fuel. It is perfect for replenishing flagging cells.

MAJOR NUTRIENTS PER AVERAGE-SIZED BANANA

105 kcal	0.39g	26.95g	3.1g	1.29g	0.43 mg	10.3 mg	422 mg
CALORIES	TOTAL FAT	CARBS	FIBRE	PROTEIN	VITAMIN B6	VITAMIN C	POTASSIUM

Bananas are undeniably high in sugar, but they shouldn't be underestimated for their health-giving anti-ageing properties. A ripe banana contains a high amount of fibre, including the prebiotic inulin, which feeds our beneficial (probiotic) gut bacteria, the first line of defence for the immune system. Keeping your gut bacteria healthy can help prevent inflammatory conditions like eczema, asthma and arthritis, and support the digestion and absorption of nutrients needed to retain optimal health and keep you looking and feeling young.

- Contain high levels of potassium, vitamin C and vitamin B6, which are all important for heart health. Athletes draw on this rich mix to support performance, recovery and muscle response. Potassium and vitamin C help transport oxygen around the body to renew and revitalize the skin.
- Help kidney function and eliminate fluid retention, reducing puffiness for a more youthful appearance.

DID YOU KNOW?

The name banana comes from the Arabic banan or 'finger'; they grow in clusters of up to 20 fruit called 'hands'.

PRACTICAL TIPS

The fruit of choice for many people with a sweet tooth, bananas are best eaten when the skin is a solid yellow colour, with no bruises. Avoid overripe bananas as, by this stage, the sugars will have broken down and the fruit will be too sweet. Bananas may not be suitable for people with phlegm and nasal congestion as they can make these conditions worse.

HEALTHY FRENCH TOAST WITH BANANAS & PECANS

There's no better way to start the day than with this very tempting and sustaining banana-and-nut-topped French toast.

SERVES 4 • PREP TIME: 20 MINS • COOK TIME: 12–17 MINS

PER SERVING: **405 kcal** CALORIES **19.4g** FAT **2.7g** SAT FAT **53.4g** CARBS **17g** SUGAR **7.6g** FIBRE **9.7g** PROTEIN **0.5g** SALT

INGREDIENTS

60 g/2¼ oz pecan nuts, roughly chopped
2 eggs
4 ripe bananas, chopped
½ tsp vanilla extract
½ tsp ground cinnamon
4 thick slices wholemeal bread
1 tbsp olive oil
½ tsp ground cinnamon, for sprinkling

1. Place the pecan nuts in a small, dry frying pan and toast over a medium heat for 3–4 minutes, tossing regularly until just toasted. Set aside.

2. Put the eggs, 2 bananas, vanilla extract and cinnamon into a blender and whizz for 1–2 minutes, or until the consistency is smooth and thick.

3. Pour the mixture into a medium, shallow dish. Place two slices of bread into the mixture and, working quickly, gently press the bread into the liquid, allowing it to soak up the mixture. Turn the slices over and repeat.

4. Meanwhile, heat half the oil in a large, non-stick frying pan over a medium–high heat. Using a spatula, remove the soaked bread from the banana mixture and place it in the pan. Cook in batches, for 2–3 minutes on each side, then remove from the pan, set aside and keep warm. Repeat for the remaining slices, adding the remaining oil if needed.

5. Top with the pecan nuts and remaining bananas, sprinkle with cinnamon and serve immediately.

LEMONS

Indispensable in many recipes, lemons are rich in vitamin C
and can help protect us from breast and other cancers.

MAJOR NUTRIENTS PER AVERAGE-SIZED LEMON

17 kcal	TRACE	5.4g	1.6g	0.6g	31mg	80mg
CALORIES	TOTAL FAT	CARBS	FIBRE	PROTEIN	VITAMIN C	POTASSIUM

The fresh, acidic flavour of lemon juice enhances both sweet and savoury foods and dishes, while the peel can be used to add flavour. The acid and antioxidants in lemon juice can help prevent foods from discolouring once peeled or cut. All parts of the lemon contain valuable nutrients and antioxidants. They are a particularly good source of vitamin C. The plant compound antioxidants include limonene, an oil that may help to prevent breast and other cancers and lower 'bad' blood cholesterol, and rutin, which has been found to strengthen veins. Lemons stimulate the taste buds and may be useful for people with a poor appetite.

- Rich in vitamin C.
- Contain disinfecting and insecticide properties.
- Rutin content may help to strengthen veins and prevent fluid retention, especially in the legs.
- Help increase appetite.

DID YOU KNOW?

An average lemon contains about 3 tablespoons of juice. The tenderizing acid in lemons makes a useful addition to marinades for meat.

PRACTICAL TIPS

Either wash thoroughly or buy unwaxed or organic lemons if you want to use the peel. You can get more juice from a lemon if you warm it for a few seconds, in the microwave or in hot water, before squeezing. The heavier the lemon, the more juice it should contain. Lemon juice, thanks to its pectin, helps jams and jellies to set. It can be used instead of vinegar in salad dressings or added to mayonnaise.

LEMON CHEESECAKE WITH ALMOND BASE

A crunchy-based, zesty and creamy cheesecake that's
perfect for when friends come over for dinner.

SERVES 8 • PREP TIME: 20 MINS, PLUS CHILLING • COOK TIME: 1 HOUR 15 MINS

PER SERVING:

402 kcal	35.6g	16.2g	11g	3.7g	2.4g	10.6g	0.5g
CALORIES	FAT	SAT FAT	CARBS	SUGAR	FIBRE	PROTEIN	SALT

INGREDIENTS

10 g/¼ oz butter, for greasing
20 g/¾ oz butter
100 g/3½ oz ground almonds
50 g/1¾ oz almonds, finely chopped
2 tbsp sugar-free smooth almond butter
2 tbsp quinoa flour
2 tbsp stevia

TOPPING

250 g/9 oz mascarpone cheese
300 g/10½ oz full-fat cream cheese
2 large eggs
finely grated zest and juice of 1 large
unwaxed lemon
1 tbsp quinoa flour
4 tbsp stevia

1. Preheat the oven to 180°C/350°F/Gas Mark 4. Lightly butter a 20-cm/8-inch round non-stick springform cake tin and line the base with baking paper.

2. To make the base, melt the butter in a small saucepan over a medium–low heat. Pour it into a large bowl and add the ground almonds, chopped almonds, almond butter, quinoa flour and stevia, then mix well. Spoon the mixture into the prepared tin and, using the back of a fork, press down into an even layer. Bake in the preheated oven for 25 minutes, then remove from the oven and reduce the oven temperature to 120°C/250°F/Gas Mark ½.

3. To make the topping, put the mascarpone cheese and cream cheese into a large bowl and beat until loose. Beat for a further 30 seconds, then add the eggs, one at a time, beating between each addition. Add the lemon zest and juice, quinoa flour and stevia, then whisk again until well mixed.

4. Pour the topping over the base. Bake for 50 minutes, or until the sides are set and the middle still has a slight wobble. Leave to cool, then cover and chill in the refrigerator for 1–2 hours.

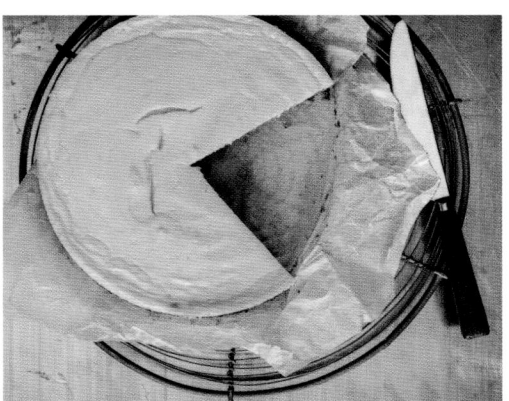

KIWI FRUIT

The kiwi fruit has an unusual amount of healthy omega-3 oils for a fruit. This, combined with its high vitamin C content, helps maintain youthful heart function.

MAJOR NUTRIENTS PER AVERAGE-SIZED KIWI FRUIT

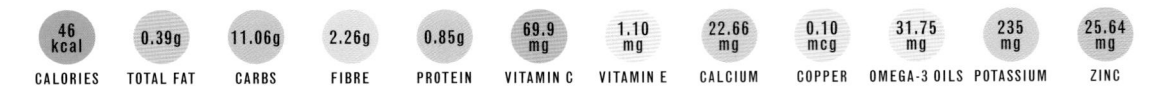

46 kcal	0.39g	11.06g	2.26g	0.85g	69.9 mg	1.10 mg	22.66 mg	0.10 mcg	31.75 mg	235 mg	25.64 mg
CALORIES	TOTAL FAT	CARBS	FIBRE	PROTEIN	VITAMIN C	VITAMIN E	CALCIUM	COPPER	OMEGA-3 OILS	POTASSIUM	ZINC

Eating the edible seeds of fruits is extremely beneficial, and the seeds of the kiwi fruit are particularly easy to swallow. As well as fibre and zinc, seeds contain all the nutrients and enzymes needed for a plant to grow, and taking them into our bodies means we are able to grow and rejuvenate too. Kiwi fruit seeds contain on average 62 per cent alpha-linoleic acid, the omega-3 oil that helps protect the heart and decrease inflammation, inside and outside the body, so preventing the diseases associated with ageing. Kiwi fruit is also a good source of copper, needed for collagen production, which promotes healthy skin, nails and muscles.

- Comparable to a banana in terms of high potassium content, keeping kidneys healthy so they can remove ageing toxins.
- Contains more vitamin C than oranges, as well as vitamin E and rehydrating omega-3 oils for a skin-nourishing combination.
- Vitamin C works with copper to produce collagen, to keep skin renewed and firm.

DID YOU KNOW?

Studies have shown that kiwi fruit may relieve symptoms of respiratory conditions such as asthma and coughs. Healthy breathing is crucial for rejuvenation and staying youthful throughout life.

PRACTICAL TIPS

Kiwi fruit can be eaten whole like an apple: eating the skin means you don't miss out on the vitamin C that lies just beneath the skin, and it vastly increases the fruit's insoluble fibre and antioxidant content. To test if a kiwi fruit is ripe, press it. You should be able to depress the skin slightly. Dried kiwi fruit slices make healthy snacks, and can be bought in health food shops and supermarkets.

SKIN-SOOTHER SMOOTHIE

Packed with healing vitamin C from the fruit, skin-protecting vitamin E
from the peanut butter and essential fatty acids (EFAs) from the linseeds,
this spectacular stripy drink might just be your skin's new best friend.

SERVES 1 • PREP TIME: 10 MINS • COOK TIME: NONE

PER SERVING:

466 kcal	13.4g	2.1g	87.5g	51.1g	15.7g	10.1g	TRACE
CALORIES	FAT	SAT FAT	CARBS	SUGAR	FIBRE	PROTEIN	SALT

INGREDIENTS
BANANA LAYER

1 banana, peeled and roughly chopped
1 tbsp smooth peanut butter
1 tbsp soya yogurt

BLUEBERRY LAYER

150 g/5½ oz blueberries
juice of ½ lemon

KIWI LAYER

3 kiwi fruit, peeled and roughly chopped
1 tbsp milled linseeds

1. Put all the ingredients for the banana layer in a blender and blend until smooth. Transfer to a jug and rinse the blender goblet.

2. To make the blueberry layer, put the blueberries and lemon juice into the blender and blend until smooth. Transfer to a separate jug and rinse the blender goblet.

3. To make the kiwi layer, place the kiwi in the blender with the linseeds and blend until smooth. Layer the three smoothie mixtures into a large glass and serve immediately.

FIGS

Fresh and dried figs are rich in fibre and high in iron,
boosting energy and promoting healthy blood.

MAJOR NUTRIENTS PER FRESH FIG

47 kcal	TRACE	12.3g	1.9g	0.5g	1.3 mg	54 mcg	22 mg	11 mg	148 mg
CALORIES	TOTAL FAT	CARBS	FIBRE	PROTEIN	VITAMIN C	BETA-CAROTENE	CALCIUM	MAGNESIUM	POTASSIUM

Figs are usually available dried, as fresh figs are easily damaged and have a very short shelf life. This delicious fruit contains good amounts of fibre, most of it soluble, which helps protect against heart disease. Figs are also a good source of several minerals and vitamin B6, with small amounts of a range of B vitamins, folate and several other vitamins and minerals. Dried figs are a concentrated source of potassium and are rich in calcium, magnesium and iron. They are, however, also high in calories, so are best eaten in moderation.

- Contain sterols, which help to lower blood cholesterol.
- Good source of natural energy and sugars.
- Good source of potassium to help prevent fluid retention.
- Dried fruit is an excellent source of iron, for healthy blood, and of calcium, for bone density.

DID YOU KNOW?

The leaves of the fig tree are edible. Fig-leaf liquid extract has anti-diabetic properties, reducing the amount of insulin needed by some people with diabetes.

PRACTICAL TIPS

Fresh figs deteriorate quickly and so should be eaten the day they are bought or picked. They are best eaten as they are but are also tasty with ham, served as a starter or as part of a dessert. Some varieties of fig have edible skin while others need to be peeled.

LAMB'S LETTUCE & CUCUMBER SALAD WITH FIGS

This unusual salad combination gets much of its flavour from the zesty dressing. The walnut oil is the perfect complement to the sweetness of the figs.

SERVES 4 • PREP TIME: 5 MINS • COOK TIME: NONE

PER SERVING:	231 kcal	20.6g	2.2g	13.7g	9.8g	2.2g	1.3g	TRACE
	CALORIES	FAT	SAT FAT	CARBS	SUGAR	FIBRE	PROTEIN	SALT

INGREDIENTS

100 g/3½ oz lamb's lettuce
½ cucumber, diced
4 ripe figs

DRESSING

1 small shallot, finely chopped
4 tbsp walnut oil
2 tbsp extra virgin olive oil
2 tbsp cider vinegar
½ tsp clear honey
salt and pepper (optional)

1. Put all the dressing ingredients into a screw-top jar, with salt and pepper, if using, and shake well to mix.

2. Put the lettuce and cucumber into a bowl and pour over half the dressing. Toss well to coat evenly, then divide between four serving plates.

3. Cut the figs into quarters and arrange 4 quarters on top of each portion. Drizzle over the remaining dressing and serve the salads immediately.

RASPBERRIES

Packed with vitamin C and antioxidants to protect the heart,
raspberries are one of the most nutritious fruits.

MAJOR NUTRIENTS PER 100 G/3½ OZ RASPBERRIES

| 52 kcal CALORIES | 0.6g TOTAL FAT | 12g CARBS | 6.5g FIBRE | 1.2g PROTEIN | 26 mg VITAMIN C | 0.6 mg VITAMIN B3 | 0.8 mg VITAMIN E | 25 mg CALCIUM | 21 mcg FOLATE | 0.7 mg IRON | 151 mg POTASSIUM | 0.4 mg ZINC |

Raspberries are the seventh-highest fruit on the ORAC scale and are therefore an extremely desirable fruit. They are best eaten raw, because cooking or processing destroys some of these antioxidants, especially anthocyanins. Anthocyanins are red and purple pigments that have been shown to help prevent both heart disease and cancers, and may also help prevent varicose veins. Raspberries also contain high levels of ellagic acid, a compound with anti-cancer properties. In addition, they are high in vitamin C and fibre, and contain good amounts of iron, which the body absorbs well because of the high levels of vitamin C.

- High antioxidant activity.
- May help to prevent varicose veins.
- One portion contains approximately half a day's recommended intake of vitamin C.
- High in fibre to help control high 'bad' cholesterol.

DID YOU KNOW?

Raspberries consist of numerous smaller fruits called drupelets, which are clustered around a central stalk core. Each drupelet contains a seed, which is why raspberries are so high in fibre.

PRACTICAL TIPS

The berries do not keep for long, so should be picked only when ripe. They do freeze very well, though, if packed in containers rather than polythene bags. Never wash raspberries before storing unless absolutely necessary – their structure is easily destroyed. The healthy soluble fibre in raspberries is pectin, which means they make excellent, easy-to-set jam.

RASPBERRY & MASCARPONE ICE CREAM

Fresh raspberries and extra creaminess from the mascarpone mean you will be fighting people off the last scoops of this classic ice cream.

SERVES 8 • PREP TIME: 20 MINS • COOK TIME: 10 MINS, PLUS FREEZING

PER SERVING:

285 kcal	28.6g	16.5g	3.9g	1.2g	0.8g	4.2g	0.1g
CALORIES	FAT	SAT FAT	CARBS	SUGAR	FIBRE	PROTEIN	SALT

INGREDIENTS

1 large egg
4 large egg yolks
2½ tbsp stevia
100 g/3½ oz mascarpone cheese
1 tsp vanilla extract
400 ml/14 fl oz double cream
80 g/2¾ oz raspberries, halved

1. Crack the egg into a large heatproof bowl, add the yolks and stevia, and whisk with a hand-held electric mixer for 30 seconds. Place over a saucepan of gently simmering water, making sure the bowl doesn't touch the water, and whisk until the mixture is pale and airy. This cooks the eggs and makes a sweet custard. Be careful not to overcook them.

2. Pour cold water into a basin and place the custard bowl in it, with the base of the bowl in the water, to cool. Continue to whisk the eggs for 2 minutes, then lift the bowl out of the water and set aside.

3. Put the mascarpone cheese and vanilla extract into a separate large bowl and whisk briefly until loose. Pour in the cream and whisk again until it holds soft peaks.

4. Using a metal spoon, gently fold the custard into the cream mixture, preserving as much air as possible. Carefully stir in the raspberries.

5. Pour the mixture into a freezerproof container, cover with a lid and freeze for 4 hours, or until set. Take the ice cream out of the freezer 10 minutes before you serve it to allow it to soften. Scoop it into glasses or small bowls and serve.

MANGOES

The mango is a nutritional superstar among fruits, being very rich in antioxidants and vitamins C and E.

MAJOR NUTRIENTS PER AVERAGE-SIZED MANGO

114 kcal	0.3g	28g	5.2g	1.4g	74mg
CALORIES	TOTAL FAT	CARBS	FIBRE	PROTEIN	VITAMIN C

Mangoes are grown throughout the tropics. Their orange flesh contains more antioxidant beta-carotene, which can protect against some cancers and heart disease, than most other fruits. They are high in vitamin C – one fruit can contain more than a whole day's RDA – and in fibre. Unlike most other fruits, they also contain a significant amount of the antioxidant vitamin E, which can boost the body's immune system and maintain healthy skin. Their medium–low glycaemic index also means they are a good fruit for dieters as they help regulate blood sugar levels.

- High levels of pectin – a soluble fibre that helps reduce 'bad' blood cholesterol.
- Rich in potassium (320 mg per fruit) for regulating blood pressure.
- Valuable source of vitamin C.

DID YOU KNOW?

Mangoes contain a special enzyme that can be a soothing digestive aid – it can also help tenderize meat.

PRACTICAL TIPS

If you buy unripe mangoes, put them in a paper bag in a dark place and they will ripen within a few days. Eat ripe mangoes raw for maximum vitamin C content, or eat them with a little fat, such as full-fat yogurt or in a salad dressed with olive oil, to better absorb their carotenes.

LAYERED POWERBOWL SMOOTHIE

This colourful smoothie, rich in antioxidants from the fruits, with additional protein
from the chlorella powder, almonds and sesame seeds, is a great breakfast.

SERVES 2 • PREP TIME: 10–15 MINS • COOK TIME: NONE

PER SERVING:

303 kcal	6.4g	1.1g	61.3g	44.2g	7.1g	6.4g	TRACE
CALORIES	FAT	SAT FAT	CARBS	SUGAR	FIBRE	PROTEIN	SALT

INGREDIENTS

1 large mango, stoned, peeled and chopped
2 kiwi fruit, peeled and chopped
½ tsp chlorella powder
*450 g/1 lb watermelon, peeled (leave the seeds in
for additional vitamin E)*
1 tbsp ground almonds
1 tsp sesame seeds
2 tbsp granola
¼ tsp ground cinnamon

1. Place the mango in a small blender and process until smooth. Divide between two glass bowls. Rinse the blender.

2. Place the kiwi and chlorella powder in the blender and process until smooth. Spoon it over the mango. Rinse the blender goblet.

3. Place the watermelon in the blender and process until smooth. Add the ground almonds and sesame seeds and process briefly to combine. Spoon it over the kiwi mixture.

4. Sprinkle with the granola and cinnamon and serve.

MELONS

The juicy flesh of the melon is rich in vitamin C and is a great source of potassium, which helps prevent fluid retention.

MAJOR NUTRIENTS PER AVERAGE-SIZED CANTALOUPE MELON

28 kcal	TRACE	6.3g	1.5g	1g	39mg	2647 mcg	315 mg
CALORIES	TOTAL FAT	CARBS	FIBRE	PROTEIN	VITAMIN C	BETA-CAROTENE	POTASSIUM

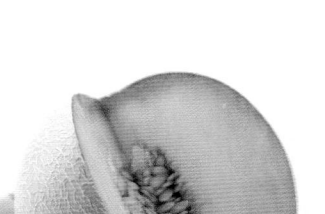

A melon contains over 92 per cent water, which can help keep the kidneys working well. The orange varieties are a great source of beta-carotene and are also high in vitamin C, although amounts vary according to variety. All melons are rich in vitamin B6 and potassium and several varieties are high in the bioflavonoid group of plant chemicals, which have anti-cancer, anti-heart disease and anti-ageing properties. Melons are also rich in soluble fibre.

- High potassium content helps prevent fluid retention and balances sodium in the body.
- Soluble fibre content helps arterial health and can help lower 'bad' blood cholesterol.
- Beta-carotene content of orange varieties is one of the highest of all fruits and vegetables.

DID YOU KNOW?

If you buy half or a quarter of a melon, it should be stored in the refrigerator, well wrapped in clingfilm, to prevent other foods absorbing its strong odour.

PRACTICAL TIPS

Unlike many fruits, melons don't ripen once picked, so choose one with a rich fragrance, which indicates it is ripe. If it has wrinkles, it is overripe. Store melons at cool to moderate room temperature.

CRUNCHY GREEK YOGURT MELON POTS

Refreshingly tangy and low in fat but also surprisingly filling and high in protein, these pretty pots are a perfect quick breakfast and ideal for a slimming diet too.

SERVES 4 • PREP TIME: 15 MINS, PLUS CHILLING • COOK TIME: NONE

PER SERVING:

234 kcal	6.3g	0.7g	28.3g	18.5g	2.6g	17.2g	0.1g
CALORIES	FAT	SAT FAT	CARBS	SUGAR	FIBRE	PROTEIN	SALT

INGREDIENTS

500 g/1 lb 2 oz fat-free Greek-style yogurt
1 tsp vanilla extract
275 g/9¾ oz cantaloupe melon,
cut into 1-cm/½-inch cubes
350 g/12 oz watermelon,
cut into 1-cm/½-inch cubes
1 tbsp sunflower seeds
1 tbsp pumpkin seeds
2 tbsp chopped almonds
60 g/2¼ oz ready-made oat granola

1. Beat together the yogurt and vanilla extract. Set half of the yogurt mixture aside. Divide the remaining yogurt mixture between four small glasses or serving dishes.

2. Spoon half the cantaloupe melon and half the watermelon evenly over the yogurt.

3. Mix the seeds, almonds and granola together in a small bowl. Spoon the seed mixture evenly over each yogurt pot. Stir in the reserved yogurt. Chill for 30 minutes before serving.

ORANGES

Vitamin C, the antioxidant vitamin that boosts the immune system and protects from the signs of ageing, is found in abundance in oranges.

MAJOR NUTRIENTS PER AVERAGE-SIZED ORANGE

65 kcal	TRACE	16g	3.4g	1g	64mg	61mg	182 mcg	238 mg
CALORIES	TOTAL FAT	CARBS	FIBRE	PROTEIN	VITAMIN C	CALCIUM	LUTEIN/ ZEAXANTHIN	POTASSIUM

Oranges are one of the least expensive sources of vitamin C, which protects against cell damage, ageing and disease. The fruit is also a good source of fibre, folate and potassium as well as calcium, which is vital for bone maintenance. They contain the carotenes zeaxanthin and lutein, both of which can help maintain eye health and protect against macular degeneration. Oranges also contain rutin, a flavonoid that can help slow down or prevent the growth of tumours, and nobiletin, an anti-inflammatory compound. All these plant compounds also help vitamin C to work more effectively.

- Can help prevent infections and the severity and duration of colds may be lessened by increasing intake of vitamin C.
- Oranges are one of the few fruits that are low on the glycaemic index, so they are a useful food for dieters and diabetics.
- Good content of soluble fibre pectin, which helps control blood cholesterol levels.
- Anti-inflammatory, so may help reduce incidence of arthritis.
- Blood oranges contain even higher levels of antioxidants in red anthocyanin pigments, which are linked with cancer prevention.

DID YOU KNOW?

You should eat some of the white pith of the orange as well as the juicy flesh because it contains high levels of fibre, useful plant chemicals and antioxidants.

PRACTICAL TIPS

Buy oranges that feel heavy to hold compared with their size – this means they should be juicy and fresh. Store them in the refrigerator to retain their vitamin C. Orange peel contains high levels of nutrients, but should be scrubbed and dried before use.

RICH ORANGE CRÊPES

Crêpes make a great weekend breakfast or brunch, when you have a little more time for preparation. These luxury pancakes give a good vitamin C boost at the start of the day.

SERVES 4 • PREP TIME: 15 MINS • COOK TIME: 10 MINS

PER SERVING:

 418 kcal CALORIES **22.6g** FAT  **13.4g** SAT FAT **46.1g** CARBS **15g** SUGAR **2.8g** FIBRE **8.4g** PROTEIN **0.3 g** SALT

INGREDIENTS

150 g/5½ oz plain flour
200 ml/7 fl oz milk
3 tbsp fresh orange juice
1 large egg
2 tbsp melted butter
2 oranges, segmented
2 tsp melted butter, for frying

ORANGE BUTTER

55 g/2 oz unsalted butter
finely grated rind and juice of 1 orange
1 tbsp caster sugar

1. To make the crêpes, put all the ingredients (excluding the segmented oranges) into a mixing bowl and whisk until smooth. Alternatively, whizz in a food processor until smooth.

2. Heat a crêpe pan until hot, lightly brush with butter and pour in a small ladleful of batter, swirling to thinly coat the surface of the pan.

3. Cook the crêpes until golden underneath, then turn and cook the other side. Remove from the pan and keep warm while you cook the remaining batter.

4. To make the orange butter, melt the butter in a small saucepan, add the orange rind and juice and the sugar and stir until the sugar has dissolved. Simmer, stirring, for 30 seconds, then remove from the heat.

5. Serve the crêpes folded over, with the orange segments and the orange butter poured over.

VARIATION

Keeping with the citrus theme, replace the orange butter with lemon butter, preparing it with 1 lemon and 2 tbsp caster sugar.

PINEAPPLES

A special compound found within pineapples can help ease the
pain of arthritis and may help prevent strokes.

MAJOR NUTRIENTS PER AVERAGE-SIZED PINEAPPLE SLICE

40 kcal	TRACE	10.6g	1.2g	0.5g	30 mg	10 mg	97 mg
CALORIES	TOTAL FAT	CARBS	FIBRE	PROTEIN	VITAMIN C	MAGNESIUM	POTASSIUM

Pineapples have long been used as a medicinal plant in various parts of the world, particularly the Americas. Apart from being a good source of vitamin C and various other vitamins and minerals, including magnesium, the pineapple contains an active substance known as bromelain. This protein has been proven to ease the inflammation associated with arthritis and joint pain, and may also help to reduce the incidence of blood clots, which can lead to heart attacks and strokes. Unfortunately, the inedible stem is the richest source of bromelain, but there is also a little in the fruit.

- May aid digestion and limit pain from arthritis and joint conditions.
- Can help to reduce the risk of blood clots.
- Good source of the antioxidant vitamin C.
- Good source of ferulic acid, which can help prevent cancer.

DID YOU KNOW?

*The bromelain in pineapples
is an effective meat tenderizer
– use a few spoonfuls of juice
and add to meat stews and curries.*

PRACTICAL TIPS

A pineapple is ripe to eat when a leaf is easily pulled from the top. To prepare, cut off the leafy top and a small layer of the base, and then slice off the tough skin and 'eyes'. Once cut into slices, remove the chewy central core. Avoid using fresh pineapple in jelly – the bromelain enzyme prevents setting. Canned pineapple contains no bromelain but retains much of its vitamin C. Pineapples are delicious simply served fresh, chopped with cereal or yogurt for breakfast, or try them cooked in brown sugar and a little butter for a tasty warm dessert.

PINEAPPLE & MINT
ICED TEA

This refreshing iced tea is infused with soothing ginger and fresh mint and delivers a bounty of vitamins and minerals, ensuring a fresh and rejuvenating thirst-quenching drink.

MAKES 500 ML/17 FL OZ • PREP TIME: 20–25 MINS • COOK TIME: 45 MINS, PLUS INFUSING

PER 500 ML/17 FL OZ:	810 kcal	1.2g	0.1g	206.8g	177.1g	13.5g	5.3g	TRACE
	CALORIES	FAT	SAT FAT	CARBS	SUGAR	FIBRE	PROTEIN	SALT

INGREDIENTS

1 pineapple
1 litre/1¾ pints water
30 g/1 oz fresh mint sprigs
5-cm/2-inch piece fresh ginger, finely sliced
125 ml/4 fl oz agave syrup
crushed ice
2 tbsp mint leaves, to decorate

1. Prepare the pineapple by slicing off the base and leaves with a sharp knife. Rest the pineapple on its base and slice off the peel until you reveal the flesh. Slice the fruit in half and remove the woody core from the centre. Cut the remaining flesh into 2-cm/¾-inch cubes.

2. Pour the water into a large saucepan and add the pineapple, mint and ginger. Stir in the agave syrup and place the saucepan over a medium–high heat. Simmer for 45 minutes, or until the liquid has reduced by half.

3. Remove from the heat and leave the tea to cool completely and infuse. This will take 4–5 hours. Using a slotted spoon, remove the mint sprigs and ginger.

4. Empty the crushed ice into a large jug and add the mint leaves. Pour over the cooled tea and stir. Serve immediately.

HINT

A jar is an interesting way to serve this tea but you could also serve in cocktail glasses or other attractive glasses.

BLACKBERRIES

Juicy blackberries are small powerhouses of health that are rich
in antioxidants to protect us from cardiovascular diseases.

MAJOR NUTRIENTS PER 100 G/3½ OZ BLACKBERRIES

25 kcal	TRACE	5g	3.1g	0.9g	15 mg	2.4 mg	41 mg	34 mcg	0.7 mg	160 mg
CALORIES	TOTAL FAT	CARBS	FIBRE	PROTEIN	VITAMIN C	VITAMIN E	CALCIUM	FOLATE	IRON	POTASSIUM

In recent years it has been discovered that these tasty fruits are potent health-protectors as well as a delicious autumn treat. They rate almost as high on the ORAC scale as blueberries. Their deep purple colour denotes that they are rich in several compounds, which can help beat heart disease, cancers and the signs of ageing. These compounds include anthocyanins and ellagic acid. Additionally, blackberries are rich in fibre and minerals, including magnesium, zinc, iron and calcium. Their high vitamin E content helps protect the heart and keeps skin healthy.

- High in ellagic acid, a chemical known to block cancer cells.
- Rich in antioxidant vitamin E and fibre.
- A good source of vitamin C, which boosts the immune system.
- A useful source of folate for healthy blood.

PRACTICAL TIPS

The freshest blackberries have a shiny, plump appearance. If they look dull they are likely to be past their best and the vitamin C content will be lower. The darker the blackberry, the more ellagic acid it is likely to contain. Cooking doesn't destroy ellagic acid, so you can use blackberries to make jam or in pies and crumbles. However, for maximum vitamin C they are best eaten raw. Blackberries freeze well, so pack them into lidded containers or open-freeze on a tray and then pack into polythene bags.

DID YOU KNOW?

Blackberries contain salicylate, which is related to the active ingredient in aspirin. For this reason, people who are allergic to aspirin may also have a reaction to blackberries.

CARDAMOM WAFFLES WITH BLACKBERRIES & FIGS

Aromatic cardamom adds a wonderful depth of flavour to these fabulous fruit-topped waffles, so dig out your waffle maker and cook up this satisfying weekend family breakfast.

SERVES 6 • PREP TIME: 25 MINS, PLUS RESTING • COOK TIME: 10–17 MINS

PER SERVING:

422 kcal	17.3g	7.8g	53.9g	23.7g	7.3g	16.1g	0.5g
CALORIES	FAT	SAT FAT	CARBS	SUGAR	FIBRE	PROTEIN	SALT

INGREDIENTS

5 large eggs, separated
pinch of salt
1 tsp ground cardamom
50 g/1¾ oz unsalted butter, melted and cooled
250 ml/8½ fl oz semi-skimmed milk
225 g/8 oz wholemeal plain flour
1 tbsp olive oil, for brushing
150 g/5½ oz Greek-style natural yogurt
6 ripe figs, quartered
200 g/7 oz blackberries
6 tbsp agave syrup, to serve

1. You will need a waffle maker for this recipe. Place the egg yolks, salt and cardamom in a bowl and beat well with a wooden spoon. Stir in the melted butter. Slowly beat in the milk until fully incorporated. Gradually add the flour until you have a thick batter.

2. In a separate bowl, whisk the egg whites until they hold stiff peaks and gently fold them into the batter. Leave the batter to rest for at least 1 hour, but preferably overnight.

3. Heat the waffle maker according to the manufacturers' instructions. Brush with a little oil and spoon the batter onto the waffle iron. Cook for 4–5 minutes, or until golden. Keep the waffles warm until you are ready to serve.

4. Serve the waffles with the yogurt, fig quarters, blackberries and agave syrup.

HINT

To keep the waffles warm, cover them with foil and place in an oven preheated to 120°C/250°F/Gas Mark ½.

APRICOTS

Fresh apricots are highly nutritious and have a low glycaemic index,
making them an excellent food for sweet-toothed dieters.

MAJOR NUTRIENTS PER 2 AVERAGE-SIZED FRESH APRICOTS

31 kcal	TRACE	7.2g	1.7g	0.9g	6mg	766 mcg	0.5 mg	766 mcg
CALORIES	TOTAL FAT	CARBS	FIBRE	PROTEIN	VITAMIN C	BETA-CAROTENE	IRON	POTASSIUM

Fresh apricots contain vitamin C, folate, potassium and vitamin E. Their high content of beta-carotene, an important antioxidant, helps to prevent some cancers. They are also ideal for weight maintenance as they are a good source of fibre and are fat-free. The semi-dried, plumped fruit is a very good source of potassium anc iron, although the drying process diminishes the vitamin C and carotene content. Fresh apricots, because they contain more water, are, weight for weight, lower in calories than dried ones.

- Contain a range of carotenes: beta-carotene for cancer prevention; lutein and zeaxanthin for eye health; and cryptoxanthin, which may help to maintain bone health.
- High in total and soluble fibre for healthy heart and circulation.
- Excellent source of potassium.

DID YOU KNOW?

Hunza apricots are a form of dried apricot that grows wild in the Hunza Valley in Kashmir, India. The fruits are left on the trees to dry and must be cooked before eating.

PRACTICAL TIPS

Fresh apricots need to be fully ripe to maximize their carotene content, and cooking them helps the carotene and soluble fibre to be better absorbed in the body. Fresh apricots are excellent in fruit crumbles or poached in white wine.

ROASTED FRUIT CRUMBLE

A healthy take on an old favourite – gooey soft fruits, topped with a nutty coconut crumble, full of fibre but also rich in antioxidants due to the colourful fruits.

SERVES 4 • PREP TIME: 15 MINS • COOK TIME: 35–40 MINS

PER SERVING:	410 kcal	22.5g	13.6g	50.7g	26.7g	9.7g	6.4g	TRACE
	CALORIES	FAT	SAT FAT	CARBS	SUGAR	FIBRE	PROTEIN	SALT

INGREDIENTS

4 apricots, stoned and quartered
1 tbsp caster sugar
200 g/7 oz raspberries
200 g/7 oz blackberries
55 g/2 oz rolled oats
40 g/1½ oz wholemeal flour
30 g/1 oz pecan nuts
10 g/¼ oz sesame seeds
60 g/2¼ oz dark muscovado sugar
60 g/2¼ oz coconut oil
coconut yogurt, to serve (optional)

1. Preheat the oven to 180°C/350°F/Gas Mark 4. Place the apricot quarters in a roasting tin and sprinkle with the sugar. Roast in the preheated oven for 15 minutes.

2. Spoon the apricots into four ovenproof dishes and sprinkle over the remaining fruit. Place the remaining ingredients in a food processor and process to very lumpy crumbs.

3. Spoon the crumble over the fruit, place the dishes on a baking sheet and bake in the oven for 20–25 minutes, until golden and bubbling. Serve with coconut yogurt, if using.

GRAPEFRUIT

An excellent source of vitamin C, eating grapefruit boosts the
immune system and protects our hearts.

MAJOR NUTRIENTS PER HALF PINK GRAPEFRUIT

30 kcal	TRACE	7.5g	1.1g	0.5g	37 mg	127 mg	770 mcg	15 mg	9 mcg
CALORIES	TOTAL FAT	CARBS	FIBRE	PROTEIN	VITAMIN C	POTASSIUM	BETA-CAROTENE	CALCIUM	FOLATE

In recent years, the pink-fleshed grapefruit has become as popular as the white- or yellow-fleshed variety. It is a little sweeter and contains more health benefits – the pink pigment indicates the presence of lycopene, the antioxidant carotene that has been shown to help prevent prostate and other cancers. Like other citrus fruits, grapefruits contain bioflavonoids, compounds that appear to increase the benefits of vitamin C, also found in this fruit in excellent amounts. Grapefruit are low on the glycaemic index and are very low in calories, so they are an important fruit for dieters. Because grapefruit juice can alter the effect of certain drugs (for example drugs that lower blood pressure), people on medication should check with their doctors before they consume the fruit.

- High in antioxidants, which can help prevent prostate and other cancers.
- Rich in vitamin C to boost the immune system.
- Excellent fruit for dieters.
- Help reduce bouts of wheezing in asthma-prone people.

DID YOU KNOW?

*The slightly bitter taste
of some grapefruit is caused
by a compound called
naringenin, which has
cholesterol-lowering properties.*

PRACTICAL TIPS

Grapefruit is delicious halved, sprinkled with demerara sugar and grilled for a short while. Try to eat some of the white pith with your grapefruit because this is high in nutrients. Grapefruit, like all citrus fruits, will contain more juice if they feel heavier.

SMOKED SALMON &
PINK GRAPEFRUIT SALAD

Citrus fruit really brings out the flavour of smoked salmon, and the pink grapefruit here adds so much more than a squeeze of lemon juice!

SERVES 2 • PREP TIME: 20 MINS • COOK TIME: NONE

PER SERVING:

246 kcal	17g	2.4g	16.5g	11.7g	3.9g	9.7g	1.7g
CALORIES	FAT	SAT FAT	CARBS	SUGAR	FIBRE	PROTEIN	SALT

INGREDIENTS

1 pink grapefruit
50 g/1¾ oz rocket
50 g/1¾ oz frisée
½ fennel bulb, thinly sliced
¼ tsp sea salt
1 tbsp extra virgin olive oil
½ tsp white wine vinegar
60 g/2¼ oz smoked salmon
1 tbsp extra virgin olive oil, for drizzling
pepper (optional)

1. Using a sharp knife, cut a slice from the top and bottom of the grapefruit. Remove the peel and white pith by cutting downwards, following the shape of the fruit as closely as possible. Cut between the flesh and membrane of each segment and ease out the flesh. Discard the membrane and set aside the flesh.

2. Put the rocket, frisée and fennel in a bowl. Sprinkle with the sea salt. Gently toss with your hands to distribute the salt. Add the oil and gently toss. Sprinkle with the vinegar, toss again and divide between two serving plates.

3. Cut the smoked salmon into bite-sized pieces and arrange on top of the salad with the grapefruit segments. Drizzle with oil, sprinkle with pepper, if using, and serve.

VARIATION
Smoked salmon works well here but you could also use other types of smoked fish, like trout.

PASSION FRUIT

Passion fruit is full of antioxidants such as the healing vitamins A and C,
which take action in the body to slow down the signs of ageing.

MAJOR NUTRIENTS PER AVERAGE-SIZED PASSION FRUIT

17 kcal	0.13g	4.21g	1.9g	0.40g	229IU	5.4 mg	134 mcg	63 mg
CALORIES	TOTAL FAT	CARBS	FIBRE	PROTEIN	VITAMIN A	VITAMIN C	BETA-CAROTENE	POTASSIUM

High in the orange spectrum of antioxidants, the vitamin A and beta-carotene content of passion fruit gives skin a youthful boost. Enjoying this fruit will also protect your skin against the sun and help avoid sun damage such as pigment changes and lines. Although we need some sunlight for health, especially to enhance mood and encourage restorative sleep cycles and bone health, we are damaged by its UV rays when it hits the skin. Many fruits, especially tropical fruit like passion fruit, which receives intense amounts of sunlight, contain vitamin A and carotenoid antioxidants to protect themselves against UV rays as they ripen. By eating these fruits, we reap the same sun-protecting properties, while also satisfying our requirements for high amounts of vitamin C.

- High levels of potassium, fibre and vitamin C combine to prevent heart disease.
- A highly alkalizing fruit, which helps fluid balance and detoxification, crucial for maintaining a youthful appearance.
- Vitamin C helps knit together the collagen that keeps skin plump and wrinkle-free.

DID YOU KNOW?

The yellow variety of this nutrient-rich fruit has more antioxidant carotenoids and is made into juice, while the purple variety has more vitamin C and is sold as fresh produce.

PRACTICAL TIPS

The seeds of passion fruit are edible, so you can scoop out the entire contents from the skin and enjoy as a delicious snack. When made into juice or to flavour foods, the seeds are usually removed. Keep the ripe fruit in the refrigerator for up to a week.

STRAWBERRY & PASSION FRUIT YOGURTS

If you fancy a light, sweet-tasting snack, these little jars of
summery freshness will give you an instant boost.

SERVES 4 • PREP TIME: 20–25 MINS, PLUS CHILLING • COOK TIME: 2–3 MINS

PER SERVING: **141 kcal** CALORIES | **3.5g** FAT | **2.8g** SAT FAT | **19.3g** CARBS | **14.6g** SUGAR | **3.2g** FIBRE | **10.4g** PROTEIN | **TRACE** SALT

INGREDIENTS

20 g ¾ oz desiccated coconut
200 g/7 oz strawberries, hulled
finely grated zest and juice of 1 lime
350 g/12 oz fat-free Greek-style yogurt
4 tsp clear honey
2 passion fruit, halved
1 tbsp dried goji berries, roughly chopped

1. Add the coconut to a dry frying pan and cook over a medium heat for 2–3 minutes, shaking the pan, until light golden in colour. Remove from the heat and leave to cool.

2. Coarsely mash the strawberries and mix with half the lime juice. Add the lime zest, remaining lime juice, the yogurt and honey to a bowl, and stir together.

3. Add three quarters of the cooled coconut to the yogurt, then scoop the seeds from the passion fruit over the top and lightly fold into the yogurt.

4. Layer alternate spoonfuls of strawberry and yogurt in four 200-ml/7-fl oz preserving jars, then sprinkle with the remaining coconut and the goji berries. Clip down the lids and chill until ready to serve. Eat within 24 hours.

VARIATION

If you don't like coconut, try adding 30 g/1 oz finely chopped hazelnuts instead for a crunchy finish (omitting Step 1).

CHERRIES

Glossy red cherries are one of the best fruit sources of antioxidants,
which help prevent many diseases associated with ageing.

MAJOR NUTRIENTS PER 80 G/2¾ OZ CHERRIES

			1.7g	0.8g			
50 kcal	TRACE	13g	1.7g	0.8g	5.6mg	68 mcg	178 mg
CALORIES	TOTAL FAT	CARBS	FIBRE	PROTEIN	VITAMIN C	LUTEIN/ ZEAXANTHIN	POTASSIUM

Although cherries contain slightly smaller amounts of vitamins and minerals than other stone fruits, they are rich in several plant compounds that have definite health benefits. They rank highly – in twelfth place – on the ORAC scale of antioxidant capacity in fruits, and the chemicals they contain include quercetin, a flavonoid that has anti-cancer and heart-protecting qualities, and cyanidin, which is an anti-inflammatory that minimizes symptoms of arthritis and gout. The soluble fibre contained in cherries is helpful for controlling 'bad' blood cholesterol levels, while the fruit is also a good source of potassium and a reasonable source of vitamin C and carotenes.

- High in antioxidants, which help protect the heart and prevent signs of ageing.
- Rich in quercetin to help prevent cancers.
- Rich in cyanidin to alleviate arthritis and inflammatory diseases.
- Soluble fibre helps improve blood cholesterol profile.

DID YOU KNOW?

Morello cherries are a sour, rather than sweet, variety of cherry and are usually used in pies and cooking.

PRACTICAL TIPS

Fresh cherries will have green stalks and a glossy skin. The deeper the colour, the more antioxidant compounds they contain, so choose red or black, rather than yellow, cherries. To preserve vitamin C, store in the refrigerator. Fresh cherries contain higher levels of antioxidants, so are best eaten raw.

CHERRY AID SMOOTHIE

This deliciously tangy drink has the sweetness of pears, the tartness of cherries and the innumerable health benefits of chia seeds. A great refresher at any time of the day.

SERVES 1 • PREP TIME: 20 MINS • COOK TIME: NONE

PER SERVING:

376 kcal	4.8g	0.6g	87.7g	57.1g	4.8g	5.2g	TRACE
CALORIES	FAT	SAT FAT	CARBS	SUGAR	FIBRE	PROTEIN	SALT

INGREDIENTS

2 pears, halved
1 tbsp chia seeds
175 g/6 oz cherries, stoned
125 ml/4 fl oz chilled water
small handful of crushed ice (optional)

1. Feed the pears through a juicer.

2. Put the chia seeds in a blender and whizz until finely ground. Add the pear juice, cherries, water and crushed ice, if using, and blend until smooth.

3. Pour into a glass and serve immediately.

RHUBARB

Rhubarb has been used as a laxative for thousands of years, to prevent the build-up of ageing toxins that can make you feel sluggish.

MAJOR NUTRIENTS PER 100 G/3½ OZ RHUBARB

21 kcal	0.2g	4.54g	1.8g	0.9g	8mg	29.3 mcg	86 mg	288 mg
CALORIES	TOTAL FAT	CARBS	FIBRE	PROTEIN	VITAMIN C	VITAMIN K	CALCIUM	POTASSIUM

Rhubarb roots and stems are rich in anthraquinones. These substances are also found in senna, aloe and cascara – all used in herbal medicine as natural laxatives. Preparations made from these plants are sometimes harsh on the gut, however, which makes dietary sources like rhubarb preferable. As part of a high-fibre diet, rhubarb will help bowel function by toning the muscle of the gut wall and ensuring the removal of ageing toxic waste without dehydrating or damaging the digestive tract. Traditionally rhubarb has been used to promote skin health and maintain a youthful appearance by following this route of cleaning the body and the detoxification pathways from the inside.

- Modulates inflammatory responses, helping restore balance to the immune system and prevent ageing diseases.
- Removes excess fats from the bloodstream, helping the circulation to deliver revitalizing oxygen and nutrients to the cells.
- Good source of vitamin K, neeced for youthful bone health.

DID YOU KNOW?

Rhubarb has been used for thousands of years by the Chinese for digestive and kidney health – both vital for retaining youth – and is also mentioned in medieval European and Arabic medical texts.

PRACTICAL TIPS

Rhubarb tastes extremely tart on its own so it always needs sweetening. Although this can have the effect of negating its healthy properties, honey or fruit juice will minimize the damage. Getting used to the tartness of rhubarb as an aspect of its distinctive flavour also reduces the temptation to over-sweeten.

PORK FILLET WITH ROASTED RHUBARB

Young pink rhubarb tempers the pork's natural sweetness and produces deliciously tangy juices.
Use a blade-end or centre-cut joint for moistness and flavour.

SERVES 4 • PREP TIME: 20 MINS • COOK TIME: 55 MINS–1 HOUR, PLUS RESTING

PER SERVING:

276 kcal	8g	2g	6.7g	4.8g	0.9g	42.4g	2g
CALORIES	FAT	SAT FAT	CARBS	SUGAR	FIBRE	PROTEIN	SALT

INGREDIENTS

800 g/1 lb 12 oz boneless pork loin
1 tbsp olive oil
1 tsp sea salt flakes
½ tsp pepper
10 small fresh rosemary sprigs
125 ml/4 fl oz chicken stock
175 g/6 oz pink rhubarb stalks, trimmed and sliced diagonally into 4-cm/1½-inch lengths
1 tbsp clear honey

1. Preheat the oven to 190°C/375°F/Gas Mark 5. Using the tip of a sharp knife, score the fat, but not the flesh, of the pork at 1-cm/½-inch intervals. Tie the meat with kitchen string to make a neat roll. You can ask your butcher to do this.

2. Place the meat in a small roasting tin. Rub with the oil and then with the salt and pepper, rubbing in well. Insert the rosemary sprigs into the slits in the fat. Roast in the preheated oven for 40 minutes.

3. Pour in the stock. Arrange the rhubarb around the meat and drizzle with the honey. Roast for a further 10–15 minutes, until the rhubarb is tender and starting to colour at the edges.

4. Transfer the pork and rhubarb to a warmed serving platter, reserving the pan juices. Make a tent over the meat with foil and leave to rest in a warm place for 10 minutes.

5. Place the roasting tin on the hob over a medium–high heat. Bubble rapidly to reduce the pan juices, including any that have flowed from the meat, for 3–4 minutes, until slightly thickened. Strain into a jug and serve with the meat.

PEARS

This fruit – known to be hypoallergenic – is antibacterial, high in fibre and contains antioxidants to help prevent cancer and gastroenteritis.

60 kcal	TRACE	15g	3.3g	0.5 g	9mg	225 mg
CALORIES	TOTAL FAT	CARBS	FIBRE	PROTEIN	VITAMIN C	POTASSIUM

Pear cultivation goes back over 3,000 years in western Asia, and there has been some evidence of its discovery as far back as the Stone Age. Pears are closely related to apples and there are many varieties. It has been found that, compared to many other fruits, they are less likely to produce an adverse or allergic response, and this makes them particularly useful as a first fruit for young children. They contain a range of useful nutrients and a good amount of fibre, which helps maintain a healthy colon.

- Safe fruit for most children and for people who suffer from food allergies.
- A good source of a range of nutrients, including vitamin C and potassium.
- Contain hydroxycinnamic acids, antioxidants that are anti-cancer and anti-bacterial and may help prevent gastroenteritis.

DID YOU KNOW?

Much of the fibre in pears is contained in the skin, so it is best simply to wash the fruit and not peel it.

PRACTICAL TIPS

Pears don't ripen well on the tree, so bought pears tend to be under-ripe. Place them in a cool to moderately warm room and, once ripe, they should be eaten within a day – they tend to spoil quickly. Pears can also discolour easily – to prevent this, sprinkle the cut sides with lemon juice. Although an ideal snack or lunch-box fruit, pears are very versatile and can be baked, sautéed or poached, and used in mixed fruit compotes, crumbles and pies.

CRUNCH-TOPPED ROAST PEARS

Soft, fragrant pears go wonderfully well with crunchy nuts and are
one of the tastiest fruits to roast in the oven.

SERVES 4 • PREP TIME: 10 MINS • COOK TIME: 20 MINS

PER SERVING:

215 kcal	5.1g	0.7g	34.4g	20.5g	5.9g	2.9g	TRACE
CALORIES	FAT	SAT FAT	CARBS	SUGAR	FIBRE	PROTEIN	SALT

INGREDIENTS

4 dessert pears, such as Comice or Williams,
each weighing about 150 g/5½ oz
200 ml/7 fl oz medium white wine
1 tbsp demerara sugar
½ tsp mixed spice
30 g/1 oz mixed nuts, toasted and chopped
15 g/½ oz rolled oats
2 tbsp wholemeal breadcrumbs
2 tsp sunflower seeds
8 sprays cooking oil spray

1. Preheat the oven to 190°C/375°F/Gas Mark 5.

2. Cut the pears in half lengthways and remove the cores. Place in a large shallow baking dish. Pour the white wine around the pears and bake in the preheated oven for 10 minutes.

3. Meanwhile, combine the sugar, spice, nuts, oats, breadcrumbs and sunflower seeds in a bowl.

4. Remove the pears from the oven, top each one with some of the nut mixture, then spray with cooking oil spray. Return to the oven for 7–8 minutes, or until the topping is golden. Serve drizzled with any juice left in the dish.

GRAPES

Grapes are rich in polyphenols – which protect our hearts, improve circulation, and help lower cholesterol – and have antifungal properties.

MAJOR NUTRIENTS PER 100 G/3½ OZ GRAPES

70 kcal	TRACE	18g	0.9g	0.7g	10.8 mg	191 mg
CALORIES	TOTAL FAT	CARBS	FIBRE	PROTEIN	VITAMIN C	POTASSIUM

All grape varieties contain beneficial compounds, mainly polyphenols, and most of these are found in the skin. Black, purple and red varieties also contain much higher levels of the flavonoid quercetin and anthocyanins – the dark pigments – and both may help prevent cancer, heart and cardiovascular disease. The antioxidant benefits of paler-coloured grapes are mainly from their catechin content. Resveratrol, another antioxidant present in all grapes, has been linked to the prevention or inhibition of cancer and heart disease, degenerative nerve disease and viral infections, and may also be linked to protection against Alzheimer's disease.

- Rich source of polyphenols, for cancer prevention and a healthy cardiovascular system.
- Quercetin can improve blood cholesterol profile and has an anti-clotting action.
- Antiviral and antifungal action.
- Good source of vitamin C.

PRACTICAL TIPS

Wash grapes before use – they may have been sprayed with pesticides – and store in the refrigerator or a cool room to preserve vitamin C content and prevent deterioration. If using in a dessert, cut at the last minute to prevent the cut side discolouring.

GRAPE & LYCHEE SMOOTHIE

This super green drink blends fragrant lychees with creamy, smooth avocado and naturally sweet grapes for the perfect pick-me-up to rehydrate and fight fatigue.

SERVES 1 • PREP TIME: 15 MINS • COOK TIME: NONE

413 kcal	**15.6g**	**2.3g**	**72.8g**	**54.6g**	**8.3g**	**6.2g**	**0.1g**
CALORIES	FAT	SAT FAT	CARBS	SUGAR	FIBRE	PROTEIN	SALT

PER SERVING:

INGREDIENTS

300 g/10½ oz green grapes
55 g/2 oz young spinach
½ ripe avocado, stoned, flesh
scooped from the skin
5 lychees, peeled and stoned
small handful of crushed ice
125 ml/4 fl oz chilled water
slice of avocado to serve (optional)

1. Feed the grapes and spinach through a juicer.

2. Pour the juice into a blender, add the avocado, lychees and crushed ice, and blend until smooth.

3. Add the water and blend again. Pour into a glass, add the avocado slice, if using, and serve immediately.

PAPAYA

The tropical papaya is extremely high in carotenes, which are linked with cancer prevention and with healthy lungs and eyes.

MAJOR NUTRIENTS PER AVERAGE-SIZED PAPAYA

120 kcal	0.4g	30g	5.5g	1.5g	180 mg	780 mg	839 mcg	2313 mcg	228 mcg	30 mg
CALORIES	TOTAL FAT	CARBS	FIBRE	PROTEIN	VITAMIN C	POTASSIUM	BETA-CAROTENE	BETA-CRYPTOXANTHIN	LUTEIN/ZEAXANTHIN	MAGNESIUM

The papaya flesh is high in fructose (fruit sugars) and relatively high in calories, so it's good as a hunger-beating snack or dessert. The flesh is also high in carotenes, which can help prevent cancer, and it is a good source of fibre. In addition, it is one of the richest fruits in potassium and is much higher in calcium than most other fruits. Papaya is also extremely high in vitamin C, and is a reasonable source of magnesium and vitamin E. It contains the enzyme papain, which breaks down protein and tenderizes meat.

- Rich in beta-carotene, which can help prevent prostate cancer.
- A good source of the carotenes lutein and zeaxanthin, which can help protect the eyes from macular degeneration.
- Rich in beta-cryptoxanthin, which can help maintain healthy lungs and may help prevent arthritis.
- Excellent source of vitamin C and fibre.
- High soluble fibre content helps control blood sugar levels by slowing sugar absorption.

DID YOU KNOW?
Papaya seeds can be dried in a low oven and used in the same way as peppercorns.

PRACTICAL TIPS

When a papaya is ripe, its skin is orange, rather than green. It can be added to a casserole to tenderize the meat. In a fruit salad, add just before serving – the papain in it can over-soften other fruits. The papain also prevents gelatine setting, so avoid using it in jelly desserts. Lime juice sprinkled on the fruit brings out its flavour.

CHICKEN, PAPAYA & AVOCADO SALAD

This delicious salad is a powerhouse of valuable nutrients, with peppery green leaves, avocado, nuts and quinoa sprouts, not to mention the star of the show, papaya.

SERVES 2 • PREP TIME: 20 MINS • COOK TIME: 10 MINS

PER SERVING:

1002 kcal	87.5g	8.7g	41.6g	21.4g	12g	40.3g	0.2g
CALORIES	FAT	SAT FAT	CARBS	SUGAR	FIBRE	PROTEIN	SALT

INGREDIENTS

2 boneless, skinless chicken breasts, each weighing about 150 g/5½ oz
2 tbsp olive oil
100 g/3½ oz peppery green salad leaves, such as rocket, mizuna, curly endive and watercress
1 large papaya, peeled, deseeded and thickly sliced
1 ripe avocado, peeled, stoned and thickly sliced
30 g/1 oz toasted hazelnuts, halved
2 tbsp red or white quinoa sprouts
salt and pepper (optional)

DRESSING

2 tbsp lime juice
6 tbsp hazelnut oil
salt and pepper (optional)

1. Place the chicken breasts on a board. With the knife parallel to the board, slice each breast in half horizontally to make four fillets in total.

2. Place the fillets between two sheets of clingfilm and pound with a rolling pin to a thickness of about 8 mm/⅜ inch.

3. Heat the oil in a large frying pan. Add the chicken and fry over a medium–high heat for 3–4 minutes on each side, until golden on the outside and no longer pink in the middle. Transfer to a warmed plate and season to taste with salt and pepper, if using.

4. Slice the chicken lengthways into 2-cm/¾-inch wide strips.

5. Divide the salad leaves between two plates. Arrange the chicken, papaya and avocado on top. Sprinkle with the hazelnuts and quinoa sprouts.

6. To make the dressing, whisk together all the ingredients until smooth and creamy. Pour over the salad and serve immediately.

PEACHES

The soft fruit of this member of the rose family makes a nutritional sweet substitute for refined sugars and provides skin-nourishing nutrients.

MAJOR NUTRIENTS PER AVERAGE-SIZED PEACH

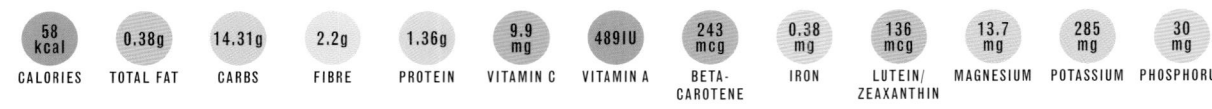

58 kcal	0.38g	14.31g	2.2g	1.36g	9.9 mg	489IU	243 mcg	0.38 mg	136 mcg	13.7 mg	285 mg	30 mg
CALORIES	TOTAL FAT	CARBS	FIBRE	PROTEIN	VITAMIN C	VITAMIN A	BETA-CAROTENE	IRON	LUTEIN/ZEAXANTHIN	MAGNESIUM	POTASSIUM	PHOSPHORUS

Like most orange fruit and vegetables, peaches are abundant in carotenoid nutrients, the antioxidants that protect fatty areas of the body, in our liver, skin, heart and other organs, including the brain, which is 60 per cent fat. These fatty areas are susceptible to damage and we rely on fat-soluble antioxidants like carotenoids and vitamin A to slow down degeneration and ageing. Peaches are also high in vitamin C, which protects what are known as watery areas of the body, in and between cells and in the bloodstream. The high boron content of peaches has been shown to promote new bone growth and reduce the risk of prostate cancer in men.

- Rich in potassium, vitamin C and iron, important for circulation and taking oxygen around the body to renew and revitalize the skin.
- Their gentle laxative effect helps maintain bowel regularity, ensuring the removal of ageing toxins.
- Contain the minerals magnesium and phosphorus, used by the nervous system for optimum brain and muscle function.

DID YOU KNOW?

Peaches have long been considered a medicinal plant and are recommended during convalescence for those suffering from fatigue or depression.

PRACTICAL TIPS

Choose fruit that is still firm and only just becoming soft, with yellowy-cream colouring between the red areas and a velvety skin. Look out for bruises as they spread quickly, and only wash immediately before eating as any damage to the skin can accelerate spoiling.

CELERIAC, FENNEL & PEACH SLAW

The peach combines well with the slightly anise undertones of the celeriac and fennel to make a rather unusually flavoured summer side dish.

SERVES 4 • PREP TIME: 10 MINS • COOK TIME: NONE

PER SERVING: 175 kcal CALORIES | 10.9g FAT | 1.7g SAT FAT | 19g CARBS | 10.6g SUGAR | 4.3g FIBRE | 2.5g PROTEIN | 0.4g SALT

INGREDIENTS

4 tbsp mayonnaise
1 tsp sriracha chilli sauce
1 tsp horseradish sauce
zest and juice of 1 lemon
½ tsp pepper
2 ripe peaches, stoned and sliced
200 g/7 oz celeriac, cut into matchsticks
1 fennel bulb, sliced
1 small red onion, sliced

1. In a large bowl, whisk together the mayonnaise, chilli sauce, horseradish sauce, lemon zest and juice and pepper.

2. Add the peaches, celeriac, fennel and onion to the bowl. Mix well to combine thoroughly, then serve immediately.

VARIATION
This slaw will work well with any soft stone fruit and is great served with pork, chicken or fish.

PLUMS

Research shows that antioxidants found in plums protect the brain
as well as the heart. They are also a good source of iron.

MAJOR NUTRIENTS PER AVERAGE-SIZED PLUM

30 kcal	TRACE	7.5g	0.9g	0.5g	6.3 mg	125 mcg	0.4 mcg	48 mcg	104 mg
CALORIES	TOTAL FAT	CARBS	FIBRE	PROTEIN	VITAMIN C	BETA-CAROTENE	IRON	LUTEIN/ ZEAXANTHIN	POTASSIUM

Plums come in a variety of colours, from the more common red and purple varieties to yellow and white. The fruits are well known for their health-giving phenolic compounds – neochlorogenic and chlorogenic acids – which are particularly effective at neutralizing the free radicals that contribute to disease and the ageing process. They seem to be especially beneficial in their antioxidant action on the fatty tissues in the brain and help prevent damage to the fats circulating in our blood. The red and purple varieties are also rich in anthocyanins, the pigments that help to prevent heart disease and cancers.

- Low glycaemic index is useful for dieters and diabetics.
- Good source of carotenes for cancer protection and eye health.
- Rich in phenolic compounds for healthy brain and strong antioxidant action.
- Source of easily absorbed iron for healthy blood and body maintenance.

DID YOU KNOW?

Plums, native to China and Europe, have been eaten for at least 2,000 years. There are also over 2,000 varieties.

PRACTICAL TIPS

Buy plums that are almost ripe, preferably still with a slight bloom on the skin, and allow to ripen at room temperature for one to two days – fully ripe plums contain the most antioxidants. Plums bought for cooking should be poached in a little water and eaten with the juices, because some of the nutrients will leach into the water.

RICE PUDDING WITH CINNAMON-POACHED PLUMS

Creamy rice pudding with cinnamon-flavoured plum compote is an incredibly warm and comforting dish that takes us right back to childhood.

SERVES 4 • PREP TIME: 15 MINS • COOK TIME: 50–55 MINS

PER SERVING:

296 kcal	7.5g	4.2g	52.6g	33.7g	2.4g	6.3g	0.1g
CALORIES	FAT	SAT FAT	CARBS	SUGAR	FIBRE	PROTEIN	SALT

INGREDIENTS
85 g/3 oz pudding rice
30 g/1 oz caster sugar
15 g/½ oz unsalted butter
500 ml/17 fl oz milk
1 thinly pared strip of orange rind

COMPOTE
500 g/1 lb 2 oz red plums, stoned and halved
1 cinnamon stick
2 tbsp golden caster sugar
juice of 1 orange

1. Put the rice, sugar and butter into a saucepan and stir in the milk and orange rind. Heat gently, stirring occasionally, until almost boiling.

2. Reduce the heat to low, then cover and simmer gently for 40–45 minutes, stirring occasionally, until the rice is tender and most of the liquid has been absorbed.

3. Meanwhile, to make the compote, put the plums, cinnamon, sugar and orange juice into a large saucepan. Heat gently until just boiling, then reduce the heat, cover and simmer for about 10 minutes, or until the plums are tender.

4. Remove the plums with a slotted spoon and discard the cinnamon. Serve the rice pudding warm with the compote.

VARIATION
This delicious fruit compote would work just as well on top of porridge or pancakes.

OLIVES

Olives offer the same health benefits as olive oil, but with extra phytosterols, lutein and vitamins A and E for an added anti-ageing boost.

MAJOR NUTRIENTS PER 100 G/3½ OZ OLIVES

145 kcal	15.32g	11.3g	3.84g	3.3g	1.03g	393IU	3.81mg
CALORIES	TOTAL FAT	MONO UN-SATURATED FAT	CARBS	FIBRE	PROTEIN	VITAMIN A	VITAMIN E

1215 mg	11145 mg	231 mcg	510 mcg	176mg	1556 mg
OMEGA-6 OILS	OMEGA-9 OILS	BETA-CAROTENE	LUTEIN/ZEAXANTHIN	PHYTOSTEROLS	SODIUM

The fatty nature of olives makes them a fantastic carrier of the fat-soluble nutrients that are so important for forming and protecting every single cell membrane in the body. This translates as wrinkle prevention, bone strength and brain clarity. The valuable oil within the olives moves these nutrients in through the digestive system so that they can be absorbed and used where needed. Taken together, the monounsaturated fats, omega-6 oils, vitamins and carotenoids in olives provide staunch support for all-round heart health. The only downside of this food is the high sodium content, which needs balancing out with potassium from other foods for the body to retain good blood pressure.

- Contain lutein and vitamin A to protect the eyes from macular degeneration, a condition associated with older age.
- Vitamins A and E ensure skin is kept lubricated; dry skin can wrinkle and age more easily.
- Vitamin E may help prevent cancer and keeps blood vessels healthily dilated.

DID YOU KNOW?

The Latin for the olive tree is Olea europaea, which literally translates as 'European oil'. The fruit of the olive has to be processed in some way – such as curing or fermenting – or it will have a very bitter taste.

PRACTICAL TIPS

Olives come in a wide range of varieties, not only green and black. Try sampling some of the different sizes, flavourings and preparations at a good-quality farmers' market or deli to discover your personal preference, and to find out which go best with other foodstuffs and drinks. Olives with stones retain their flavour better.

CRACKED MARINATED OLIVES

These traditionally flavoured olives will up the ante at your next drinks party.
They will keep in the fridge for several weeks.

SERVES 8 • PREP TIME: 30 MINS, PLUS STANDING AND MARINATING • COOK TIME: NONE

PER SERVING:	83 kcal	7.8g	1g	4.3g	0.3g	1.9g	0.6g	0.7g
	CALORIES	FAT	SAT FAT	CARBS	SUGAR	FIBRE	PROTEIN	SALT

INGREDIENTS

450 g/1 lb canned unstoned
large green olives, drained
4 garlic cloves, peeled
2 tsp coriander seeds
1 small lemon
4 fresh thyme sprigs
4 feathery fennel stalks
2 small fresh red chillies (optional)
extra virgin olive oil, for marinating
pepper (optional)

1. To allow the flavours of the marinade to penetrate completely, place the olives on a chopping board and, using a rolling pin, bash them lightly so that they crack slightly. Alternatively, use a sharp knife to cut a lengthways slit in each olive as far as the stone. Using the flat side of a broad knife, lightly crush each garlic clove. Using a pestle and mortar, crack the coriander seeds. Cut the lemon, with its rind, into small chunks.

2. Put the olives, garlic, coriander seeds, lemon chunks, thyme sprigs, fennel and chillies, if using, into a large bowl and toss together. Season with pepper, if using. Tightly pack the ingredients into a glass jar with a lid. Pour in enough oil to cover the olives, then seal the jar tightly.

3. Leave the olives at room temperature for 24 hours, then marinate in the refrigerator for at least 1 week but preferably 2 weeks. From time to time, gently give the jar a shake to re-mix the ingredients. Remove from the refrigerator and leave to come to room temperature, then remove the olives from the oil and serve.

HINT

*Serve these marinated olives with plenty of cocktail sticks to
make this tasty snack easier to eat.*

POMEGRANATE

Pomegranate juice has been found to contain around three times the protective dose of antioxidant polyphenols of green tea.

MAJOR NUTRIENTS PER MEDIUM POMEGRANATE

234 kcal	3.3g	52.7g	11.3g	4.7g	28.8 mg	28mg	107 mcg	0.85 mg	34mg	666 mg	1.4 mcg
CALORIES	TOTAL FAT	CARBS	FIBRE	PROTEIN	VITAMIN C	CALCIUM	FOLATE	IRON	MAGNESIUM	POTASSIUM	SELENIUM

Polyphenols are a group of compounds in plant foods which are important nutrients because of their antioxidant, anti-inflammatory, and anti-cancer health benefits. Risk of high blood pressure, heart diseases, degenerative diseases of the nervous system, and several types of cancer, including prostate cancer, can all be reduced with the help of a diet rich in polyphenols. Pomegranate seeds and their juice contain such high levels of three major types – tannins, anthocyanins, and ellagic acid – that a study of healthy juices found pomegranate juice came out top, beating both acai and blueberry juice. The fruits are also a good source of iron for healthy blood, and are very high in total dietary fibre and soluble fibre to help control blood sugars and reduce LDL cholesterol and total cholesterol levels. Lastly one average fruit contains nearly half a day's recommended vitamin C intake and a third of a day's vitamin E requirement.

- Rich in polyphenols for a range of health benefits.
- Excellent source of dietary fibre for improved blood cholesterol profile.
- High in vitamins C and E.
- Good source of iron.

DID YOU KNOW?

Pomegranates were the primary symbol of Aphrodite, the Greek goddess of love who gave her name to 'aphrodisiac'. An average pomegranate contains about 600 seeds.

PRACTICAL TIPS

The easiest way to extract the seeds from the pith is to halve the fruit and use a small spoon to scoop them out, or a very ripe fruit can be halved and squeezed so that the seeds drop out. The seeds are probably best eaten raw and are ideal for scattering onto sweet or savoury salads, stirred into yogurt or added to a smoothie.

GINGERED CARROT
& POMEGRANATE SALAD

Turn the humble carrot into an exotic, fresh-tasting salad with a little
Middle Eastern magic with the help of jewel-like pomegranate!

SERVES 4 • PREP TIME: 20–25 MINS • COOK TIME: NONE

PER SERVING:	166 kcal	10.9g	1.5g	16.8g	9.9g	3.6g	1.8g	0.2g
	CALORIES	FAT	SAT FAT	CARBS	SUGAR	FIBRE	PROTEIN	SALT

INGREDIENTS

350 g/12 oz carrots, finely grated
5-cm/2-inch piece fresh ginger, peeled and grated
1 small pomegranate, quartered
50 g/1¾ oz ready-to-eat sprouting seeds,
such as alfalfa and radish sprouts

DRESSING

3 tbsp light olive oil
3 tsp red wine vinegar
3 tsp pomegranate molasses
salt and pepper (optional)

1. Put the carrots and ginger in a salad bowl. Flex the
pomegranate pieces to pop out the seeds, prising any stubborn
ones out with the tip of a small knife, and add to the bowl.

2. To make the dressing, put the oil, vinegar and pomegranate
molasses in a jam jar, season with salt and pepper, if using,
screw on the lid and shake well. Drizzle over the salad and toss
gently together. Cover and leave to marinate in the refrigerator
for 30 minutes.

3. Sprinkle the sprouting seeds over the salad and serve.

DRIED APRICOTS

Dried apricots are a nutritious and concentrated source of energy, nutrients and fibre and are low on the glycaemic index.

MAJOR NUTRIENTS PER 30G/1 OZ (3 PIECES) DRIED APRICOTS

72 kcal	TRACE	18.8g	2.2g	1g	TRACE	1297 mcg	0.8 mg	349 mg
CALORIES	TOTAL FAT	CARBS	FIBRE	PROTEIN	VITAMIN C	BETA-CAROTENE	IRON	POTASSIUM

Apricots are rich in the plant compound beta-carotene, and dried apricots are a particularly valuable source. Beta-carotene is an antioxidant which can protect against heart disease and ageing and some cancers. It also converts into vitamin A in the body, which is vital to maintain bones and vision, for healthy skin and the immune system. The good iron content in the dried fruits is another immune system booster. Dried apricots contain catechins, antioxidants with anti-inflammatory action, as well as helping to control blood pressure. Containing twice the fibre, weight for weight, of fresh apricots, dried apricots are a good source of heart-friendly soluble fibre, and are one of the lowest fruits on the glycaemic index at a value of 30 and thus a useful snack for dieters and those with diabetes as they are only slowly absorbed into the bloodstream.

- Contain high levels of beta-carotene for a variety of important health benefits.
- Low GI fruit is a good aid to weight control.
- High in total fibre and soluble fibre to help protect the heart.
- Excellent source of iron to boost immunity and keep blood healthy.

DID YOU KNOW?

Dried apricots and other dried fruits that are produced commercially are usually preserved with the aid of sulphites, which are thought to trigger asthma in susceptible people. Organic dried fruits do not contain sulphites.

PRACTICAL TIPS

Try poaching dried apricots in a little water until tender. This helps the carotenes and soluble fibre to be absorbed by the body. Dried apricots can be used in savoury dishes, such as couscous salad or Moroccan tagines. Be careful, however, if you are allergic to aspirin, as dried apricots contain salicylate, a natural substance similar to the active ingredient in aspirin.

CHEWY APRICOT & ALMOND ENERGY BARS

These flapjack-style, dairy-free energy bars are great for carrying with you for a healthy mid-morning snack.

MAKES 15 • PREP TIME: 25 MINS • COOK TIME: 30 MINS, PLUS COOLING

PER BAR:	235 kcal	14g	7.2g	26.6g	14.6g	3.5g	4.2g	TRACE
	CALORIES	FAT	SAT FAT	CARBS	SUGAR	FIBRE	PROTEIN	SALT

INGREDIENTS

115 g/4 oz coconut oil
85 g/3 oz light muscovado sugar
60 g/2¼ oz almond butter,
or other nut butter
1 dessert apple, cored and roughly grated
150 g/5½ oz porridge oats
40 g/1½ oz brown rice flour
55 g/2 oz unblanched almonds, roughly chopped
40 g/1½ oz sunflower seeds
200 g/7 oz dried apricots, diced

1. Preheat the oven to 180°C/350°F/Gas Mark 4. Line a 20-cm/8-inch shallow square cake tin with non-stick baking paper.

2. Heat the oil and sugar in a medium-sized saucepan over a low heat until the oil has melted and the sugar is dissolved. Remove from the heat and stir in the almond butter until melted.

3. Add the apple, oats, flour, almonds and sunflower seeds, and mix together well.

4. Spoon two thirds of the mixture into the prepared tin and press down firmly. Sprinkle over the apricots and press firmly into the base layer, then dot the remaining oat mixture over the top in a thin layer so that some of the apricots are still visible.

5. Bake in the preheated oven for about 25 minutes, until the top is golden brown. Remove from the oven and leave to cool in the tin until almost cold, then cut into 15 small rectangles. Leave to cool completely and serve.

HINT
To store, lift the bars out of the tin, separate and pack into a plastic container. Store in the refrigerator for up to three days.

PRUNES

A prune is any species of dried plum. They are highly concentrated sources of fibre and are very effective at flushing ageing toxins out of the body.

MAJOR NUTRIENTS PER 100 G/3½ OZ PRUNES

240 kcal	0.38g	63.88g	7.1g	2.18g	43 mg	41 mg	394 mcg	148 mcg
CALORIES	TOTAL FAT	CARBS	FIBRE	PROTEIN	CALCIUM	MAGNESIUM	BETA-CAROTENE	LUTEIN/ZEAXANTHIN

The host of antioxidants contained in prunes ensures that they are very high on the ORAC scale. Most of these protective and disease-preventing antioxidants are phenolic compounds, or water-soluble antioxidants like vitamin C and rutin, both of which keep your veins healthy and so help prevent bruising and varicose veins, support circulation and heart function, and transport nutrients to the skin for healing. Prunes and prune juice are common home remedies for constipation, partly because of their fibre content: the soluble fibre helps speed up toxic waste elimination, while the insoluble fibre helps to bulk out stools.

- The insoluble fibre in prunes makes you feel full, and thus they regulate appetite to help you mainta n weight levels.
- Prunes release their sugars very slowly, preventing these sugars from causing accelerated ageing of the skin.
- About 60 per cent of the soluble fibre in prunes comes from pectin, which helps remove damaging and ageing toxic metals such as lead and mercury from the body.

DID YOU KNOW?

In recent times, the popularity of prunes as a culinary ingredient has increased. This may be partly due to a campaign in the US, which has remarketed them as 'dried plums'.

PRACTICAL TIPS

Make a simple purée by liquidizing prunes and dried apricots with some boiling water and cinnamon. This less sugary alternative to jam makes a great sweetener for yogurt and porridge. Prunes work well in savoury dishes, such as Moroccan tagines, providing complementary sweet tones to slow-cooked meats.

COMPOTE OF DRIED FRUITS

Made entirely with dried fruit, this compote is a good winter standby. It is also very versatile – eat it on its own as a dessert, or with porridge, yogurt or quark for breakfast.

SERVES 4 • PREP TIME: 5 MINS • COOK TIME: 20 MINS

PER SERVING:	349 kcal	0.7g	0.1g	80.5g	73g	8.3g	2.9g	0.1g
	CALORIES	FAT	SAT FAT	CARBS	SUGAR	FIBRE	PROTEIN	SALT

INGREDIENTS

140 g/5 oz ready-to-eat dried apricots, halved
140 g/5 oz ready-to-eat prunes
140 g/5 oz ready-to-eat
dried apple rings, halved
55 g/2 oz dried cranberries
500 ml/17 fl oz orange juice
2 pieces stem ginger in syrup,
drained and chopped, 2 tbsp syrup reserved

1. Put the apricots, prunes, apple rings and cranberries into a saucepan and pour over the orange juice.

2. Bring to the boil over a medium heat, then stir in the ginger and reserved syrup. Reduce the heat to low, cover and simmer gently for about 15 minutes, until the fruit is soft.

3. Lift out the fruit with a slotted spoon and place in a serving dish. Simmer the juice, uncovered, for 3–4 minutes, until reduced and slightly thickened. Pour the syrup over the fruit and serve warm or cold.

VEGETABLES
& SALADS

KALE

Deep green kale contains the highest levels of antioxidants of all vegetables and is a very good source of vitamin C.

MAJOR NUTRIENTS PER 100 G/3½ OZ KALE

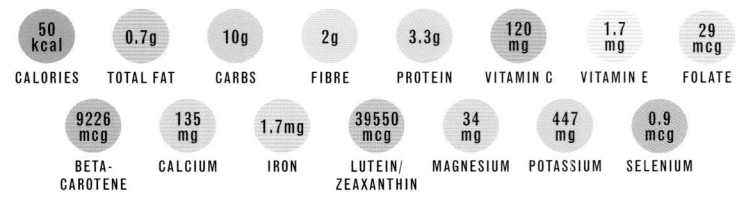

50 kcal	0.7g	10g	2g	3.3g	120 mg	1.7 mg	29 mcg
CALORIES	TOTAL FAT	CARBS	FIBRE	PROTEIN	VITAMIN C	VITAMIN E	FOLATE

9226 mcg	135 mg	1.7mg	39550 mcg	34 mg	447 mg	0.9 mcg
BETA-CAROTENE	CALCIUM	IRON	LUTEIN/ ZEAXANTHIN	MAGNESIUM	POTASSIUM	SELENIUM

Kale is one of the most nutritious members of the Brassica family. It rates as the vegetable highest in antioxidant capacity on the ORAC scale, and contains more calcium and iron than any other vegetable. A single portion contains twice the recommended daily amount of vitamin C, which helps the vegetable's high iron content to be absorbed in our bodies. One portion also gives about a fifth of the daily calcium requirement for an adult. Kale is rich in selenium, which helps fight cancer, and it contains magnesium and vitamin E for a healthy heart. The range of nutrients kale provides will keep skin young-looking and healthy.

- Rich in flavonoids and antioxidants to fight cancers.
- Contains indoles, which can help lower 'bad' cholesterol and prevent cancer.
- Calcium-rich for healthy bones.
- Extremely rich in carotenes to protect eyes.

DID YOU KNOW?

Kale contains naturally occurring substances that can interfere with the functioning of the thyroid gland – those with thyroid problems may not want to eat kale.

PRACTICAL TIPS

Wash kale before use as the curly leaves may contain sand or soil. Don't discard the deep green outer leaves – these contain rich amounts of carotenes and indoles. Kale is good steamed or stir-fried and its strong taste goes well with bacon, eggs and cheese. Kale, like spinach, shrinks a lot during cooking, so make sure you add plenty to the pan.

CRUNCHY PARMESAN & KALE CRISPS

This recipe for kale crisps is one of the simplest you'll ever make.
They're deliciously crisp, with a salty kick from the Parmesan.

SERVES 4 • PREP TIME: 10 MINS • COOK TIME: 15 MINS

PER SERVING:

153 kcal	10.2g	4.6g	5.8g	0.2g	1g	10.6g	1.4g
CALORIES	FAT	SAT FAT	CARBS	SUGAR	FIBRE	PROTEIN	SALT

INGREDIENTS

200 g/7 oz kale, woody stalks removed
1 tbsp olive oil
pinch of cayenne pepper
100 g/3½ oz Parmesan cheese, finely grated
sea salt (optional)

1. Preheat the oven to 180°C/350°F/Gas Mark 4. Put the kale and oil in a bowl, season with the cayenne pepper and salt, if using, then toss.

2. Arrange the kale in a single layer on a large baking sheet. Sprinkle the cheese over the kale. Bake in the preheated oven for 10–15 minutes, or until the leaves are dry and crisp but just a little brown at the edges.

3. Leave to cool and crisp up for 5 minutes, then serve.

MUSHROOMS

The compounds in mushrooms, which boost the immune system, help to prevent cancers, infections and auto-immune diseases such as arthritis and lupus.

MAJOR NUTRIENTS PER 85 G/3 OZ MUSHROOMS

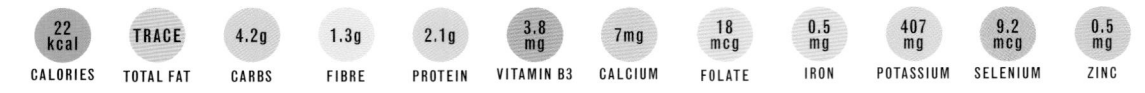

22 kcal	TRACE	4.2g	1.3g	2.1g	3.8 mg	7mg	18 mcg	0.5 mg	407 mg	9.2 mcg	0.5 mg
CALORIES	TOTAL FAT	CARBS	FIBRE	PROTEIN	VITAMIN B3	CALCIUM	FOLATE	IRON	POTASSIUM	SELENIUM	ZINC

Most of the mushrooms that we buy are the young, white-skinned button mushrooms and the older, darker gilled flat mushrooms, but there are several others, such as Chinese shiitake mushrooms, ceps and wild mushrooms. While the amount of beneficial compounds varies according to their variety and age (older, darker ones have more benefits), most mushrooms are rich in plant chemicals, which help boost the immune system. An active component of mushrooms that may be beneficial is glutamic acid, a naturally occurring form of monosodium glutamate. Mushrooms are also a useful source of protein.

• Contain compounds that can help prevent cancers and auto-immune diseases.
• Ideal source of healthy protein for vegetarians and dieters.
• Rich in the anti-cancer antioxidant mineral selenium.
• Good source of B vitamins, including folate and niacin, which has cholesterol-lowering properties.

DID YOU KNOW?
You should not pick mushrooms from the wild unless you get them checked for safety by a fungi expert. Several varieties look harmless but are poisonous.

PRACTICAL TIPS
Store mushrooms in the refrigerator in a paper bag rather than a polythene bag, to help them breathe. Most mushrooms shouldn't need washing but if any compost clings to them, gently wipe with kitchen paper. Don't peel or remove the stalks – these contain much of their goodness.

ROAST MUSHROOM & GARLIC SOUP

Large, meaty immune-boosting mushrooms make this soup a real winner when you're feeling hungry but don't fancy a meat-based meal.

SERVES 1 • PREP TIME: 20 MINS • COOK TIME: 40–50 MINS

PER SERVING:

205 kcal	7.7g	1.9g	26.2g	6.4g	5.3g	10.1g	2.8g
CALORIES	FAT	SAT FAT	CARBS	SUGAR	FIBRE	PROTEIN	SALT

INGREDIENTS

2 open-cap mushrooms, wiped clean
2 garlic cloves, peeled
1 slice wholemeal bread, cut into small cubes
1 tsp olive oil
10 g/¼ oz dried ceps
250 ml/8½ fl oz vegetable stock
1 tsp fresh thyme leaves
1 tsp Worcestershire sauce
1 tsp half-fat crème fraîche (optional)
freshly ground black pepper (optional)
1 fresh thyme sprig, to garnish

1. Preheat the oven to 180°C/350°F/Gas Mark 4.

2. Loosely wrap the open-cap mushrooms and garlic in foil and place in the preheated oven. Bake for 10 minutes, open the foil, and bake for a further 5 minutes.

3. To prepare the croûtons, drizzle the bread cubes with the oil, place on a baking sheet and bake for 10–15 minutes, or until golden brown.

4. Meanwhile, put the ceps, stock and thyme leaves in a lidded saucepan.

5. When the open-cap mushrooms are cooked, remove from the oven, slice and add them to the pan with the Worcestershire sauce, garlic, mushroom juices and pepper, if using. Cover and simmer for 15 minutes over a low heat.

6. Leave to cool slightly, then purée half the soup in a blender for a few seconds. Return to the pan and reheat gently. Stir in the crème fraîche, if using, and add pepper to taste, if using.

7. Transfer to a warmed bowl, sprinkle over the croûtons and thyme sprig and serve immediately.

RED CABBAGE

This vegetable is rich in compounds that protect us
from cancers and the signs of ageing.

MAJOR NUTRIENTS PER 100 G/3½ OZ RED CABBAGE

31 kcal	TRACE	7.4g	2.1g	1.4g	0.4 mg	57mg
CALORIES	TOTAL FAT	CARBS	FIBRE	PROTEIN	VITAMIN B3	VITAMIN C

670 mg	45 mg	18 mcg	0.8 mg	329 mcg	243 mg	0.6 mcg
BETA-CAROTENE	CALCIUM	FOLATE	IRON	LUTEIN/ZEAXANTHIN	POTASSIUM	SELENIUM

A member of the Brassica family, purple-red cabbage is high in nutrients and contains protective plant compounds. These include: indoles, which have been linked with protection against hormone-based cancers such as breast, uterine and ovarian; sulphorophane, which can help block cancer-causing chemicals; and monoterpenes, which protect body cells from damage by free radicals. Red cabbage is much higher in immunity-boosting carotenes than other cabbages – lycopene is linked with protection from prostate cancer, and anthocyanins may protect against Alzheimer's disease. Red cabbage is also higher in vitamin C than the pale varieties and is a good source of minerals, including calcium and selenium.

- Contains a variety of cancer-fighting compounds.
- Low in calories, with a low glycaemic index – ideal for dieters.
- Rich in the antioxidant vitamin C.
- Anthocyanin content may protect against Alzheimer's disease.

DID YOU KNOW?

Cabbage leaves have natural antiseptic properties and can be applied directly to wounds and bruises to help relieve pain and promote healing.

PRACTICAL TIPS

Thinly sliced red cabbage can be used raw in coleslaw instead of white cabbage. Sprinkle with lemon juice or salad dressing to prevent it turning grey. Once cut, red cabbage should be used within one to two days. When cooking, steaming is the method that preserves the maximum nutrients, so try not to overcook.

TURKEY GOUJONS WITH RED CABBAGE & KALE SLAW

Forget deep-fried chicken; this oven-baked, crispy-coated
turkey version is quick and easy to make and healthier!

SERVES 4 • PREP TIME: 20 MINS • COOK TIME: 15 MINS

PER SERVING:	471 kcal	27g	4.2g	21.3g	8.6g	9.2g	38.4g	1.8g
	CALORIES	FAT	SAT FAT	CARBS	SUGAR	FIBRE	PROTEIN	SALT

INGREDIENTS

70 g/2½ oz linseeds
40 g/1½ oz sesame seeds
2 eggs
450 g/1 lb skinless and boneless turkey breast,
thinly sliced
3 tbsp virgin olive oil
sea salt and pepper (optional)

RED CABBAGE & KALE SLAW

115 g/4 oz red cabbage, thinly shredded
30 g/1 oz kale, thinly shredded
1 carrot, coarsely grated
1 dessert apple, cored and coarsely grated
1 tsp caraway seeds
60 g/2¼ oz Greek-style natural yogurt

1. Preheat the oven to 220°C/425°F/Gas Mark 7 and put a large baking sheet in it to heat.

2. To make the slaw, put the red cabbage, kale and carrot in a bowl and mix well. Add the apple, caraway seeds and yogurt, season with salt and pepper, if using, and mix well. Cover and chill in the refrigerator until needed.

3. Put the linseeds in a spice mill or blender and process until coarsely ground. Add the sesame seeds and process for a few seconds. Tip the mixture onto a plate.

4. Crack the eggs into a shallow dish, season with salt and pepper, if using, and lightly beat with a fork.

5. Dip each turkey slice into the beaten egg, then lift out with a fork and dip both sides into the seed mixture to coat. Brush the hot baking sheet with a little oil, add the turkey slices in a single layer, then drizzle with a little extra oil.

6. Bake the turkey, turning the slices once and moving them from the corners into the centre of the baking sheet, for 15 minutes, or until golden brown and cooked through. Cut one of the larger slices in half to check that the meat is no longer pink. Any juices that run out should be clear and piping hot with steam rising. Serve the goujons with the slaw.

SWEET POTATOES

The orange-fleshed sweet potato is high in carotenes and cholesterol-lowering compounds, and is an ideal food for dieters to ward off hunger with.

MAJOR NUTRIENTS PER 150 G/5½ OZ SWEET POTATO

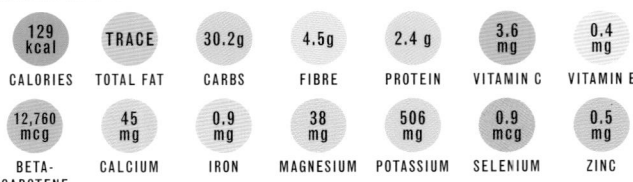

129 kcal	**TRACE**	**30.2g**	**4.5g**	**2.4 g**	**3.6 mg**	**0.4 mg**
CALORIES	TOTAL FAT	CARBS	FIBRE	PROTEIN	VITAMIN C	VITAMIN E
12,760 mcg	**45 mg**	**0.9 mg**	**38 mg**	**506 mg**	**0.9 mcg**	**0.5 mg**
BETA-CAROTENE	CALCIUM	IRON	MAGNESIUM	POTASSIUM	SELENIUM	ZINC

Sweet potatoes have a creamy texture and a sweet, slightly spicy flavour. There are two varieties, one with creamy white flesh – also called yams – and the other with orange flesh. The orange variety contains the most nutrients and is the variety referred to here. Sweet potatoes are richer in nutrients than potatoes and lower on the glycaemic index, and so are of benefit for diabetics and dieters and for regulating blood sugar levels. They also contain plant sterols and pectin that can help lower 'bad' blood cholesterol. They are extremely high in beta-carotene as well as being an excellent source of vitamin E, magnesium and selenium.

- Carotenes have strong anti-cancer action.
- Sterols and pectin content help reduce 'bad' cholesterol.
- Low glycaemic index – good for dieters.
- Antioxidants and vitamin E help improve skin conditions.
- High potassium content helps regulate body fluids and prevent fluid retention.

DID YOU KNOW?

Research has found that sweet potatoes are one of the oldest foods in the world, existing since prehistoric times. They contain naturally occurring substances that can crystallize, and people with kidney or gall bladder problems may be advised not to eat them.

PRACTICAL TIPS

Sweet potatoes can be substituted for normal potatoes in many recipes but, unlike potatoes, their skins are often waxed or treated with chemicals and are therefore not always suitable for eating. They can be added to curries, pasta, casseroles and soups, or roasted, mashed with oil, or baked, halved and served drizzled with oil. The addition of oil helps with the absorption of carotene.

SMOKY PAPRIKA SWEET POTATO CHIPS

Starchy and sweet, with crunchy edges and fluffy insides, these chips make
a really satisfying snack. Always use the best paprika you can find.

SERVES 2 • PREP TIME: 10 MINS • COOK TIME: 40 MINS

PER SERVING:

399 kcal	28.4g	10.4g	32.8g	8.8g	5g	4g	1.1g
CALORIES	FAT	SAT FAT	CARBS	SUGAR	FIBRE	PROTEIN	SALT

INGREDIENTS

*300 g/10½ oz sweet potatoes,
scrubbed and cut into chips*
2 tbsp olive oil
1 heaped tbsp smoked paprika
sea salt and pepper (optional)

SOURED CREAM DIP

4 chives, finely snipped
150 g/5½ oz soured cream

1. Preheat the oven to 180°C/350°F/Gas Mark 4. Put the sweet
potatoes, oil and paprika in a large bowl, season with salt and
pepper, if using, and toss well.

2. Arrange the chips in a single layer on a large baking sheet.
Bake in the preheated oven for 30–40 minutes, or until crisp.

3. To make the dip, put the chives and soured cream in a bowl
and mix. Season with salt and pepper, if using, and divide
between two small dipping bowls.

4. Line two larger bowls with kitchen paper. Transfer the chips
to the bowls and serve immediately with the dip.

ONIONS

The onion is a top health food, containing sulphur compounds that are natural antibiotics offering protection from cancers and heart disease.

MAJOR NUTRIENTS PER 150 G/5½ OZ ONION

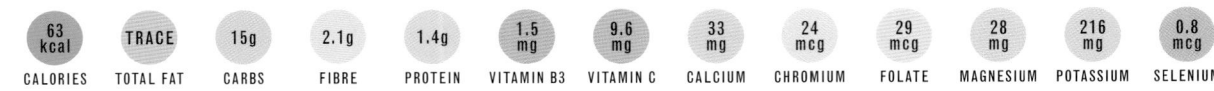

63 kcal	TRACE	15g	2.1g	1.4g	1.5 mg	9.6 mg	33 mg	24 mcg	29 mcg	28 mg	216 mg	0.8 mcg
CALORIES	TOTAL FAT	CARBS	FIBRE	PROTEIN	VITAMIN B3	VITAMIN C	CALCIUM	CHROMIUM	FOLATE	MAGNESIUM	POTASSIUM	SELENIUM

Onions are rich in the powerful compound diallyl sulphide, which gives them their strong smell and helps prevent cancer by blocking the effects of carcinogens (cancer-causing particles) in the body. Onions also contain numerous flavonoids, such as quercetin, and these antioxidant compounds help prevent blood clots and protect against heart disease and cancer. The vegetable also has anti-inflammatory and antibacterial action and can help minimize the nasal congestion of a cold. In addition, onions are very rich in chromium, a trace mineral that helps cells respond to insulin, and are a good source of vitamin C and other trace elements.

- Can help protect against several cancers, including lung cancer.
- Help protect the heart and circulatory system and may increase 'good' blood cholesterol.
- Anti-inflammatory, which may help symptoms of arthritis.
- Antibacterial and may help control colds.
- Can help regulate insulin response.

DID YOU KNOW?

If you cook onions quickly at a high heat, you destroy a large percentage of the beneficial sulphide compounds that they contain.

PRACTICAL TIPS

Stored in an airy, dry, cool place without touching each other, most onions will last for several months, although the vitamin C content will diminish over time. To cook, onions should be gently sautéed in oil to retain maximum nutrients. Mild onions can be thinly sliced and eaten raw.

SWEET ROOTS BOWL

Root vegetables are full of starch and sugar, so they're great for giving your energy levels a long-term boost. Using tahini in dressings increases your intake of protein and essential fats.

SERVES 4 • PREP TIME: 12 MINS • COOK TIME: 35–40 MINS

PER SERVING:

402 kcal	18.4g	2.3g	54.2g	11.8g	9.5g	10.1g	0.3g
CALORIES	FAT	SAT FAT	CARBS	SUGAR	FIBRE	PROTEIN	SALT

INGREDIENTS

2 sweet potatoes, cut into chunks
2 beetroot, cut into chunks
2 red onions, cut into wedges
2 tbsp olive oil
2 tsp cumin seeds
75 g/2¾ oz brown rice
4 tbsp tahini
juice of 1 lemon
½ tsp pepper
½ tsp clear honey
200 g/7 oz kale, shredded
2 tbsp flaked almonds, toasted

1. Preheat the oven to 200°C/400°F/Gas Mark 6. Place the sweet potatoes, beetroot and onions in a bowl with the oil and cumin seeds and toss together to coat with the oil.

2. Tip into a roasting tin and roast in the preheated oven for 35–40 minutes, until tender.

3. Meanwhile, cook the rice according to the packet instructions. Whisk together the tahini, lemon juice, pepper and honey.

4. Stir the kale into the root vegetables 10 minutes before the end of the roasting time.

5. Drain the rice and divide between four warmed bowls. Toss the vegetables with the dressing and serve on top of the rice, sprinkled with the toasted almonds.

VARIATION
Instead of rice, try serving the root vegetables over protein-packed quinoa.

TOMATOES

Tomatoes are one of the healthiest salad foods because they contain lycopene, which offers protection from prostate cancer, and compounds to help prevent blood clots.

MAJOR NUTRIENTS PER 100 G/3½ OZ TOMATO

18 kcal	0.2g	3.9g	1.2g	0.9g	12.7 mg	123 mcg	2573 mcg	237 mg
CALORIES	TOTAL FAT	CARBS	FIBRE	PROTEIN	VITAMIN C	LUTEIN/ ZEAXANTHIN	LYCOPENE	POTASSIUM

Tomatoes are our major source of dietary lycopene, a carotene antioxidant that fights heart disease and may help to prevent prostate cancer. Tomatoes also have an anticoagulant effect because of the salicylates contained in them, and they contain several other antioxidants, including vitamin C, quercetin and lutein. Tomatoes are low in calories but high in potassium, and contain useful amounts of fibre.

- Excellent source of lycopene, which helps prevent prostate cancer.
- One medium tomato contains nearly a quarter of the day's recommended intake of vitamin C for an adult.
- Rich in potassium to help regulate body fluids.
- Quercetin and lutein content helps prevent cataracts and keep eyes and heart healthy.
- Contain salicylates, which have an anticoagulant effect.

DID YOU KNOW?

Lycopene is actually more active in processed tomato products such as ketchup, tomato purée and tomato juice than it is in the raw tomato.

PRACTICAL TIPS

The riper and redder the tomato, the higher its lycopene content. Vine-ripened tomatoes also contain more lycopene than those ripened after picking. The tomato skin is richer in nutrients than the flesh and the central seed part is high in salicylates, so avoid peeling and don't deseed unless necessary. The lycopene in tomatoes is better absorbed in your body if it is eaten with something that contains oil, such as a salad dressing.

SLOW-COOKED
TOMATO PASTA SAUCE

This is the traditional Italian tomato-based pasta sauce. The flavours deepen
during the slow simmering, so resist the temptation to rush this stage.

MAKES 750 ML/ 1¼ PINTS • PREP TIME: 20 MINS • COOK TIME: 1 HOUR 40 MINS

PER 750 ML/1¼ PINTS:

805 kcal	53.3g	7.3g	79.2g	49.3g	20.6g	15.7g	0.2g
CALORIES	FAT	SAT FAT	CARBS	SUGAR	FIBRE	PROTEIN	SALT

INGREDIENTS

50 ml/2 fl oz olive oil
1 onion, chopped
5 garlic cloves, finely sliced
2 tbsp roughly chopped fresh flat-leaf parsley
2 tbsp roughly chopped fresh basil
1.5 kg/3 lb 5 oz tomatoes, roughly chopped
1 tsp brown sugar
1 tbsp red wine vinegar
salt and pepper (optional)

1. Heat the oil in a heavy-based saucepan over a medium heat.
Add the onion and fry gently until soft and almost golden. Add
the garlic and herbs and fry for 30 seconds before carefully
pouring in the chopped tomatoes, including the seeds and skin.

2. Stir in the sugar and vinegar. Season with salt and pepper,
if using, then reduce the heat to medium–low and simmer the
sauce, uncovered, for 1½ hours, or until the tomatoes have
broken down and the sauce has thickened. Stir occasionally to
prevent anything catching on the base of the pan.

3. Leave to cool slightly and serve mixed into pasta or spaghetti,
or as required.

ARTICHOKES

Globe artichokes are low in calories and ideal for dieters, and their
cynarin content helps maintain liver health.

MAJOR NUTRIENTS PER AVERAGE-SIZED ARTICHOKE

60 kcal	TRACE	13.4g	6.5g	4.2g	12 mg	54 mg	65 mcg	1.5 mg	557 mcg	425 mg	72 mg
CALORIES	TOTAL FAT	CARBS	FIBRE	PROTEIN	VITAMIN C	CALCIUM	FOLATE	IRON	LUTEIN/ ZEAXANTHIN	POTASSIUM	MAGNESIUM

A delicious delicacy, globe artichokes are the unopened flowers of a large
perennial plant. The whole vegetable can be served as an appetizer, but
only the tender leaf bases and more nutritious central heart are edible.
Artichokes are one of the richest vegetable sources of a range of minerals,
including calcium, iron, magnesium and potassium. They are very high in
fibre, and contain cynarin, which is said to boost liver function.

- Very rich source of minerals, including calcium, iron and the
  antioxidant mineral magnesium for bone and heart health.
- Very high in fibre, with a high proportion of soluble fibre for healthy
  blood cholesterol.
- Good source of vitamin C and folate.
- Low in calories and low on the glycaemic index.

DID YOU KNOW?

*Iron, copper and aluminium
cookware will cause artichokes
to oxidize and discolour, so use
stainless steel, glass or enamel.*

PRACTICAL TIPS

Very small baby artichokes can be eaten whole but, when using larger
ones, snap off the stem, cut off the top third of the artichoke and remove
the tough outer leaves individually by hand. Simmer in boiling water
containing a little lemon juice for 20 minutes, or until the leaves are easy
to remove. Eat only the creamy bases of each leaf. Once the leaves are
removed, the bristly choke should be pulled out to reveal the tender heart,
which is delicious served hot with a dressing, cold in a salad or with pasta.

AVOCADO, ARTICHOKE & ALMOND SALAD

This beautiful salad is full of healthy ingredients, giving you masses of heart-friendly monounsaturated fats and a huge boost of fibre.

SERVES 4 • PREP TIME: 15 MINS • COOK TIME: NONE

PER SERVING:

364 kcal CALORIES	24g FAT	3g SAT FAT	31g CARBS	4.1g SUGAR	13.4g FIBRE	9g PROTEIN	1.4g SALT

INGREDIENTS

1 red mini cos lettuce, tough outer leaves discarded
6 canned or bottled artichoke hearts in water, drained and patted dry, about 250 g/9 oz drained weight
1 small yellow pepper, deseeded and thinly sliced
2 ripe avocados, peeled, stoned and sliced
50 g/1¾ oz lamb's lettuce
40 g/1½ oz flaked almonds
4 radishes, finely chopped
8 dark rye crispbreads, to serve

DRESSING

3 tbsp balsamic vinegar
1 tbsp olive oil
½ tsp salt
pepper (optional)

1. Cut 1.5 cm/⅝ inch from the base of the cos lettuce. Peel off the outer leaves and reserve. Cut the heart lengthways into eight pieces and arrange on a serving platter with the reserved leaves.

2. Halve the artichoke hearts and add to the serving platter with the yellow pepper and avocados.

3. Scatter over the lamb's lettuce, flaked almonds and radishes.

4. To make the dressing, combine the vinegar, oil, salt, and pepper, if using, whisking together thoroughly, then drizzle over the salad.

5. Serve immediately with the crispbreads.

VARIATION
For a more substantial meal, this salad would go well served with some salmon, chicken or pork.

CAULIFLOWER

Cauliflower contains the same potent cleansing and rejuvenating sulphur compounds as the other members of the Brassica family, such as Brussels sprouts.

MAJOR NUTRIENTS PER 100 G/3½ OZ CAULIFLOWER

25 kcal	0g	5g	2.5g	2g	0.65 mg	0.22 mg	46 mg	57mg
CALORIES	TOTAL FAT	CARBS	FIBRE	PROTEIN	VITAMIN B5	VITAMIN B6	VITAMIN C	FOLATE

One of these compounds, sulphoraphane, has been found to help prevent adult-onset diabetes and destroy invading microbes like bacteria and viruses. It can also work as an antioxidant through enzymes produced in the liver, helping repair areas of the body that have been damaged. Research has shown that this wonder substance helps prevent cancer and the progression of tumours by stopping cancer cells spreading and actively killing them off. Another sulphur compound in cauliflower, indole-3-carbinol, appears to lower oestrogen, thereby helping to prevent cancers of the breast and prostate as well as regulating female hormones, keeping women youthful post menopause.

- Source of vitamin B6, used to unlock energy from the food we eat, for skin and bone renewal.
- Vitamin C helps the liver remove damaging, ageing toxins.
- Vitamin C and vitamin B5 support the adrenal glands and so help us cope with stress, an important factor in staying young.

DID YOU KNOW?

A purple cauliflower variety, called Purple Cape, has recently been developed so that fans of cauliflower can take on beneficial proanthocyanidins, the antioxidants also found in purple sprouting broccoli.

PRACTICAL TIPS

Serve raw florets with dips or use in a salad. Remove the outer leaves and steam a whole cauliflower for about 10 minutes or separate into florets and steam for about 6 minutes. While cooking, test regularly with a knife to make sure it doesn't overcook. Over-cooked cauliflower evokes memories of nasty school dinners, but cooked properly it is crunchy and delicious.

BASIL & LEMON
CAULIFLOWER RICE

Raw cauliflower is pulsed in a food processor to resemble rice grains, then
pan-fried with celery and garlic to make this nutritious side dish.

SERVES 4 • PREP TIME: 20–25 MINS • COOK TIME: 15–20 MINS

PER SERVING:

182 kcal	14.4g	1.3g	11.4g	3.7g	4.7g	5.7g	0.1g
CALORIES	FAT	SAT FAT	CARBS	SUGAR	FIBRE	PROTEIN	SALT

INGREDIENTS

70 g/2½ oz unskinned hazelnuts, roughly chopped
500 g/1 lb 2 oz head of cauliflower
1 tbsp olive oil
2 celery sticks, roughly chopped
3 garlic cloves, roughly chopped
30 g/1 oz fresh basil, roughly chopped
zest and juice of 1 lemon
70 g/2½ oz watercress, chopped
salt and pepper (optional)

1. Add the chopped hazelnuts to a large, dry frying pan and toast over a medium heat until golden. Remove from the pan and set aside.

2. Remove the core from the cauliflower and divide up the florets. Place in a food processor and pulse until the cauliflower resembles rice grains. Place in a bowl and set aside.

3. Add the oil to a frying pan over a medium heat and fry the celery and garlic for about 5–6 minutes, or until soft.

4. Add the cauliflower rice to the frying pan and stir to combine. Cook, stirring occasionally, for 8–10 minutes. Remove from the heat and leave to cool for a few minutes before adding the basil, lemon zest and juice, hazelnuts and watercress. Season with salt and pepper, if using, and serve immediately.

HINT
Cauliflower rice can be used as a substitute for traditional rice in other recipes, experiment with flavour combinations.

GARLIC

Valued as a health-protector for thousands of years, garlic bulbs are a useful antibiotic, and can also reduce the risk of both heart disease and cancer.

MAJOR NUTRIENTS PER 2 GARLIC CLOVES

9 kcal	TRACE	2g	TRACE	0.4g	2mg	11 mg	24 mg	1 mcg
CALORIES	TOTAL FAT	CARBS	FIBRE	PROTEIN	VITAMIN C	CALCIUM	POTASSIUM	SELENIUM

Although often used only in small quantities, garlic can still make an impact on health. It is rich in powerful sulphur compounds that cause its strong odour but are the main source of its health benefits. Research has found that garlic can help minimize the risk of both heart disease and many types of cancer. It is also a powerful antibiotic and inhibits fungal infections such as athlete's foot. It also appears to minimize stomach ulcers. Eaten in reasonable quantity, it is also a good source of vitamin C, selenium, potassium and calcium. Garlic should be crushed or chopped and left to stand for a few minutes before cooking.

- May prevent formation of blood clots and arterial plaque and help prevent heart disease.
- Regular garlic consumption may significantly reduce the risk of colon, stomach and prostate cancer.
- Natural antibiotic, antiviral and antifungal.
- Can help prevent stomach ulcers.

DID YOU KNOW?

Cooking meat at high temperatures, as when grilling or barbecuing, can have a carcinogenic effect, but when garlic is used with the meat it reduces the production of the cancer-promoting chemicals.

PRACTICAL TIPS

Choose large, firm undamaged bulbs and store in a container with air holes, in a dark, cool, dry place. Peel the garlic by lightly crushing the clove with the flat side of a cleaver or knife and just lightly cook – long cooking destroys its beneficial compounds.

GARLIC & HERB BREAD SPIRAL

A delicious alternative to the garlic bread often served as an accompaniment to pizza. The inclusion of parsley will help neutralize any strong odours!

SERVES 6 • PREP TIME: 30 MINS, PLUS RISING • COOK TIME: 20–25 MINS

PER SERVING:

 488 kcal CALORIES
 20.3g FAT
 8.9g SAT FAT
 60.6g CARBS
 0.9g SUGAR
 2.5g FIBRE
 14.8g PROTEIN
1.8g SALT

INGREDIENTS

1 tbsp vegetable oil, for greasing
500 g/1 lb 2 oz strong white flour
1 sachet easy-blend dried yeast
1½ tsp salt
350 ml/12 fl oz lukewarm water
2 tbsp vegetable oil
10 g/¼ oz strong white flour, for dusting
85 g/3 oz butter, melted and cooled
3 garlic cloves, crushed
2 tbsp chopped fresh parsley
2 tbsp snipped fresh chives
1 egg, beaten, for glazing
sea salt flakes, for sprinkling (optional)

1. Brush a large baking sheet with oil. Combine the flour, yeast and salt in a mixing bowl. Stir in the water and half the oil, mixing to a soft, sticky dough.

2. Turn out the dough onto a lightly floured surface and knead until smooth and no longer sticky. Return to the bowl, cover and leave in a warm place for about 1 hour until doubled in size.

3. Meanwhile, preheat the oven to 240°C/475°F/Gas Mark 9. Mix the butter, garlic, herbs and remaining oil together. Roll out the dough to a 33 x 23-cm/13 x 9-inch rectangle and spread the herb mix evenly over the dough to within 1 cm/½ inch of the edge.

4. Roll up the dough from one long side and place on the prepared baking sheet, join underneath. Cut into 12 thick slices and arrange, cut side down, on the baking sheet, about 2 cm/¾ inch apart.

5. Cover and leave to rise in a warm place until doubled in size and springy to the touch. Brush with egg and sprinkle with sea salt flakes, if using. Bake in the preheated oven for 20–25 minutes, until golden brown and firm. Transfer to a wire rack and leave to cool.

BROCCOLI

Of all the vegetables in the Brassica family, broccoli has shown the
highest levels of protection against prostate cancer.

MAJOR NUTRIENTS PER 100 G/3½ OZ BROCCOLI

34 kcal	0.4g	6.6g	2.6g	2.8g	89 mg	361 mcg	47 mg	1403 mcg	2.5 mcg
CALORIES	TOTAL FAT	CARBS	FIBRE	PROTEIN	VITAMIN C	BETA-CAROTENE	CALCIUM	LUTEIN/ZEAXANTHIN	SELENIUM

Broccoli comes in several varieties but the darker the colour, the more beneficial nutrients the vegetable contains. It contains sulphoraphane and indoles, which have strong anti-cancer effects, particularly against breast and colon cancer. Broccoli is also high in flavonoids, which have been linked with a significant reduction in ovarian cancer. The chemicals in broccoli protect against stomach ulcers, stomach and lung cancer and possibly skin cancer. They also act as a detoxifier, helping lower 'bad' blood cholesterol, boosting the immune system, and protecting against cataracts.

- Rich in a variety of nutrients that protect against some cancers.
- Contains chemicals that help to lower 'bad' cholesterol and protect against heart disease.
- Lutein and zeaxanthin help prevent macular degeneration.
- Helps eradicate the Helicobacter pylori bacteria.
- High calcium content helps build and protect bones.
- Excellent source of the antioxidants vitamin C and selenium.
- 3–5 servings a week offer protection against cancer.

DID YOU KNOW?

You can eat the leaves of the broccoli as well as the stalks and florets. They contain as much goodness and taste great, too!

PRACTICAL TIPS

Look for heads rich with colour and avoid any broccoli with pale yellow or brown patches on the florets. Store in the refrigerator and use within a few days of purchase. Frozen broccoli contains all the nutrients of fresh broccoli. Cook by lightly steaming or stir-frying.

ROASTED BROCCOLI WITH PINE NUTS & PARMESAN

This is a good side dish to serve with any roast meat or fish, but it would also make a nutritious lunch or light supper dish, served with crusty white bread.

SERVES 4 • PREP TIME: 20 MINS • COOK TIME: 25 MINS

PER SERVING:

340 kcal	28.9g	4.2g	17.2g	4.1g	6.2g	8.8g	1.9g
CALORIES	FAT	SAT FAT	CARBS	SUGAR	FIBRE	PROTEIN	SALT

INGREDIENTS

1 head of broccoli, weighing 800 g/1 lb 12 oz
6 tbsp olive oil
1 tsp sea salt
¼ tsp pepper
4 tbsp toasted pine nuts
grated rind of ½ lemon
30 g/1 oz Parmesan cheese shavings
4 lemon wedges, to garnish

1. Preheat the oven to 230°C/450°F/Gas Mark 8. Cut off the broccoli crown where it meets the stalk. Remove the outer peel from the stalk. Slice the stalk crossways into 8-cm/3¼-inch pieces, then quarter each slice lengthways. Cut the crown into 4-cm/1½-inch wide wedges.

2. Put the broccoli wedges and stalks in a bowl. Sprinkle with the oil, salt and pepper, gently tossing to coat. Spread out in a large roasting tin. Cover tightly with foil and roast on the bottom rack of the preheated oven for 10 minutes.

3. Remove the foil, then roast for a further 5–8 minutes, until just starting to brown. Turn the stalks and wedges over, and roast for a further 3–5 minutes, until tender.

4. Tip into a shallow, warmed serving dish, together with any cooking juices. Sprinkle with the pine nuts and lemon rind, tossing to mix. Scatter the cheese shavings over the top.

5. Garnish with lemon wedges and serve hot, warm or at room temperature.

ASPARAGUS

The distinctive asparagus is an anti-inflammatory and contains a
type of fibre that keeps the digestive system healthy.

MAJOR NUTRIENTS PER 10 ASPARAGUS SPEARS

24 kcal	TRACE	4.7g	2.5g	2.6g	6.7 mg	1.36 mg	29 mg	62 mcg	2.6 mg	17 mg	242 mg
CALORIES	TOTAL FAT	CARBS	FIBRE	PROTEIN	VITAMIN C	VITAMIN E	CALCIUM	FOLATE	IRON	MAGNESIUM	POTASSIUM

The plant chemical glutathione contained in asparagus has
been found to be anti-inflammatory and may help rheumatoid arthritis
symptoms. The vegetable is also rich in the soluble fibre oligosaccharide,
which acts as a prebiotic in the gut by stimulating the growth of 'friendly'
bacteria. It is also a valuable source of vitamin C, folate, magnesium,
potassium and iron. Unusually for a vegetable, it is a good source of vitamin
E, an antioxidant that helps keep the heart and immune system healthy.

- Glutathione content is anti-inflammatory.
- Fibre content acts as a prebiotic for gut health.
- Good source of a wide range of important vitamins, including
  vitamin E.
- Rich in iron, promotes energy and healing and helps
  fight infection.

DID YOU KNOW?

*Asparagus contains purines,
compounds that encourage the
production of uric acid in the body,
which can trigger an attack of
gout. Gout sufferers should avoid
asparagus, or only consume it in
moderation.*

PRACTICAL TIPS

Asparagus doesn't store well and should be eaten as soon as possible
after picking. If necessary, store in a polythene bag in the refrigerator for
one to two days. If possible, cook the spears upright so that the delicate
tips don't overcook before the stalks are tender. Large spears can also
be brushed with oil and grilled for 2–3 minutes on each side, until tender.
Small, thin asparagus spears can be used in quiches, soups and risottos.

BROWN RICE RISOTTO PRIMAVERA

Loaded with fresh spring vegetables for vitality, this brown rice risotto provides a delicious and balanced meat-free meal.

SERVES 4 • PREP TIME: 20–25 MINS • COOK TIME: 45–50 MINS

PER SERVING:

433 kcal	16.8g	8.1g	59.6g	5.4g	5g	13.6g	3.7g
CALORIES	FAT	SAT FAT	CARBS	SUGAR	FIBRE	PROTEIN	SALT

INGREDIENTS

1.2 litres/2 pints vegetable stock
1 tbsp olive oil
1 large leek, thinly sliced, white and green parts kept separate
2 garlic cloves, finely chopped
250 g/9 oz short-grain brown rice
150 g/5½ oz baby carrots, tops trimmed, halved lengthways
100 g/3½ oz asparagus spears, woody stems removed
225 g/8 oz courgettes, cut into cubes
30 g/1 oz butter
70 g/2½ oz finely grated Parmesan cheese
60 g/2¼ oz mixed baby spinach, watercress and rocket leaves

1. Bring the stock to the boil in a saucepan.

2. Meanwhile, heat the oil in a large frying pan over a medium heat. Add the white leek slices and garlic and cook for 3–4 minutes, or until soft but not brown.

3. Stir the rice into the pan and cook for 1 minute. Pour in half of the hot stock, bring back to the boil, then cover and simmer for 15 minutes.

4. Add the carrots and half of the remaining stock and stir again. Cover and cook for 15 minutes.

5. Add the green leek slices, asparagus and courgettes to the rice, then add a little extra stock. Re-cover and cook for 5–6 minutes, or until the vegetables and rice are just tender.

6. Remove from the heat, stir in the butter and two thirds of the cheese, then add a little more stock if needed. Top with the mixed leaves, cover with the lid, and warm through for 1–2 minutes, or until the leaves are just beginning to wilt.

7. Spoon the risotto into shallow bowls, sprinkle with the remaining cheese and serve immediately.

LEEKS

As a member of the onion family, leeks have many similar benefits, including an ability to reduce 'bad' blood cholesterol and protect against heart disease.

MAJOR NUTRIENTS PER AVERAGE-SIZED LEEK

61 kcal	0.3g	14g	1.8g	1.5g	12 mg	0.9 mg
CALORIES	TOTAL FAT	CARBS	FIBRE	PROTEIN	VITAMIN C	VITAMIN E

1000 mcg	59 mg	64 mcg	2.1 mg	1900 mcg	28 mg	180 mg
BETA-CAROTENE	CALCIUM	FOLATE	IRON	LUTEIN/ZEAXANTHIN	MAGNESIUM	POTASSIUM

Leeks have a distinct, slightly sweet onion flavour but are milder than most onions. The long thick stems have a lower white area and dark green tops, which are edible but usually removed because they can be tough and strong-tasting. Leeks have been shown to reduce total 'bad' blood cholesterol while raising 'good' cholesterol, and so can help to prevent heart and arterial disease. Regular consumption is also linked with a reduction in the risk of prostate, ovarian and colon cancer. It is the allylic sulfides in the plants that appear to confer the benefits. They are also rich in vitamin C, fibre, vitamin E, folate and several important minerals.

- Lower total 'bad' blood cholesterol and raise 'good' cholesterol.
- Anti-cancer action.
- Mildly diuretic to help prevent fluid retention.
- High in carotenes, including lutein and zeaxanthin, for eye health.

DID YOU KNOW?

In Ancient Greece, leeks were prized for their beneficial effects on the throat. The leek is now the national emblem of Wales.

PRACTICAL TIPS

Wash leeks thoroughly before using – they may contain soil between the tight leaves. The more of the green section of the leek that you use, the more of the beneficial nutrients you will retain. Steam, bake or stir-fry leeks, rather than boil, to retain their vitamins. The darker green parts take a little longer to cook than the white part so, if chopped, add the green parts to the pan first.

ROASTED LEEKS WITH PARSLEY

Leeks are given the Mediterranean treatment in this quickly prepared dish. Roasted until slightly charred, they make a tasty accompaniment to fish or roast lamb.

SERVES 4 • PREP TIME: 10 MINS • COOK TIME: 15–20 MINS

PER SERVING: **181 kcal** CALORIES | **10.6g** FAT | **1.4g** SAT FAT | **21.3g** CARBS | **5.8g** SUGAR | **2.7g** FIBRE | **2.3g** PROTEIN | **0.1g** SALT

INGREDIENTS

4 large leeks, trimmed and halved lengthways
3 tbsp extra virgin olive oil
1 tbsp chopped fresh flat-leaf parsley
sea salt flakes and pepper (optional)

1. Preheat the oven to 240°C/475°F/Gas Mark 9. Pack the leeks in a single layer in a shallow casserole into which they fit tightly.

2. Brush with the oil, taking care that it goes into the crevices. Sprinkle with the parsley and salt and pepper, if using, turning to coat.

3. Roast in the preheated oven for 15–20 minutes, turning once, until the leeks begin to blacken at the edges.

CARROTS

The richest in carotenes of all plant foods, carrots offer protection from cancers and cardiovascular disease, and help keep eyes and lungs healthy.

MAJOR NUTRIENTS PER 100 G/3½ OZ CARROTS

41 kcal	TRACE	9.6g	2.8g	0.9g	6mg	0.7 mg	8285 mcg	33 mg	256 mcg	320 mg
CALORIES	TOTAL FAT	CARBS	FIBRE	PROTEIN	VITAMIN C	VITAMIN E	BETA-CAROTENE	CALCIUM	LUTEIN/ ZEAXANTHIN	POTASSIUM

Carrots are one of the most nutritious root vegetables. They are an excellent source of antioxidant compounds, and the richest vegetable source of carotenes, which give them their bright orange colour. These compounds help protect against cardiovascular disease and cancer. Carotenes may reduce the incidence of heart disease by about 45 per cent, promote good vision and help maintain healthy lungs. They are also rich in fibre, antioxidant vitamins C and E, calcium and potassium. A chemical in carrots, falcarinol, has been shown to suppress tumours in animals by a third.

- High carotene content protects against high blood cholesterol and heart disease.
- May offer protection against some cancers and emphysema.
- People who eat at least five carrots a week are nearly two thirds less likely to have a stroke than those who don't.
- Carrots help to protect sight and night vision.
- Carrots contain a good range of vitamins, minerals and fibre.

DID YOU KNOW?

A very high intake of carrots can cause the skin to appear orange. Called carotanemia, it is a harmless condition.

PRACTICAL TIPS

The darker orange the carrot, the more carotenes it will contain. Remove any green on the stalk end of the carrot before cooking as this can be mildly toxic. The nutrients in carrots are more available to the body when a carrot is cooked, rather than raw, and adding a little oil during cooking helps the carotenes to be absorbed.

CARROT CAKE MUFFINS

These delicious carrot, raisin and walnut muffins are surprisingly low in sugar and fat, and are packed with fibre and vitamin A-rich carrots.

MAKES 10 • PREP TIME: 20–25 MINS • COOK TIME: 25 MINS

PER MUFFIN:

| 318 kcal CALORIES | 12.5g FAT | 4.2g SAT FAT | 47g CARBS | 9g SUGAR | 7.9g FIBRE | 9g PROTEIN | 1g SALT |

INGREDIENTS

450 g/1 lb plain wholemeal flour
1 tsp bicarbonate of soda
1 tsp baking powder
½ tsp salt
1 tsp ground cinnamon
¼ tsp ground ginger
2 tbsp rapeseed oil
1 egg
2 egg whites
3 tbsp stevia granules
2 tsp vanilla extract
125 g/4½ oz unsweetened apple sauce
80 ml/2¾ fl oz unsweetened almond milk
450 g/1 lb carrots
80 g/2¾ oz raisins
60 g/2¼ oz walnuts, chopped
60 g/2¼ oz desiccated coconut

1. Preheat the oven to 180°C/350°F/Gas Mark 4. Line ten holes in a 12-hole muffin tin with paper cases.

2. Sift together the flour, bicarbonate of soda, baking powder, salt, cinnamon and ginger into a bowl, tipping in any bran left in the sieve.

3. Beat together the oil, egg, egg whites, stevia granules and vanilla extract in a bowl until creamy, then stir in the apple sauce and almond milk.

4. Peel and grate the carrots, then add to the liquid ingredients with the raisins, walnuts and half the desiccated coconut. Add the flour mixture, stirring until just combined.

5. Divide the mixture between the paper cases. Bake in the preheated oven for 25 minutes, or until a skewer inserted into the centre of a muffin comes out clean.

6. Leave to cool in the tin until cool enough to handle, then transfer to a wire rack and leave to cool completely. Decorate with the remaining desiccated coconut or wrap in polythene bags and freeze for up to 1 month.

BEANSPROUTS

Beansprouts are a very low-calorie source of many nutrients,
including vitamin C, protein, calcium and folate.

MAJOR NUTRIENTS PER 100 G/3½ OZ RAW BEANSPROUTS

30 kcal	TRACE	6g	1.8g	3g	13 mg	13 mg	61 mcg	0.9 mg	21 mg	149 mg
CALORIES	TOTAL FAT	CARBS	FIBRE	PROTEIN	VITAMIN C	CALCIUM	FOLATE	IRON	MAGNESIUM	POTASSIUM

While you can sprout many types of bean, many of the sprouted seeds available in the shops are from the mung bean. Other sprouts you may find include alfalfa, azuki, lentil and pea. Beansprouts are a very low-calorie source of nutrients and thus are very useful for dieters. Dried beans contain no vitamin C, but once they are sprouted using water, they contain good levels of the vitamin. Beansprouts are also a good source of protein and calcium, and are rich in folate, the vitamin important for healthy blood and essential for a healthy foetus in pregnant women.

- Low in calories and a rich source of very low-fat protein.
- Good source of vitamin C.
- Very good source of folate.
- Good source of several minerals, including iron, magnesium, calcium and potassium.

DID YOU KNOW?

Raw sprouts, especially alfalfa sprouts and mung bean sprouts, have a higher than average risk of being contaminated with E. coli or salmonella bacteria, which can cause food poisoning. Be sure to wash all sprouts thoroughly before consuming.

PRACTICAL TIPS

Most beans can be easily sprouted by putting a layer on damp kitchen paper in a dark place for several days and watering daily. You can also purchase dedicated sprouters. Beansprouts quickly lose their vitamin C after sprouting, so eat them as soon as possible. They can be used raw in salads and spring rolls, stir-fried or lightly steamed, or used as a garnish.

CHICKEN CHOW MEIN

Beansprouts add delicious crunch and valuable nutrients to many standard Chinese dishes. They lend themselves particularly well to quick cooking, as in stir-fries like this one.

SERVES 4 • PREP TIME: 20 MINS • COOK TIME: 15 MINS

PER SERVING:

 485 kcal CALORIES

 15.8g FAT

 2.6g SAT FAT

 52.3g CARBS

 4.8g SUGAR

 4.4g FIBRE

 33.4g PROTEIN

1.8g SALT

INGREDIENTS

250 g/9 oz dried medium Chinese egg noodles
2 tbsp sunflower oil
280 g/10 oz cooked chicken breasts, shredded
1 garlic clove, finely chopped
1 red pepper, thinly sliced
100 g/3½ oz shiitake mushrooms, sliced
6 spring onions, sliced
100 g/3½ oz beansprouts
3 tbsp soy sauce
1 tbsp sesame oil

1. Place the noodles in a large bowl or dish and break them up slightly. Pour over enough boiling water to cover and set aside while preparing the other ingredients.

2. Heat the sunflower oil in a preheated wok or frying pan over a medium heat. Add the chicken, garlic, red pepper, mushrooms, spring onions and beansprouts and stir-fry for about 5 minutes.

3. Drain the noodles thoroughly, then add them to the wok, toss well and stir-fry for a further 5 minutes. Drizzle over the soy sauce and sesame oil and toss until thoroughly combined. Transfer to warmed serving bowls and serve immediately.

PEAS

Either freshly picked or bought frozen, peas are a rich source of vitamin C,
fibre and protein, with a high proportion of lutein for eye health.

MAJOR NUTRIENTS PER 100 G/3½ OZ SHELLED PEAS

81 kcal	0.4g	14.5g	5.1g	5.4g	40 mg	2.1 mg
CALORIES	TOTAL FAT	CARBS	FIBRE	PROTEIN	VITAMIN C	VITAMIN B3
56 mg	65 mcg	1.5 mg	2477 mcg	33 mg	244 mg	1.2 mg
CALCIUM	FOLATE	IRON	LUTEIN/ ZEAXANTHIN	MAGNESIUM	POTASSIUM	ZINC

Peas are rich in a wide range of useful vitamins and minerals. They are
particularly high in antioxidant vitamin C, folate and vitamin B3, and their
very high lutein and zeaxanthin content means that they help protect the
eyes from macular degeneration. The B vitamins they contain may also help
protect the bones from osteoporosis, and help to decrease the risk of strokes
by keeping levels of the amino acid homocysteine low in the blood. Peas,
high in protein, are very useful for vegetarians. In addition, their high fibre
content partly comprises pectin, a jelly-like substance that helps to lower
'bad' blood cholesterol and may also help prevent heart and arterial disease.

- Contain several heart-friendly nutrients and chemicals.
- Rich in carotenes to protect eyes and reduce risk of cancers.
- Very high in total and soluble fibre to lower cholesterol.
- Very rich in vitamin C.

DID YOU KNOW?

*Frozen peas – usually frozen
within hours of harvesting
– can often contain more vitamin
C and other nutrients than fresh
peas in their pods, which may be
several days old.*

PRACTICAL TIPS

When buying peas in the pod choose those that aren't packed in too
tightly. Older peas become almost square, lose their flavour, and become
mealy because the sugars have been converted to starches. Young pods
can be eaten with the peas inside and young peas can be eaten raw.
To cook, steam lightly or boil in minimal water, as the vitamin C content
diminishes in water.

PESTO SALMON WITH SPRING VEG

Spring vegetables are so tasty they don't need much doing to them, just gentle steaming and a little lemon dressing. The dressing cuts through the richness of the pesto salmon perfectly.

SERVES 4 • PREP TIME: 15 MINS • COOK TIME: 10–12 MINS

PER SERVING:

646 kcal	42.9g	7.6g	21.9g	7.7g	9.7g	42g	0.7g
CALORIES	FAT	SAT FAT	CARBS	SUGAR	FIBRE	PROTEIN	SALT

INGREDIENTS

200 g/7 oz fresh or frozen peas
200 g/7 oz fresh broad beans
200 g/7 oz asparagus, woody stems discarded
200 g/7 oz baby carrots, scrubbed
4 skinless salmon fillets, each weighing 150 g/5½ oz
4 tbsp ready-made pesto
3 tbsp extra virgin olive oil
grated rind and juice of 1 lemon
2 tbsp sunflower seeds, toasted
2 tbsp pumpkin seeds, toasted
2 tbsp shredded fresh basil

1. Place all the vegetables in a steamer and cook for 10–12 minutes, until tender.

2. Meanwhile, preheat the grill to hot and line a baking sheet with foil. Place the salmon on the prepared baking sheet and spoon over the pesto. Cook under the grill for 3–4 minutes on each side.

3. Mix the oil with the lemon rind and juice and toss with the cooked vegetables.

4. Divide the vegetables between four warmed shallow bowls and top each one with a salmon fillet.

5. Sprinkle with the sunflower seeds, pumpkin seeds and shredded basil and serve.

HINT
Use really young broad beans. You won't have to skin them, which will save you a lot of time, and they taste delicious!

SPINACH

Contrary to popular belief, spinach doesn't contain as much iron as originally thought but, nevertheless, it has many excellent health benefits.

MAJOR NUTRIENTS PER 100 G/3½ OZ SPINACH

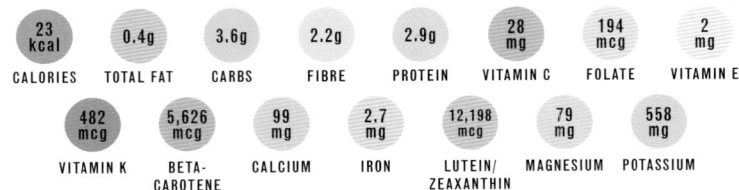

23 kcal	0.4g	3.6g	2.2g	2.9g	28 mg	194 mcg	2 mg
CALORIES	TOTAL FAT	CARBS	FIBRE	PROTEIN	VITAMIN C	FOLATE	VITAMIN E

482 mcg	5,626 mcg	99 mg	2.7 mg	12,198 mcg	79 mg	558 mg
VITAMIN K	BETA-CAROTENE	CALCIUM	IRON	LUTEIN/ ZEAXANTHIN	MAGNESIUM	POTASSIUM

Researchers have found many flavonoid compounds in spinach act as antioxidants and fight against stomach, skin, breast, prostate and other cancers. Spinach is also extremely high in carotenes, which protect eyesight. It is also particularly rich in vitamin K, which helps to boost bone strength and may help to prevent osteoporosis. In addition, spinach also contains peptides, which are aspects of protein that have been shown to lower blood pressure, and its relatively high vitamin E content may help protect the brain from cognitive decline as we age.

- Flavonoid and carotene content protects against many cancers.
- Vitamin C, folate and carotene content helps maintain artery health and prevent atherosclerosis.
- Helps keep eyes healthy.
- Vitamin K content boosts bone density.

DID YOU KNOW?

Like cheese, chocolate and wine, spinach contains the chemical tyramine, which increases the release of stimulating brain chemicals. If you don't sleep well, avoid these foods close to bedtime.

PRACTICAL TIPS

Avoid buying spinach with any yellowing leaves. The carotenes in spinach are better absorbed when the leaves are cooked rather than eaten raw, and also if eaten with a little oil. Steaming or stir-frying retains the most antioxidants. To cook, simply wash the leaves and cook in only the water still clinging to the leaves, stirring if necessary.

PRAWNS WITH SPINACH

The quick cooking of this lightly spiced dish helps retain the important nutrients provided by the spinach. Make sure the spinach leaves are as dry as possible before adding them.

SERVES 4 • PREP TIME: 15 MINS • COOK TIME: 20 MINS

PER SERVING:

410 kcal	39.3g	6.6g	6.1g	1.6g	2.7g	10.7g	2.5g
CALORIES	FAT	SAT FAT	CARBS	SUGAR	FIBRE	PROTEIN	SALT

INGREDIENTS

150 ml/5 fl oz vegetable oil
½ tsp mustard seeds
½ tsp onion seeds
2 tomatoes, sliced
350 g/12 oz fresh spinach, roughly chopped
1 tsp finely chopped fresh ginger
1 garlic clove, crushed
1 tsp chilli powder
1 tsp salt
225 g/8 oz frozen prawns, thawed and drained

1. Heat the oil in a large frying pan. Add the mustard and onion seeds to the pan.

2. Reduce the heat and add the tomatoes, spinach, ginger, garlic, chilli powder and salt and stir-fry for 5–7 minutes.

3. Add the prawns, stir until well combined, then cover and simmer over a low heat for 7–10 minutes.

4. Spoon the mixture into a warmed serving dish and serve hot.

LETTUCE

Mildly sedative, lettuce can help promote sleep. It is also a useful,
low-calorie high-fibre food for dieters.

MAJOR NUTRIENTS PER 85 G/3 OZ LETTUCE

14 kcal	0.2g	2.6g	1.7g	1g	19 mg	 2787 mcg	26 mg	109 mcg	0.8 mg	1850 mcg	198 mg
CALORIES	TOTAL FAT	CARBS	FIBRE	PROTEIN	VITAMIN C	BETA-CAROTENE	CALCIUM	FOLATE	IRON	LUTEIN/ ZEAXANTHIN	POTASSIUM

There are dozens of different types of lettuce available both in the shops
and to buy as seed but, when choosing for health reasons, it makes sense
to pick varieties that are either mid- or deep green or with red tinges.
These contain more carotenes and vitamin C than the paler lettuces. Cos
lettuce, for example, contains five times as much vitamin C and more beta-
carotene than iceberg lettuce. These more colourful heads will contain
good amounts of folate, potassium and iron. Lettuce is high in fibre, very
low in calories and low on the glycaemic index.

- Nutritious low-calorie food for dieters.
- High in antioxidant vitamin C and carotenes
  for disease prevention.
- Mildly sedative.
- High in folate for heart and arterial health.

DID YOU KNOW?

*In most countries, lettuce
is usually eaten raw, but
in France it is cooked with
peas. In China it is often
used in stir-fries and other
cooked dishes.*

PRACTICAL TIPS

Using a clean tea towel or a salad spinner, wash non-organic lettuces well
before use, because sometimes it contains high levels of pesticide residues
and bacteria. If a whole lettuce is too much for one meal, pick leaves from
the outside rather than cutting it in half, as the cut side will turn brown.
Eating lettuce with oil increases absorption of carotenes, but add dressing
just before serving so that the leaves do not deteriorate.

LETTUCE ELIXIR JUICE

Lettuce, celery and apple all have a high water content, so they are useful in helping the body to flush out toxins. This cleansing drink also tastes delicious!

SERVES 1 • PREP TIME: 10–15 MINS • COOK TIME: NONE

PER SERVING:

157 kcal	1.2g	0.1g	35.8g	23.6g	2.7g	5g	0.5g
CALORIES	FAT	SAT FAT	CARBS	SUGAR	FIBRE	PROTEIN	SALT

INGREDIENTS
100 g/3½ oz cos lettuce, roughly chopped
4 celery sticks, roughly chopped
1 green apple, halved
30 g/1 oz fresh flat-leaf parsley
1 tsp spirulina powder
crushed ice, to serve
1 cos lettuce leaf, to garnish

1. Feed the lettuce, celery and apple through a juicer with the parsley.

2. Stir through the spirulina powder until combined.

3. Pour over crushed ice and serve immediately, garnished with the lettuce leaf.

BRUSSELS SPROUTS

Containing many health-giving nutrients, Brussels sprouts
offer high levels of protection against cancers.

MAJOR NUTRIENTS PER 100 G/3½ OZ BRUSSELS SPROUTS

43 kcal	0.3g	9g	3.8g	3.4g	85 mg	450 mcg	42 mg	61 mcg	1590 mcg	23 mg	1.6 mcg	0.4 mg
CALORIES	TOTAL FAT	CARBS	FIBRE	PROTEIN	VITAMIN C	BETA-CAROTENE	CALCIUM	FOLATE	LUTEIN/ ZEAXANTHIN	MAGNESIUM	SELENIUM	ZINC

Brussels sprouts are an important winter vegetable, providing high levels of vitamin C and many other immune-boosting nutrients. They are rich in the sulphoraphane compound, which is a detoxifier and has been shown to help the body clear itself of potential carcinogens. Brussels sprouts have been shown to help prevent DNA damage when eaten regularly and may help minimize the spread of breast cancer. They even contain small amounts of beneficial omega-3 fats, zinc and selenium, a mineral many adults do not eat in the recommended daily amount. People who eat large quantities of Brussels sprouts and other Brassicas have a much lower risk of prostate, colorectal and lung cancer.

- Rich in indoles and other compounds to protect against cancer; may reduce the spread of cancer.
- Extremely rich in immune-boosting vitamin C.
- Indole content can help lower 'bad' blood cholesterol.
- Very high in fibre for colon health.

DID YOU KNOW?

Brussels sprouts are thought to come from a region in Belgium near Brussels. They were not widely used until the early twentieth century.

PRACTICAL TIPS

Select bright green sprouts with tight heads and no sign of yellow leaves. Lightly steaming or quickly boiling Brussels sprouts is the best way to cook them and preserve their nutrients. Don't overcook because much of the vitamin C content will be destroyed. Overcooking also alters their flavour and gives them an unwelcome odour.

SPROUT TONIC SMOOTHIE

Brussels sprouts might seem like a Christmas dinner staple, but drinking them
in a smoothie like this means you can get your greens all year round.

SERVES 1 • PREP TIME: 10–15 MINS • COOK TIME: NO COOK

PER SERVING:

	162 kcal	2.7g	0g	31.8g	15.2g	5g	4.2g	0.5g
	CALORIES	FAT	SAT FAT	CARBS	SUGAR	FIBRE	PROTEIN	SALT

INGREDIENTS

75 g/2¾ oz Brussels sprouts
30 g/1 oz beetroot leaves
30 g/1 oz chard
250 ml/9 fl oz unsweetened rice milk

1. Put the Brussels sprouts, beetroot leaves and chard into a blender.

2. Pour over the rice milk and blend until smooth and creamy. Pour into a glass and serve immediately.

HINT

Boost this juice's nutritional power and get your skin
glowing by adding 2 teaspoons of açai powder.

GREEN BEANS

Green beans, peas and beans (pulses) are all legumes, with a high protein content
that is essential for the revitalization of the skin, bones and muscles.

MAJOR NUTRIENTS PER 100 G/3½ OZ GREEN BEANS

									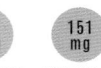		25 mg
31 kcal	0.1g	7.1g	3.6g	1.8g	16 mg	0.6 mg	0.8 mg	21 mcg	151 mg	0.7 mg	25 mg
CALORIES	TOTAL FAT	CARBS	FIBRE	PROTEIN	VITAMIN C	VITAMIN B2	VITAMIN B3	VITAMIN B5	VITAMIN B6	CHOLINE	FOLATE

Plant protein is an important part of any diet, whether you eat animal
products or not. We need protein for all structures in the body, to do the
continual work of rebuilding skin, bone, teeth, hair and nails. The effects of
too little protein are a dull complexion, lank hair and brittle nails. Whereas
animal protein is acid-forming in the body, protein derived from plants like
beans is more alkaline, the optimal state when it comes to detoxification,
repair and regulation of the metabolism. Plant sources also come with
good levels of fibre that help clear harmful waste from the body, promote
good digestion and aid full absorption of the wide range of nutrients we
need to stay young.

- Vitamin B6 and folate reduce blood levels of homocysteine, a
  substance that can create the risk of heart disease.
- B vitamins unlock energy from all the food we eat so that it can be
  used as fuel for all cell repair. Deficiency symptoms include dull skin
  and hair, poor nail health, cracked lips and spots, as well as fatigue,
  anxiety, insomnia and depression.
- Contains choline, which helps move fatty deposits out of the liver and
  protects us from the harmful and ageing effects of alcohol.

DID YOU KNOW?

*Green beans are the unripe fruit
of any bean plant. There are three
main types: French beans, runner
beans and snap beans.*

PRACTICAL TIPS

Buy beans loose where possible so that you can select those with a
smooth feel, bright green colour and a pleasing snap when broken in half.

BEAN SALAD WITH FETA

A little soft feta goes a long way in this salad, adding salty seasoning
to the crunchy beans and radishes and the sweet tomatoes.

SERVES 4 • PREP TIME: 15 MINS • COOK TIME: 10 MINS

PER SERVING:

249 kcal	21.2g	5.2g	11.9g	6.3g	3.6g	5.2g	0.4g
CALORIES	FAT	SAT FAT	CARBS	SUGAR	FIBRE	PROTEIN	SALT

INGREDIENTS

350 g/12 oz green beans
1 red onion, finely chopped
3 tbsp finely chopped fresh coriander
2 radishes, thinly sliced
75 g/2¾ oz feta cheese (drained weight), crumbled
1 tsp finely chopped fresh oregano
2 tbsp red wine vinegar
5 tbsp extra virgin olive oil
225 g/8 oz tomatoes, cut into wedges
pepper (optional)

1. Bring a saucepan of water to the boil. Add the beans, bring back to the boil, then simmer for 5 minutes, or until tender. Drain, rinse with cold water, then drain again. Cut them in half and transfer them to a salad bowl. Add the onion, coriander, radishes and cheese.

2. Sprinkle the oregano over the salad, then season to taste with pepper, if using.

3. To make the dressing, put the vinegar and oil in a bowl and whisk to combine. Drizzle over the salad, add the tomatoes, toss gently together and serve.

PUMPKIN

Pumpkins contain the orange nutrients alpha and beta-carotene and lutein, powerful anti-ageing nutrients that protect you against skin damage from sunlight.

MAJOR NUTRIENTS PER 100 G/3½ OZ PUMPKIN

13 kcal	0.1g	6.5g	0.5g	1g	9mg	1.06 mg	0.11 mg	0.06 mg	3100 mcg	16 mcg	1500 mcg	12 mg	
CALORIES	TOTAL FAT	CARBS	FIBRE	PROTEIN	VITAMIN C	VITAMIN E	VITAMIN B2	VITAMIN B6	BETA-CAROTENE	FOLATE	LUTEIN/ZEAXANTHIN	PHYTOSTEROLS	

These fat-soluble carotenoids are needed to protect fatty areas in, for example, the skin, heart, eyes, brain and liver. As a winter vegetable, pumpkin is well placed to protect us when we need it most. We eat more fat in the winter and lay down more fat stores for insulation and to use as energy during the cold months. The seeds of the pumpkin are especially nutrient-rich, while the flesh contains malic acid – also found in apples and plums – which is needed by every cell in the body for renewal and to make repairs. In combination with the protective carotenoids, it helps keep skin firm, bones strong and organs youthful.

- Contains phytosterols, needed for immune function and cholesterol regulation.
- Contains vitamin B2 to activate folate, and vitamin B6 to process fats and proteins from food to repair and rejuvenate body tissues and mucous membranes.
- Vitamin E supports fertility and young-looking skin.

DID YOU KNOW?

The name pumpkin originally comes from the Greek peponi, meaning 'large melon'. The French then called it pompon, and the British opted for pumpion, before finally taking the American name.

PRACTICAL TIPS

Like most squash, pumpkin can be boiled, steamed, baked or roasted, and used to make both sweet and savoury dishes. Pumpkin is sometimes oversweetened, especially in some traditional American dishes, which masks its delicate flavour. Experiment with less sugar if using in sweet recipes.

PUMPKIN, FETA & ADUKI BEAN PARCELS

Served crisp, golden and freshly baked from the oven, these fantastic feta, bean and pumpkin-packed filo parcels provide a wholesome, meat-free lunch or supper for all the family to enjoy.

MAKES 6 • PREP TIME: 40 MINS • COOK TIME: 45–50 MINS

PER PARCEL:

 213 kcal — CALORIES
 13.4g — FAT
 7.3g — SAT FAT
 18.4g — CARBS
 2.6g — SUGAR
 1.9g — FIBRE
 6g — PROTEIN
0.7g — SALT

INGREDIENTS

500 g/1 lb 2 oz pumpkin, cut into
2-cm/¾-inch cubes
4 shallots, quartered
1 tsp smoked paprika
1 tbsp olive oil
200 g/7 oz canned aduki beans, drained
and rinsed
2 tbsp roughly chopped fresh parsley
zest of 1 lemon
100 g/3½ oz feta cheese, crumbled
3 sheets filo pastry,
each measuring 40 x 30 cm/16 x 12 inches
50 g/1¾ oz butter, melted
pepper (optional)
1 tbsp chopped watercress, to garnish

1. Preheat the oven to 200°C/400°F/Gas Mark 6. Place the pumpkin and shallots in a shallow roasting tin in an even layer and sprinkle with the paprika. Drizzle over the oil and mix well. Roast in the preheated oven for 20–25 minutes, or until the pumpkin is slightly golden and soft. Do not switch off the oven.

2. Place the pumpkin mixture in a large bowl. Using a potato masher, mash until the cubes have broken down. Stir in the beans, parsley, lemon zest and cheese. Mix until all the ingredients are well combined. Season with pepper, if using.

3. Cut a filo sheet in half to create two long lengths of pastry (approximately 40 x 15 cm/16 x 6 inch) and brush one pastry length all over with melted butter. Keep the remaining pastry covered with a damp tea towel to prevent it drying out.

4. Spoon a sixth of the pumpkin mixture on one end of the pastry length. Fold this edge up to meet one side to start the shape of a triangle. Fold the bottom point of the pastry up, sealing in the filling, then complete the triangle by folding again in the opposite direction. Keep folding until you reach the top and lightly brush with a little more melted butter. Repeat with the other sheets of filo until you have six triangles.

5. Place the parcels on a baking tray and cook for 25 minutes, or until golden. Garnish with watercress and serve immediately.

BEETROOT

This colourful sweet root may not be the richest vegetable in terms of nutrients, but it certainly should not be overlooked and is invaluable during the winter season.

MAJOR NUTRIENTS PER 100 G/3½ OZ BEETROOT

36 kcal	TRACE	7.6g	1.9g	1.7g	5mg	20 mg	150 mcg	1.0 mg	23 mg	380 mg
CALORIES	TOTAL FAT	CARBS	FIBRE	PROTEIN	VITAMIN C	CALCIUM	FOLATE	IRON	MAGNESIUM	POTASSIUM

Beetroot comes in white and gold varieties as well as the classic purple-red, which is the best source of nutrients. Betaine, which gives it its deep colour, is even more potent an antioxidant than polyphenols in its effect on lowering blood pressure. A scientific study also found that the high levels of nitrates in beetroot juice work like aspirin to prevent blood clots, and help to protect the lining of the blood vessels. Red beetroot is also rich in anthocyanins, which may help to prevent colon and other cancers.

- Contain betaine to lower blood pressure and may be anti-inflammatory.
- Contain nitrates to help prevent blood clots.
- Anthocyanins can help prevent cancers.
- A good source of iron, magnesium and folate.

DID YOU KNOW?

Beetroot was originally cultivated for its nutritious leaves, which can still be eaten when young, cooked in the same way as spinach.

PRACTICAL TIPS

Cooked beetroot will keep in an airtight container for a few days in the refrigerator, or you can purée cooked beetroot and freeze it. To cook, cut off the leaves, leaving about 5 cm/2 inches of stalk and the root intact. This will prevent the beetroot 'bleeding' as it cooks. Beetroot can be boiled whole for about 50 minutes, or brushed with a little oil and baked in foil at 200°C/400°F/Gas Mark 6 for 1 hour. The skins can then be easily rubbed off. Beetroot can also be used raw, peeled and finely grated into salads or salsa, or juiced.

BEETROOT BROWNIE BITES

The addition of beetroot to these brownies not only adds depth of colour and texture, but reduces the guilt associated with a luscious sweet treat!

MAKES 36 PIECES • PREP TIME: 25 MINS • COOK TIME: 30–35 MINS

PER BITE:	75 kcal	4g	1.5g	10g	7g	0.5g	1.5g	TRACE
	CALORIES	FAT	SAT FAT	CARBS	SUGAR	FIBRE	PROTEIN	SALT

INGREDIENTS

1 tbsp sunflower oil, for oiling
150 g/5½ oz plain chocolate,
broken into small pieces
2 eggs
1 tsp vanilla extract
150 g/5½ oz dark muscovado sugar
85 ml/3 fl oz sunflower oil
225 g/8 oz cooked beetroot, grated
100 g/3½ oz self-raising flour
3 tbsp cocoa powder

1. Preheat the oven to 180°C/350°F/Gas Mark 4. Lightly oil a 20-cm/8-inch square baking tin and line with baking paper.

2. Place the chocolate in a heatproof bowl set over a pan of gently simmering water and heat until just melted. Remove from the heat.

3. Place the eggs, vanilla extract and sugar in a bowl and whisk at high speed for 3–4 minutes, or until pale and frothy. Beat in the oil. Stir in the beetroot, then sift in the flour and cocoa and fold in. Add the melted chocolate and stir evenly.

4. Spoon the mixture into the prepared tin and bake in the preheated oven for 25–30 minutes, or until just firm to the touch. Leave to cool in the tin, then turn out onto a wire rack and leave to cool completely.

5. Cut into about 36 bite-sized squares and serve.

HINT

This makes 36 bite-sized squares but you can of course cut them into slightly larger squares and serve with ice cream for dessert.

FENNEL

Fennel bulbs are rich in a variety of antioxidants,
which can reduce inflammation and help to prevent cancer.

MAJOR NUTRIENTS PER HALF FENNEL BULB

12 kcal	TRACE	1.8g	2.4g	0.9g	5mg	140 mg	24 mg	42 mcg	440 mg	0.7 mcg
CALORIES	TOTAL FAT	CARBS	FIBRE	PROTEIN	VITAMIN C	BETA-CAROTENE	CALCIUM	FOLATE	POTASSIUM	SELENIUM

Fennel is grown for its thick, crunchy bulbous base. It is refreshing, slightly sweet and has a strong anise flavour. Fennel contains a potent combination of plant chemicals, which give it strong antioxidant activity. One of the most interesting compounds in fennel is anethole. In animal studies, the anethole in fennel has been shown to reduce inflammation and to help prevent the occurrence of cancer. It is also a very good source of fibre, folate and potassium, and contains a wide range of other nutrients including vitamin C, selenium, niacin (vitamin B3) and iron. The very high potassium content means that fennel is a diuretic, helping to eliminate surplus fluid from the body.

- Diuretic, digestive aid and anti-flatulent.
- Very low in calories, making it an ideal food for dieters.
- Anti-inflammatory.
- Rich in antioxidant compounds for disease prevention.

DID YOU KNOW?

Bulb fennel is closely related to the fennel herb, and the leafy tops of the bulb can be chopped and used in a similar way to the herb.

PRACTICAL TIPS

Choose bulbs that are firm and solid with a slight gloss and healthy looking leaf tops. Store in the refrigerator – fennel bulbs lose their flavour after a few days. Fennel is delicious thinly sliced raw in salads and goes particularly well with fish. Try baking small whole fish in foil, on a bed of thinly sliced fennel. Fennel can also be quartered, browned in oil, then braised with a little vegetable stock. It loses quite a lot of its anise flavour when cooked.

FENNEL & APPLE JUICE

This vibrant green juice is packed with fennel, mint, spinach, apple
and lime. It's a healthy and delicious way to start the day.

SERVES 1 • PREP TIME: 10–15 MINS • COOK TIME: NONE

PER SERVING:	225 kcal	1.5g	0.3g	55.9g	29.6g	4.3g	7.4g	0.5g
	CALORIES	FAT	SAT FAT	CARBS	SUGAR	FIBRE	PROTEIN	SALT

INGREDIENTS

100 g/3½ oz spinach
20 g/¾ oz fresh mint
1 large fennel bulb, roughly chopped
1 green apple, halved
*1 lime, zest and pith removed, deseeded and
roughly chopped*
crushed ice, to serve (optional)

1. Feed the spinach, mint, fennel, apple and lime through
a juicer.

2. Stir well and pour over the crushed ice, if using. Serve
immediately.

HINT
*For best results wash vegetables in cold water to clean
– don't soak or you'll lose nutrients.*

PEPPERS

The bright colours of peppers contain high levels of carotenes for heart health and cancer protection, and are also a rich source of vitamin C.

MAJOR NUTRIENTS PER AVERAGE-SIZED PEPPER

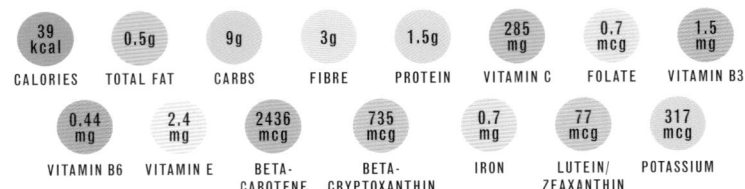

39 kcal	0.5g	9g	3g	1.5g	285 mg	0.7 mcg	1.5 mg
CALORIES	TOTAL FAT	CARBS	FIBRE	PROTEIN	VITAMIN C	FOLATE	VITAMIN B3

0.44 mg	2.4 mg	2436 mcg	735 mcg	0.7 mg	77 mcg	317 mcg
VITAMIN B6	VITAMIN E	BETA-CAROTENE	BETA-CRYPTOXANTHIN	IRON	LUTEIN/ZEAXANTHIN	POTASSIUM

Peppers come in a variety of colours, but red and orange peppers contain the highest levels of vitamin B6 and carotenes. However, all of them are extremely rich in vitamin C, with an average serving providing more than a day's recommended intake. In general, the deeper the colour of the pepper, the more beneficial plant compounds it contains. These include bioflavonoids, to protect against cancer, and phenols, which help block the action of cancer-causing chemicals in the body. Peppers also contain plant sterols, which may have an anti-cancer effect.

- Rich source of a range of vitamins, minerals and plant chemicals.
- Extremely rich in antioxidant vitamin C and excellent source of antioxidant vitamin E.
- Several components are strongly anti-cancer.
- High lutein levels protect from macular degeneration.
- Good source of vitamin B6 for reducing blood homocysteine levels; high levels of this have been linked to increased risk of heart disease, stroke, Alzheimer's disease and osteoporosis.

DID YOU KNOW?

Peppers are native to South America and date back about 5,000 years. They were introduced to Europe in the Middle Ages by Spanish and Portuguese explorers.

PRACTICAL TIPS

The carotenes in peppers are made more available to the body if the peppers are cooked and eaten with a little oil. Try stir-frying thinly sliced peppers or deseed and halve the peppers, brush with oil and roast. If using raw in a salad, drizzle over some olive oil to help absorption. Fresh peppers can be deseeded, sliced and frozen in polythene bags.

STUFFED PEPPERS WITH CHICKPEAS & BULGAR WHEAT

These tasty low-fat peppers, stuffed with fibre-rich chickpeas and bulgar wheat, are simple to cook yet good enough to cook for a special occasion.

SERVES 4 • PREP TIME: 10 MINS, PLUS SOAKING • COOK TIME: 35 MINS

PER SERVING:

291 kcal	9.5g	2.9g	41.2g	13.7g	8.2g	11g	1.6g
CALORIES	FAT	SAT FAT	CARBS	SUGAR	FIBRE	PROTEIN	SALT

INGREDIENTS

12 sprays cooking oil spray
2 large red peppers
2 large yellow peppers
1 vegetable stock cube
175 ml/6 fl oz boiling water
85 g/3 oz bulgar wheat
125 g/4½ oz canned chickpeas, drained and rinsed
30 g/1 oz flaked almonds, toasted
30 g/1 oz raisins
4 large sun-dried tomatoes, chopped
4 spring onions, finely chopped
½ tsp smoked paprika
3 tbsp chopped fresh basil
50 g/1¾ oz feta cheese, finely crumbled

1. Preheat the oven to 190°C/375°F/Gas Mark 5. Spray a baking tray with 4 sprays of the cooking oil spray. Halve the red peppers and yellow peppers from stalk to base, discarding the cores and seeds but leaving the stalks in place. Place cut-side down on the prepared tray and roast in the preheated oven for 20 minutes.

2. Meanwhile, prepare the bulgar wheat. Dissolve the stock cube in the boiling water in a heatproof bowl and stir in the bulgar wheat. Set aside for 15 minutes, then fluff up with a fork.

3. Add the chickpeas, almonds, raisins, tomatoes, spring onions, paprika and basil to the bulgar wheat and stir well to combine.

4. Remove the peppers from the oven and stuff with the bulgar wheat mixture. Sprinkle a little cheese over the top of each stuffed pepper and spray with the remaining cooking oil spray. Roast for a further 15 minutes, or until the tops are light golden and the peppers are tender when pierced with a sharp knife. Serve immediately.

HINT
These make a great starter or can be served as a side for any kind of grilled meat or fish.

SEAWEED

Rich in iodine for healthy thyroid action, zinc for fertility and calcium
for healthy bones, seaweed is highly nutritious.

MAJOR NUTRIENTS PER 50 G/1¾ OZ KELP

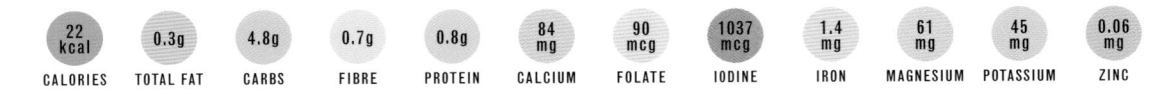

22 kcal	0.3g	4.8g	0.7g	0.8g	84 mg	90 mcg	1037 mcg	1.4 mg	61 mg	45 mg	0.06 mg
CALORIES	TOTAL FAT	CARBS	FIBRE	PROTEIN	CALCIUM	FOLATE	IODINE	IRON	MAGNESIUM	POTASSIUM	ZINC

While there are thousands of different varieties of seaweed, only a few
are widely available or commonly used as a vegetable. Often found dried,
the most well known are flat, dark green kelp (also known as kombu),
dark red dulse, green or purple nori and dark green or brown wakame.
The nutritional value of the types varies, but they are usually rich in iron,
calcium, zinc, magnesium and iodine, a mineral that can help to boost
the action of the thyroid gland, regulate the body's metabolism and aid
hearing. Seaweed is also rich in folate and low in calories.

- Rich in easily absorbed minerals and ideal for vegetarians.
- Good food for dieters as seaweed is low in calories and contains a gel-
  like substance called agar, which helps you to feel full for longer.
- May be antiviral and anti-cancer.
- Excellent source of iodine to help the body's metabolism.

DID YOU KNOW?

*Most types of seaweed are high
in sodium (the sea is very salty)
and are therefore not suitable for
anyone on a low-sodium diet.*

PRACTICAL TIPS

Fresh seaweed for consumption should be sourced from unpolluted
waters. It can be chopped and used in soups or stir-fried as a garnish.
Laver, a type of seaweed, is used in parts of the UK to make a flat bread
that is shallow fried. Dried seaweed can be reconstituted according to
the packet instructions and used in a similar way. Large sheets of nori are
used to wrap sushi.

SUSHI ROLL BOWL

Sushi is very healthy: the omega-3 fats in the fish are linked to heart protection and improved circulation; rice provides energy; and wasabi aids cancer prevention.

SERVES 4 • PREP TIME: 15 MINS, PLUS COOLING • COOK TIME: 10 MINS

PER SERVING:

572 kcal	17.7g	3.1g	70.1g	2.2g	7.6g	32g	2.4g
CALORIES	FAT	SAT FAT	CARBS	SUGAR	FIBRE	PROTEIN	SALT

INGREDIENTS

300 g/10½ oz sushi rice

2 tbsp rice vinegar

1 tsp caster sugar

1 large avocado, peeled, stoned and sliced

200 g/7 oz raw tuna, sliced

200 g/7 oz raw salmon, sliced

juice of ½ lemon

4 sheets nori seaweed, shredded

¼ cucumber, cut into matchsticks

2 tbsp snipped fresh chives

1 tbsp black sesame seeds

4 tbsp soy sauce, to serve

1. Cook the rice according to the packet instructions. When all the water has been absorbed and the rice is cooked, stir through the vinegar and sugar, then cover and leave to cool.

2. Divide the rice between four bowls.

3. Top each bowl with slices of avocado, tuna and salmon.

4. Squeeze over the lemon juice, then add the nori, cucumber, chives and sesame seeds.

5. Serve with the soy sauce.

CUCUMBER

Cucumber is a squash long used for its cooling effects, inside and outside the body, reducing inflammation and speeding repair for young-looking skin.

MAJOR NUTRIENTS PER 100 G/3½ OZ CUCUMBER, WITH PEEL

16 kcal	0.11g	3.63g	0.5g	0.65g	2.8 mg	0.26 mg	13 mg	TRACE	147 mg	TRACE
CALORIES	TOTAL FAT	CARBS	FIBRE	PROTEIN	VITAMIN C	VITAMIN B5	MAGNESIUM	MOLYBDENUM	POTASSIUM	SILICA

As well as drinking fluids directly, we need to receive water from the plant foods we eat. The high water content of cucumber makes it a hydrating food that prevents dryness and wrinkling of the skin, as well as helping to remove the toxins that can age us. Cucumber is a recommended food in the DASH (Dietary Approaches to Stop Hypertension) diet as it is rich in potassium, magnesium and fibre, so it works naturally to reduce high blood pressure by balancing the fluid in the body. The vitamin C and caffeic acid in cucumbers also help rid the body of excess fluid as they both help prevent water retention.

- Source of silica, a trace mineral needed for a healthy complexion.
- Cucumber juice is known to alleviate the symptoms of rheumatic conditions and keep joints healthy and young.
- Contains the trace mineral molybdenum, which is needed to keep bones and teeth strong and healthy.

DID YOU KNOW?

The saying 'cool as a cucumber' comes from the fact that the inside of a cucumber can be 11°C/20°F cooler than the outside air.

PRACTICAL TIPS

Cucumber combines well with other vegetables and fruits. Include its skin in juices and salads for maximum nutrition. The juice can be applied directly to cuts, burns and skin conditions to bring immediate cooling relief, or you can purée the whole vegetable in a blender for use as a rejuvenating poultice or face mask, with avocado if you have some. Cucumber slices placed on the eyes will reduce puffiness and signs of tiredness.

CUCUMBER SOOTHER JUICE

This light, fresh-tasting juice made with the addition of soothing aloe vera gel can help to reduce digestive problems such as heartburn.

SERVES 1 • PREP TIME: 10 MINS • COOK TIME: NONE

PER SERVING:

 259 kcal
CALORIES

 0.8g
FAT

 TRACE
SAT FAT

 67.9g
CARBS

 43.1g
SUGAR

 3.2g
FIBRE

 2.2g
PROTEIN

TRACE
SALT

INGREDIENTS

1 large pear, halved
100 g/3½ oz cucumber, roughly chopped
1 green apple, halved
10 g/¼ oz fresh mint
1 tbsp aloe vera gel
crushed ice, to serve (optional)
1 cucumber slice, to garnish
1 fresh mint sprig, to garnish

1. Feed the pear, cucumber, apple and mint through a juicer.

2. Stir through the aloe vera gel until combined. Pour the crushed ice, if using, into a glass, then pour in the juice.

3. Serve immediately, garnished with a cucumber slice and a sprig of mint.

PAK CHOI

This is a cruciferous vegetable in the same family as cabbage, broccoli, kale and Brussels sprouts, and offers the same protective and rejuvenating properties.

MAJOR NUTRIENTS PER 100 G/3½ OZ PAK CHOI

13 kcal	0.2g	2.2g	1g	1.5g	4468 IU	45 mg	2681 mcg	105 mg	66 mcg	19 mg
CALORIES	TOTAL FAT	CARBS	FIBRE	PROTEIN	VITAMIN A	VITAMIN C	BETA-CAROTENE	CALCIUM	FOLATE	MAGNESIUM

The anti-cancer properties of cruciferous vegetables are well documented. Research in Singapore found that these vegetables, including pak choi, reduce the risk of lung cancer in non-smokers by 30 per cent and in smokers by an astonishing 69 per cent. Pak choi also enhances and balances all aspects of liver detoxification, a remedy against the ravaging effects of stress, pollution and the ageing factors in our modern environment. Pak choi contains a higher amount of vitamin A than other cabbages and so particularly protects the liver from ageing damage from sugar, alcohol and medications as it is stored in high amounts in this organ.

- High calcium content keeps bones, teeth and joints healthy and prevents osteoporosis; also supports heart health and optimum brain function.
- Contains beta-carotene that can be converted to vitamin A and used to fight toxins that cause premature ageing.
- Vitamin C enables all other antioxidants to work effectively and so protect and repair the skin, bones, brain and heart to keep you looking and feeling young.

DID YOU KNOW?

Pak choi literally means 'white vegetable' in Chinese. The variety that is used today is similar to one cultivated in the fourteenth century.

PRACTICAL TIPS

Typically used in stir-fries and soups like miso, pak choi is quicker to cook and lighter than other cabbage, and tastes particularly good when it retains its crunchiness. Darker varieties may need longer to cook than the smaller, light ones.

PAK CHOI WITH RED ONIONS & CASHEW NUTS

Pak choi is an ideal vegetable for stir-frying, which retains its characteristic crunchiness. Given further crunch with roasted cashew nuts, this colourful dish is a tasty treat.

SERVES 4 • PREP TIME: 20 MINS • COOK TIME: 20 MINS

PER SERVING:	263 kcal	18.6g	3.5g	21.8g	9.6g	3.2g	6g	0.2g
	CALORIES	FAT	SAT FAT	CARBS	SUGAR	FIBRE	PROTEIN	SALT

INGREDIENTS

2 tbsp groundnut oil
2 red onions, cut into thin wedges
175 g/6 oz red cabbage, thinly shredded
225 g/8 oz pak choi, separated into leaves
2 tbsp plum sauce
100 g/3½ oz roasted cashew nuts, to garnish

1. Heat the oil in a large preheated wok or frying pan until it is really hot. Add the onion wedges to the wok and stir-fry for about 5 minutes, or until the onions are just beginning to brown.

2. Add the cabbage and stir-fry for a further 5 minutes.

3. Add the pak choi leaves and stir-fry for about 2–3 minutes, or until the leaves have just wilted. Drizzle the plum sauce over the vegetables, toss together until well mixed and heat until the liquid is bubbling.

4. Garnish with the roasted cashew nuts and transfer to warmed serving bowls. Serve immediately.

SAUERKRAUT

Sauerkraut is finely shredded cabbage that has been fermented by health-giving bacteria. It has a long history as a highly nutritious, anti-ageing food.

MAJOR NUTRIENTS PER 100 G/3½ OZ SAUERKRAUT (INCLUDING LIQUID)

19 kcal	0.14g	4.3g	2.9g	0.9g	15 mg	0.13 mg	1.5 mg
CALORIES	TOTAL FAT	CARBS	FIBRE	PROTEIN	VITAMIN C	VITAMIN B6	IRON

Sauerkraut is among many traditional fermented foods associated with a youthful digestive system. This is due to the support these foods give to the 1–1.5 kg/2 lb 4 oz–3 lb 5 oz of probiotic bacteria covering the lining of our digestive tract and other mucous membranes like the throat. These are our first line of immune defence against bacteria, yeasts and viruses. They effectively regulate the intestinal environment. sorting out any diarrhoea or constipation problems, preventing inflammatory conditions and intolerances, and by ensuring the immune response reacts only to genuine threats and does not overreact to harmless agents like food.

- Contains a high amount of glutamine, the amino acid found in muscle that is crucial for youthful movement and strength.
- Includes all the health benefits of the cruciferous cabbage it is made from. Like broccoli and Brussels sprouts, it contains revitalizing and detoxifying sulphur chemicals.
- Sauerkraut juice helps respiration. A good intake of oxygen to replenish body cells is a crucial factor in staying young.

DID YOU KNOW?

Before the Royal Navy made the change to limes, Captain James Cook took sauerkraut on his sea voyages as a vitamin C-rich preventative to scurvy. The lactic acid bacteria in sauerkraut gives it its distinctive taste.

PRACTICAL TIPS

The lactic acid in sauerkraut can be mildly upsetting for people who are not used to it, but starting with small amounts and building up can help address the bacterial gut imbalance that is the reason for this. Its sourness is then a welcome complement to meat, cheese and salads.

LAYERED PORK & SPICED SAUERKRAUT SOUP

This delicious soup is a great way to introduce valuable probiotics to your diet, helping to boost your immune system, keep your digestive tract healthy and contribute to a feeling of well-being.

SERVES 4 • PREP TIME: 20 MINS • COOK TIME: 1 HOUR

PER SERVING:

 207 kcal — CALORIES

 6.6g — FAT

 1.7g — SAT FAT

 20.6g — CARBS

10.1g — SUGAR

5.8g — FIBRE

18.9g — PROTEIN

2.9g — SALT

INGREDIENTS

1 tbsp olive oil
350 g/12 oz pork fillet, thinly sliced
1 onion, chopped
2 garlic cloves, finely chopped
900 ml/1½ pints chicken stock
1 tsp fennel seeds
1 tsp English mustard
175 g/6 oz Brussels sprouts, thinly sliced
1 tsp caraway seeds
115 g/4 oz carrots, coarsely grated
1 dessert apple, cored and coarsely grated
175 g/6 oz sauerkraut, drained
70 g/2½ oz gherkins, drained and diced
2 tbsp chopped fresh dill
salt and pepper (optional)

1. Heat the oil in a saucepan, add the pork and fry, stirring, for 5 minutes until brown all over. Add the onion and fry for 5 minutes until lightly coloured.

2. Mix in the garlic and stock, then add the fennel seeds and mustard. Bring to the boil, cover and simmer for 30 minutes.

3. When the pork is almost cooked, mix the sprouts with the caraway seeds and steam for 5 minutes until just tender.

4. Divide half the pork mixture between four large heatproof tumblers, arranging it on the base. Mix the carrot and apple and spoon into the glasses, then top with the sprouts, followed by the remaining pork. Mix the sauerkraut with the gherkins and the chopped dill, then spoon the mixture into the glasses.

5. Season the hot broth with salt and pepper to taste, if using, then pour it into the tumblers until all the vegetables are just covered. Serve immediately.

HINT
Choose a chicken stock that is low in salt and not too highly flavoured or it will dominate the other flavours in the soup.

PURPLE SPROUTING BROCCOLI

This purple, long-stalked variety of broccoli contains the same health benefits as its stockier cousin, but has the added bonus of antioxidant proanthocyanidins.

MAJOR NUTRIENTS PER 100 G/3½ OZ PURPLE SPROUTING BROCCOLI

3 kcal	0.37g	6.64g	2.6g	2.82g	89.2 mg	0.57 mg	361 mcg	47 mg	1121 mcg
CALORIES	TOTAL FAT	CARBS	FIBRE	PROTEIN	VITAMIN C	VITAMIN B5	BETA-CAROTENE	CALCIUM	LUTEIN/ZEAXANTHIN

The proanthocyanidins, which give purple sprouting broccoli its colour, are the same protective polyphenols found in dark red and purple berries, which promote circulation and glowing skin, and protect veins and arteries to support heart and brain health. The characteristic taste of cruciferous vegetables comes from sulphurous compounds called isothiocyanates, which have been shown to have a strongly protective effect in people showing a genetic predisposition for lung cancer. Another sulphur compound, sulforaphane, triggers our natural detoxification enzymes.

- Contains the rare vegetable fibre calcium pectate, which holds cholesterol in the liver, limiting its release into the bloodstream.
- Source of the trace mineral chromium, which enables the hormone insulin to move sugar from the bloodstream to cells, so helping to prevent adult-onset diabetes.
- Vitamin C and the carotenoids beta-carotene and lutein provide further antioxidant protection for youthful-looking skin.
- Contains vitamin B5, needed to release energy from the plant foods we eat, encouraging age-defying vigour.

DID YOU KNOW?

Although it has only come back into fashion in the last 30 years, purple sprouting broccoli is the most ancient of broccolis, and was cultivated by the Romans.

PRACTICAL TIPS

Cook broccoli only lightly, preferably by steaming, to ensure that it remains slightly crunchy. The sprouting variety has a finer stalk than the fatter vegetable so can be eaten whole. Broccoli works well in stir-fries, or served cold in salads.

PURPLE SPROUTING BROCCOLI SALAD

Salads are a great way of ensuring that you are eating enough greens. Here, lightly steamed purple sprouting broccoli is combined with cabbage, beetroot and cranberries.

SERVES 4 • PREP TIME: 10–15 MINS • COOK TIME: 15–20 MINS

PER SERVING:	229 kcal	10.9g	1.4g	29.5g	13g	5.9g	6.1g	0.3g
	CALORIES	FAT	SAT FAT	CARBS	SUGAR	FIBRE	PROTEIN	SALT

INGREDIENTS

200 g/7 oz purple sprouting broccoli
250 g/9 oz red cabbage, shredded
115 g/4 oz cooked beetroot in natural juices (drained weight), cut into matchsticks
2 tbsp dried cranberries
3 tbsp balsamic vinegar

CROÛTONS

2 tbsp olive oil
85 g/3 oz rustic wholegrain bread, torn into small pieces
1 tbsp sunflower seeds
1 tbsp linseeds

1. Put the broccoli in the top of a steamer, cover and set over a saucepan of simmering water. Steam for 3–5 minutes, or until tender. Cool under cold running water, then cut the stems in half and the lower stems in half again lengthways, and transfer them to a salad bowl.

2. Add the red cabbage, beetroot and cranberries to the bowl.

3. To make the croûtons, heat the oil in a frying pan over a medium heat, add the bread and fry for 3–4 minutes, stirring, until just beginning to brown. Add the sunflower seeds and linseeds and cook for a further 2–3 minutes, until lightly toasted.

4. Drizzle the balsamic vinegar over the salad and toss gently together. Sprinkle with the croûtons and seeds and serve.

HINT

Steaming is the method of cooking vegetables that preserves the most nutrients. Try cooking all your vegetables in this way.

SQUASH

Orange-fleshed squash offers protection against lung cancer,
and is particularly rich in vitamins C and E.

68 kcal	TRACE	17.5g	3g	1.5g	1.8 mg	31 mg	2.2 mg
CALORIES	TOTAL FAT	CARBS	FIBRE	PROTEIN	VITAMIN B3	VITAMIN C	VITAMIN E

6339 mcg	5207 mcg	72 mg	41 mcg	1mg	51 mg	528 mg
BETA-CAROTENE	BETA-CRYPTOXANTHIN	CALCIUM	FOLATE	IRON	MAGNESIUM	POTASSIUM

Squashes are related to pumpkin, cucumber and melon, and have a slightly nutty flavour that is ideal in both sweet and savoury cooking. The orange-fleshed varieties, such as butternut, tend to contain the highest levels of beneficial nutrients. Butternut squash is one of our richest sources of beta-cryptoxanthin, a carotene that is linked with protection from lung cancer. The other carotenes it contains reduce the risk of colon cancer and prostate problems in men. They may also help reduce the inflammation associated with conditions such as asthma and arthritis. The vegetable is also a very good source of several vitamins and minerals, including antioxidant vitamins C and E, calcium, iron and magnesium.

- Contains protective chemicals against lung and colon cancers.
- Anti-inflammatory.
- Rich in a range of vitamins and minerals.
- High-fibre source of complex carbohydrates.

DID YOU KNOW?

Don't throw away nutritious squash seeds – they can be dried in a low oven and eaten in the same way as pumpkin seeds.

PRACTICAL TIPS

All winter squashes can be stored for up to six months in a cool, dry, dark, airy, frost-free place. To prepare, cut in half with a sharp knife and scoop out the seeds. Squashes can be stuffed and baked, or skinned, sliced and roasted as an alternative to potatoes. Roast squash makes an excellent soup. The carotenes in squash are better absorbed if eaten with a little oil.

SQUASH, KALE & FARRO STEW

You'll feel warmer just looking at this colourful and health-boosting vegetable stew! Farro is ideal for adding to soups and stews – use it for bulking out instead of barley or rice.

SERVES 6 • PREP TIME: 30 MINS • COOK TIME: 55 MINS

PER SERVING:

 246 kcal CALORIES   7.2g FAT   1.5g SAT FAT   38.4g CARBS   9.4g SUGAR   6.4g FIBRE   9.2g PROTEIN   1.1g SALT

INGREDIENTS

1 dense-fleshed squash,
such as Kabocha or Crown Prince, weighing
about 1.25 kg/2 lb 12 oz
2 tbsp vegetable oil
1 onion, finely chopped
2 tsp dried oregano
2 garlic cloves, finely sliced
400 g/14 oz canned chopped tomatoes
750 ml/1¼ pints vegetable stock
125 g/4½ oz quick-cook farro, rinsed
250 g/9 oz kale, sliced into ribbons
400 g/14 oz canned chickpeas,
drained and rinsed
6 tbsp chopped fresh coriander
juice of 1 lime
salt and pepper (optional)

1. Cut the squash into quarters, peel and deseed. Cut the flesh into large cubes (you will need about 650 g/1 lb 7 oz).

2. Heat the oil in a flameproof casserole or heavy-based saucepan. Add the onion and fry over a medium heat for 5 minutes until translucent. Add the oregano and garlic and fry for 2 minutes.

3. Add the squash and cook, covered, for 10 minutes.

4. Add the tomatoes, stock and farro, cover and bring to the boil. Reduce the heat to a gentle simmer and cook for 20 minutes, stirring occasionally.

5. Add the kale and chickpeas. Cook for a further 15 minutes, or until the kale is just tender.

6. Season to taste with salt and pepper, if using. Stir in the coriander and lime juice just before serving.

HINT
For best results, chop the squash into equal-sized cubes to ensure even cooking.

WATERCRESS

Peppery watercress leaves are rich in vitamin C and also contain chemicals to help protect against lung cancer.

MAJOR NUTRIENTS PER 30 G/1 OZ WATERCRESS

3 kcal	TRACE	0.3g	TRACE	0.6g	11mg	62 mcg	705 mcg	30 mg	1442 mcg	83 mg
CALORIES	TOTAL FAT	CARBS	FIBRE	PROTEIN	VITAMIN C	VITAMIN K	BETA-CAROTENE	CALCIUM	LUTEIN/ ZEAXANTHIN	POTASSIUM

Watercress leaves are a powerhouse of nutrients – even if eaten in small quantities – and provide good amounts of vitamins C and K, potassium and calcium. They are also a great source of carotenes and lutein for eye health. Watercress is rich in a variety of plant chemicals that can help prevent or minimize cancers, including phenylethyl isothiocynate, which can help to block the action of cells that are linked with lung cancer. Watercress is also said to detoxify the liver and cleanse the blood, and the benzyl oils it contains are powerful antibiotics. It can also help improve night blindness and the sun-sensitive condition called porphyria.

- Helps prevent lung and other cancers.
- Detoxifying and blood cleansing.
- Can improve eye health and night blindness.
- High in vitamin K for bone health and healthy blood.

DID YOU KNOW?

It is best to buy commercially produced watercress rather than searching for wild watercress, as this mainly grows in polluted waters and may carry bacteria.

PRACTICAL TIPS

Buy watercress that has no yellowing or wilting leaves, and store in a polythene bag in the refrigerator or, if bunched, put the bunch in a mug of water up to leaf height. Wash watercress before use and shake to remove excess water. Increase your intake of watercress by using it in a soup with onion and potato. Watercress also goes very well with fresh orange segments in a salad.

FIG, GOAT'S CHEESE & WATERCRESS SALAD

This light salad makes an elegant starter, light lunch or delicious summer supper.
It also works very well served as a side dish for spicy lamb dishes.

SERVES 4 • PREP TIME: 10 MINS • COOK TIME: NONE

PER SERVING:

 205 kcal CALORIES 12g FAT 3.1g SAT FAT 21.4g CARBS 17.1g SUGAR 3.5g FIBRE 6.1g PROTEIN 0.6g SALT

INGREDIENTS

6 figs, halved lengthways
85 g/3 oz watercress
60 g/2¼ oz soft goat's cheese
40 g/1½ oz blanched almonds, toasted

DRESSING

2 tbsp finely chopped fresh mint
juice of ½ lemon
1 tbsp clear honey
1 tbsp extra virgin olive oil
pinch of sea salt
pinch of pepper

1. To make the dressing, whisk the mint, lemon juice, honey and oil together in a small jug and season with the salt and pepper.

2. Put the figs in a small bowl, drizzle over a tablespoon of the dressing and mix gently.

3. Pile the watercress onto a large serving plate. Drizzle the remaining dressing over the salad and toss. Scatter the figs, cheese and almonds over the watercress. Serve immediately.

RADICCHIO

The red pigments of radicchio provide anti-cancer compounds to protect the heart, and compounds to help prevent blood clots.

MAJOR NUTRIENTS PER 50 G/1¾ OZ RADICCHIO

12 kcal	TRACE	2.2g	0.5g	0.7g	4mg	10 mg	30 mcg	4416 mcg	151 mg	0.5 mg
CALORIES	TOTAL FAT	CARBS	FIBRE	PROTEIN	VITAMIN C	CALCIUM	FOLATE	LUTEIN/ ZEAXANTHIN	POTASSIUM	SELENIUM

Tightly packed heads of radicchio, sometimes known as Italian chicory, have a strong, slightly bitter flavour that can lift a mixed leaf salad and provide contrasting colour. The astringent taste awakens the palate and promotes the secretion of hydrochloric acid, which aids digestion. Radicchio is rich in phenolic compounds, such as quercetin glycosides, which help prevent precancerous substances from causing damage in the body, and anthocyanins, which help protect against both cancer and heart disease. The total phenolic content in red forms of radicchio is about 4–5 times higher than in green varieties. Radicchio also contains good levels of vitamin C, potassium and folate.

- Acts as a digestive aid.
- Contains high levels of cancer-blocking compounds.
- Protection against heart disease.
- Rich in lutein and zeaxanthin for eye health.

DID YOU KNOW?

The two most commonly available types of red radicchio are Verona, with a small, loose head, burgundy leaves and white ribs, and Treviso, which has a tighter, more tapered head and leaves that are narrower and more pointed.

PRACTICAL TIPS

Look for firm heads with crisp, colourful leaves and no signs of wilting or browning. Store in a polythene bag in the refrigerator for up to five days. Although usually served raw in salads, radicchio heads can be quartered, basted with olive oil, lemon juice and seasoning, and lightly grilled or baked. Radicchio can also be sautéed in oil and drizzled with balsamic vinegar.

RADICCHIO CAESAR SALAD

The classic Caesar salad is made with cos lettuce, but here ruby-red radicchio is used instead.
Its bittersweet flavour goes well with Parmesan and pancetta and the mustard dressing.

SERVES 2 • PREP TIME: 20 MINS • COOK TIME: 5 MINS

PER SERVING:

453 kcal	34.8g	8g	21.9g	1.7g	1.8g	14g	2.2g
CALORIES	FAT	SAT FAT	CARBS	SUGAR	FIBRE	PROTEIN	SALT

INGREDIENTS
4 thin slices of pancetta
½ head of radicchio, tough outer leaves discarded
and coarse stems removed
55 g/2 oz ready-made croûtons
4 anchovies in oil, drained
30 g/1 oz freshly grated Parmesan cheese

DRESSING
2 tsp lemon juice
1 tsp Dijon mustard
1 small garlic clove, crushed
dash of Worcestershire sauce
3 tbsp extra virgin olive oil
salt and pepper (optional)

1. To make the dressing, combine the lemon juice, mustard, garlic and Worcestershire sauce in a small bowl. Add salt and pepper, if using, then gradually whisk in the oil until thick.

2. Add the pancetta to a dry frying pan and fry for 2–3 minutes, until crisp. Drain on kitchen paper. Break into bite-sized pieces and set aside.

3. Tear the radicchio leaves into bite-sized pieces. Place in a salad bowl with the croûtons, anchovies and cheese. Whisk the dressing, pour over the leaves and toss to coat.

4. Top the salad with the pancetta and serve immediately.

VARIATION
If you don't have anchovies replace them with a
teaspoon of capers in brine.

CELERY

High in potassium and calcium, celery helps to reduce fluid
retention and prevent high blood pressure.

MAJOR NUTRIENTS PER 100 G/3½ OZ CELERY STICK

14 kcal	TRACE	3g	1.6g	0.7g	3mg	35 mcg	40 mg	36 mcg	11 mg	260 mg
CALORIES	TOTAL FAT	CARBS	FIBRE	PROTEIN	VITAMIN C	VITAMIN K	CALCIUM	FOLATE	MAGNESIUM	POTASSIUM

Celery has long been regarded as an ideal food for dieters because of its
high water content and therefore its low calorie load. In fact, celery is a
useful and healthy vegetable for many other reasons. It is a good source
of potassium and is also surprisingly high in calcium, vital for healthy
bones, healthy blood pressure levels and nerve function. The darker green
stalks and the leaves of celery contain carotenes and more of the minerals
and vitamin C than the paler leaves, so don't discard them. Celery also
contains the compounds polyacetalenes and phthalides, which may protect
from inflammation and high blood pressure.

- Low in calories and fat and high in fibre.
- Good source of potassium.
- Calcium content protects bones and may help regulate
  blood pressure.
- May offer protection from inflammation.

DID YOU KNOW?

*Celery can contain high levels of
nitrates, which have been linked
with an increased risk of cancer.
However, research has found
that vegetables high in nitrates
also usually contain high levels of
nitrate-neutralizing chemicals.*

PRACTICAL TIPS

Choose celery heads with leaves that look bright green and fresh. Store in
a polythene bag or wrap in clingfilm to prevent the stalks going limp. Celery
is ideal for adding flavour and bulk to soups and stews and quartered
heads can be braised in vegetable stock for an excellent accompaniment
to fish, poultry or game. The leaves can be added to salads and stir-fries or
used as a garnish.

GREEN ENVY SMOOTHIE

This smoothie packs a real nutritional punch and your friends will be green with
envy when they see you glowing with health and full of energy.

SERVES 1 • PREP TIME: 10 MINS • COOK TIME: NONE

PER SERVING:

163 kcal	1.2g	0.2g	38g	21.4g	10.5g	6g	0.6g
CALORIES	FAT	SAT FAT	CARBS	SUGAR	FIBRE	PROTEIN	SALT

INGREDIENTS

1 green apple
4 celery sticks
150 g/5½ oz cucumber
100 g/3½ oz spinach
20 g/¾ oz fresh mint
1 tsp chlorophyll powder
ice cubes, to serve
celery sticks to garnish (optional)

1. Roughly chop the apple, the celery sticks and the cucumber.

2. Put the spinach, mint, apple, celery and cucumber through a juicer.

3. Stir through the chlorophyll powder until combined. Fill a glass with ice, pour in the juice and serve immediately, garnished with a trimmed celery stick, if using.

RADISHES

Radishes are among the most nutritious of plant roots, and have traditionally been used to help maintain a youthful appearance and control weight.

MAJOR NUTRIENTS PER 2 RADISHES

2 kcal	0g	0.30g	0.2g	0.06g	1.4 mg	2 mg	2 mcg	20 mg
CALORIES	TOTAL FAT	CARBS	FIBRE	PROTEIN	VITAMIN C	CALCIUM	FOLATE	POTASSIUM

Radishes have long been used to treat thyroid conditions. This is because they contain a chemical called raphanin, which, according to researchers, regulates the thyroid gland by tempering its tendency to produce too little or too much thyroid hormone. Low function or hypothyroidism is more common, especially as we age, when the thyroid can slow down and result in weight gain, cold hands and fatigue. Radishes also have good levels of the trace mineral molybdenum, which helps balance blood sugar levels, again supporting the thyroid in its job of managing body weight and energy use.

- The chemical xylogen in radishes reduces infection and inflammation, thereby strengthening the immune system to help prevent disease and premature ageing.
- The slightly bitter taste encourages bile flow, helping with the digestion of fats and the regulation of cholesterol to maintain a trim figure and healthy weight.
- Potassium regulates blood pressure to keep the heart healthy and able to pump revitalizing nutrients around the body.

DID YOU KNOW?

Radishes are used in traditional Chinese medicine to provide kidney, digestive and liver support and to reduce mucus, sinusitis and throat problems.

PRACTICAL TIPS

As well as being a colourful, crisp and sharp salad vegetable, radishes taste very refreshing in juices. To combat nasal congestion, try whizzing together six radishes, one cucumber and one apple. Mooli is a long, white radish used in Asian cooking that can be eaten raw in salads.

PAN-COOKED TUNA WITH RADISH RELISH

Borrowing from the Japanese tradition of pickling vegetables, the radishes and cucumber are marinated in a delicious mix of sweet and sour, which goes very well with the tuna.

SERVES 4 • PREP TIME: 15 MINS, PLUS MARINATING • COOK TIME: 10 MINS

PER SERVING:

279 kcal	12.1g	1.5g	2.2g	1g	0.7g	38.3g	1.3g
CALORIES	FAT	SAT FAT	CARBS	SUGAR	FIBRE	PROTEIN	SALT

INGREDIENTS

4 tuna steaks, each weighing 150 g/5½ oz
1 tbsp sesame seeds
cooked rice, to serve (optional)

MARINADE

2 tbsp dark soy sauce
2 tbsp sunflower oil
1 tbsp sesame oil
1 tbsp rice vinegar
1 tsp grated fresh ginger

RELISH

½ cucumber, peeled
1 bunch red radishes, trimmed

1. Place the tuna steaks in a dish and sprinkle over the sesame seeds, pressing them in with the back of a spoon so they stick to the fish.

2. To make the marinade, whisk together all the ingredients. Transfer 3 tablespoons of the marinade to a medium-sized bowl. Pour the remaining marinade over the fish, turning each steak to coat lightly. Cover and marinate in the refrigerator for 1 hour.

3. Slice the cucumber and radishes very thinly and add to the marinade in the bowl. Toss the vegetables to coat, then cover and chill.

4. Heat a large, heavy-based frying pan over a high heat. Add the steaks and cook for 3–4 minutes on each side, depending on the thickness of the fish. Serve immediately with the radish relish and rice, if using.

VARIATION
You could use any firm-fleshed fish steaks or fillets for this dish, although tuna is a typically Asian ingredient.

SAVOY CABBAGE

The green leaves of the Savoy contain a range of nutrients and plant chemicals to help fight cancer, and they are also rich in minerals and vitamin C.

MAJOR NUTRIENTS PER 100 G/3½ OZ SAVOY CABBAGE

27 kcal	TRACE	6g	3g	2g	31 mg	600 mcg	35 mg	3 mcg	28 mg	230 mg	0.9 mcg
CALORIES	TOTAL FAT	CARBS	FIBRE	PROTEIN	VITAMIN C	BETA-CAROTENE	CALCIUM	FOLATE	MAGNESIUM	POTASSIUM	SELENIUM

Savoy, and other dark green cabbages are rich in plant chemicals, which may inhibit the growth of cancerous tumours, and which seem to have particular benefit in offering protection from colon, lung and hormone-based cancers, such as breast cancer, probably by increasing the metabolism of oestrogen. Cabbage is also very rich in vitamin C, folate, fibre and minerals, and is a source of B vitamins, vitamin K, iron and beta-carotene. Its other benefits are that its juice is a traditional remedy for peptic ulcers and its indoles can help lower 'bad' cholesterol.

- High in several nutrients, including vitamin C and calcium.
- Proven anti-cancer and anti-inflammatory effect.
- Helps protect against high 'bad' cholesterol and heart disease.
- Can treat peptic ulcers.

DID YOU KNOW?

This popular crinkle-leaf cabbage was originally grown in the Savoie, an Alpine region bordering Italy and France, and it is from here that it got its name.

PRACTICAL TIPS

Store the cabbage in the refrigerator in a polythene bag to retain its vitamin C and freshness. To retain most of its nutrients, cook lightly by steaming or stir-frying for a few minutes. To avoid that distinctive cabbage odour, don't overcook – cooking with a dash of vinegar also helps.

GRAPE & CABBAGE BOOSTER

Naturally sweet pears and grapes can disguise the taste of vegetables such as cabbage in a juice. The pumpkin seeds are finely ground, so no one will know they are there!

SERVES 1 • PREP TIME: 15 MINS • COOK TIME: NONE

PER SERVING:

 416 kcal CALORIES

 5.7g FAT

 0.9g SAT FAT

 94.5g CARBS

 62.6g SUGAR

 6.3g FIBRE

 9.3g PROTEIN

0.1g SALT

INGREDIENTS

2 pears, halved
¼ small head of Savoy cabbage, roughly chopped
1 tbsp pumpkin seeds
150 g/5½ oz seedless green grapes
small handful of crushed ice (optional)

1. Feed the pears and cabbage through a juicer.

2. Put the pumpkin seeds into a blender and whizz until finely ground, then add the grapes and crushed ice, if using, and blend. Pour in the pear juice mix and blend until smooth.

3. Pour into a glass and serve immediately.

POTATOES

Potatoes are rich in minerals that you need for the effective functioning of your brain and muscles, to keep you thinking and moving youthfully.

MAJOR NUTRIENTS PER 100 G/3½ OZ POTATOES

77 kcal	0.1g	19g	2.2g	2g	0.25 mg	20 mg	421 mg
CALORIES	TOTAL FAT	CARBS	FIBRE	PROTEIN	VITAMIN B6	VITAMIN C	POTASSIUM

The high starchy carbohydrate content of potatoes makes them number one on the satiety index, which scores foods according to how much they satisfy our hunger right after eating them. Healthy boiled potatoes are actually three times as satisfying as fried potatoes and can be very helpful in curbing cravings for sweet, unhealthy foods that lead to ageing weight gain. Potatoes also provide dense fuel for people who exercise and can help regulate energy and weight.

- Source of kukoamines, also found in goji berries, which, along with the high potassium content, help lower blood pressure.
- Contains vitamin B6, needed to produce the neurotransmitter GABA that helps us cope with stress, a major factor in staying young.
- Vitamin C protects sensitive brain and nerve cells from toxins, helping to keep our brains sharp and our muscles responsive.

DID YOU KNOW?

Potatoes are the most grown and eaten vegetable in the world, but their high starch content excludes them from our 'five-a-day' fruit and vegetable count.

PRACTICAL TIPS

Most nutrients in potatoes are found just under the skins, and removing these also cuts out the rich fibre there. The older and larger potatoes have a higher score on the glycaemic index, meaning that their sugars hit the bloodstream quicker, upsetting blood sugar balance. New potatoes with their skins intact are the healthiest option.

NEW POTATOES WITH GARLIC & CHILLI BUTTER

Nothing beats the flavour of those first potatoes of the season, even though we can now get new potatoes all year round. Garlic, chilli and fresh coriander add the perfect touch.

SERVES 4 • PREP TIME: 10 MINS • COOK TIME: 20 MINS

PER SERVING:

198 kcal	8.3g	5.2g	28.8g	2.6g	4.4g	3.3g	1g
CALORIES	FAT	SAT FAT	CARBS	SUGAR	FIBRE	PROTEIN	SALT

INGREDIENTS

1–2 tsp salt
700 g/1 lb 9 oz baby new potatoes
40 g/1½ oz butter
1 garlic clove, finely chopped
1 red chilli, deseeded and finely chopped
salt and pepper (optional)
1 tbsp chopped fresh coriander leaves, to garnish

1. Add the salt to a large saucepan of water and bring to the boil. Add the potatoes, bring back to the boil and cook for 15 minutes, or until tender. Drain well.

2. Melt the butter in a separate large saucepan, add the garlic and chilli and gently stir-fry for 30 seconds, without browning.

3. Add the potatoes and stir to coat in the butter, then season with salt and pepper, if using. Sprinkle with the coriander and serve hot.

ROCKET

This deep green, peppery salad leaf contains carotenes,
which have several cancer-preventing qualities.

MAJOR NUTRIENTS PER 15 G/½ OZ ROCKET

4 kcal	TRACE	0.5g	0.2g	0.4g	2.3 mg	214 mcg	24 mg	15 mcg	533 mcg	55 mg
CALORIES	TOTAL FAT	CARBS	FIBRE	PROTEIN	VITAMIN C	BETA-CAROTENE	CALCIUM	FOLATE	LUTEIN/ ZEAXANTHIN	POTASSIUM

Rocket, a member of the Brassica family that grows wild across much of Europe, is closely related to the mustard plant. It is a small plant with elongated, serrated leaves. Today, much of the rocket we buy is cultivated, but wild rocket leaves contain more of the protective plant chemicals than cultivated hybrids. The leaves are rich in carotenes and are an excellent source of lutein and zeaxanthin for eye health, including cataracts. The indoles contained in rocket and other Brassicas are linked with protection from colon cancer. The leaves also supply good amounts of folate – especially important in pregnancy because it helps protect the foetus – and calcium for healthy bones and heart.

- Contains carotenes to protect against cancers.
- Lutein content helps protect eye health, especially in the elderly.
- Contains indoles, linked with a reduction in the risk of colon cancer.
- Good source of calcium for bone protection.

DID YOU KNOW?

Rocket grows quickly from seed and is ideal for window boxes or tubs.

PRACTICAL TIPS

When buying rocket, the deeper the colour of the leaves, the more carotenes they contain. Rocket can be used in salads or as a garnish. Alternatively, it can be stirred into pasta instead of spinach, added to soup, made into a pesto or added to the top of a pizza. It doesn't keep fresh for long, so use within one to two days.

ROCKET FUEL SOUP

The mild spice from the rocket and mustard leaves is softened by the avocado
and coconut milk, creating a creamy but healthy soup.

SERVES 1 • PREP TIME: 10 MINS • COOK TIME: NONE

PER SERVING:	379 kcal CALORIES	37.9g FAT	25.2g SAT FAT	11.9g CARBS	4.4g SUGAR	6.1g FIBRE	5.4g PROTEIN	TRACE SALT

INGREDIENTS

30 g/1 oz rocket
20 g/¾ oz mustard leaves
200 ml/7 fl oz chilled water
½ avocado, stoned and flesh scooped from skin
125 ml/4 fl oz coconut milk
10 g/¼ oz rocket leaves, to garnish

1. Put the rocket, mustard leaves and water into a blender and blend until smooth.

2. Add the avocado to the blender with the coconut milk and blend until smooth and creamy.

3. Serve immediately or chill in the refrigerator. Stir well just before serving, garnished with a few rocket leaves.

MEAT, FISH, DAIRY & EGGS

TURKEY

A low-fat protein source, turkey helps promote a positive
outlook as well as high levels of energy and vitality.

MAJOR NUTRIENTS PER 100 G/3½ OZ SKINLESS TURKEY

111 kcal	0.65g	0.21g	0.11g	0mg	0mg	24.6g	6.23 mg	0.72 mg	0.58 mg	1.17 mg	4.02g	1.24 mg
CALORIES	TOTAL FAT	SATURATED FAT	MONO UN-SATURATED FAT	CARBS	FIBRE	PROTEIN	VITAMIN B3	VITAMIN B5	VITAMIN B6	IRON	GLUTAMIC ACID	ZINC

Turkey is known for its high tryptophan content. a protein constituent
from which the body makes the mood-, sleep- and appetite-regulating
brain chemical serotonin. This is believed to be one of the reasons that we
fall asleep after a heavy Christmas meal: the serotonin encourages us to
rest, which is a crucial component of staying young. Turkey's high protein
content also helps control appetite by balancing blood sugar levels, so
curbing sugar cravings and energy fluctuations. The white meat of turkey is
considered healthier than the brown meat due to its lower fat content, but
the difference is small. In fact, the brown meat can actually help raise your
metabolism more, making you more efficient at burning fuel, more likely to
lose weight, and less susceptible to overeating.

- Iron supports energy levels by producing the cells that your body uses
  for fuel and helping muscles store rejuvenating oxygen.
- Glutamic acid helps balance blood sugar and combat the ageing
  effects of stress.
- Contains the zinc that is needed to make serotonin, which makes you
  feel good. It is also vital in the process of repair to the body and helps
  you maintain a youthful appearance.

DID YOU KNOW?

*The Aztecs domesticated the
turkey and used its feathers
decoratively. It was associated with
Tezcatlipoca, their god of tricks.*

PRACTICAL TIPS

Turkey can be a lower-fat alternative to chicken, with many similar health
benefits. A free-range bird, which has had a healthy diet itself and lived
more naturally, will be leaner, taste better and lose less water when cooked
than a battery bird. Cook a whole turkey by roasting.

RED CABBAGE, TURKEY & QUINOA PILAF

Red cabbage comes into its own here, adding rich colour to this magnificent dish. Cranberries and Brazil nuts add flavour and crunch, while quinoa provides a moist and fluffy base.

SERVES 4 • PREP TIME: 30 MINS • COOK TIME: 55 MINS

PER SERVING:

 697 kcal CALORIES 34.8g FAT 7.3g SAT FAT 64.6g CARBS 22.9g SUGAR 10.3g FIBRE 37.2g PROTEIN 1.7g SALT

INGREDIENTS

90 g/3¼ oz white quinoa
90 g/3¼ oz red quinoa
½ tsp salt
4 tbsp vegetable oil
1 large red onion, halved and sliced
1 tsp cumin seeds, crushed
10-cm/4-inch cinnamon stick, broken
½ head of red cabbage, core removed,
leaves sliced into ribbons
250–300 ml/8½–10 fl oz chicken stock
¼ tsp pepper
350 g/12 oz cooked turkey, roughly chopped
2 carrots, shaved into ribbons
85 g/3 oz dried cranberries
85 g/3 oz Brazil nuts, roughly chopped
handful of fresh flat-leaf parsley leaves, to garnish

1. Combine the white quinoa and red quinoa, then place in a sieve and rinse under cold running water. Put in a saucepan with the salt and enough water to cover by 15 mm/⅝ inch. Bring to the boil, cover and simmer over a very low heat for 15 minutes. Remove from the heat but leave the pan covered for 5 minutes to allow the grains to swell. Fluff up the grains with a fork and set aside.

2. Heat the oil in a large frying pan over a medium–high heat. Add the onion with the cumin seeds and cinnamon and fry for 5 minutes, until the onion is soft but not coloured.

3. Add the cabbage, 250 ml/8½ fl oz of the stock and the pepper. Cover and cook over a medium heat for 15–20 minutes until the cabbage is just tender. Add the turkey, carrots, cranberries and Brazil nuts. Fry, uncovered, for 5 minutes, until the turkey is heated through.

4. Gently stir in the cooked quinoa. Add the remaining stock if the mixture seems dry. Cook for 2 minutes to heat through. Garnish with parsley and serve immediately.

CHICKEN

Grandma was right – scientists have confirmed that chicken soup
boosts the immune system and helps fight colds and flu.

MAJOR NUTRIENTS PER 150 G/5½ OZ SKINLESS CHICKEN

166 kcal	4g	30.5g	11.8g	1.5g	0.6 mg	0.5 mcg	15mg	1.5mg	34mg	356 mg	25 mcg	1.8mg
CALORIES	TOTAL FAT	PROTEIN	VITAMIN B3	VITAMIN B5	VITAMIN B6	VITAMIN B12	CALCIUM	IRON	MAGNESIUM	POTASSIUM	SELENIUM	ZINC

Scientists believe that chicken soup relieves the symptoms of colds and
flu by stimulating the production of infection-fighting cells. Using chicken
bones in the soup greatly boosts the effect. A portion of lean chicken meat
contains nearly half of the daily recommended intake of protein for an
adult woman, a whole day's intake of niacin (vitamin B3), and makes a large
contribution to our intake of minerals such as iron, the antioxidant zinc and
potassium. Chicken is rich in selenium, one of the minerals that is often
lacking in our diets, and which has strong anti-cancer action. Studies also
show that organic chicken contains higher levels of omega-3 fats, vitamin E
and other nutrients than non-organic meat.

- Helps boost immune system and protect against cancer.
- Niacin content helps protect against Alzheimer's disease and
  cognitive decline.
- Vitamin B content helps release energy from our food.
- Vitamin B6 content helps protect arteries from damage from
  homocysteine, a risk factor for heart disease.

DID YOU KNOW?

*Chicken fat is in its skin.
For it to be a low-fat food,
you need to remove all the skin
before cooking or eating it.*

PRACTICAL TIPS

Fresh chicken should be kept covered in a refrigerator for no more than
three days – longer storage increases bacteria count. Do not wash before
cooking as this can spread bacteria. Use a separate chopping board for
preparing raw chicken and wash hands and utensils carefully.

CHICKEN & KIMCHI SOUP

Kimchi is a fermented vegetable pickle thought to help promote the growth of healthy bacteria in the gut, which can be suppressed by a diet high in sugar and processed foods.

SERVES 4 • PREP TIME: 20 MINS • COOK TIME: 45–50 MINS

PER SERVING: **179 kcal** CALORIES **6.6g** FAT **1.8g** SAT FAT **12.8g** CARBS **6.6g** SUGAR **2.8g** FIBRE **16.7g** PROTEIN **2.9g** SALT

INGREDIENTS

2 tsp rice bran oil

4 boneless, skinless chicken thighs, 300 g/10½ oz total weight

4 spring onions, thinly sliced

115 g/4 oz carrots, thinly sliced

1 red pepper, cored, deseeded and diced

900 ml/1½ pints chicken stock

1 tbsp brown rice miso

2 tbsp mirin

175 g/6 oz bottled kimchi, sliced, with the sauce clinging to the pickle

1. Heat the oil in a saucepan, then add the chicken and fry for 5 minutes until lightly browned on both sides. Add the spring onions, carrots and red pepper. Stir in the stock, miso and mirin.

2. Bring to the boil, then cover and simmer for 30 minutes until the chicken is cooked through and there are no pink juices when the thickest part of the meat is pierced with a knife. Lift the chicken out with a slotted spoon, then shred into strips using two forks.

3. Return the chicken to the soup and add the kimchi, then heat through, ladle into warmed bowls and serve immediately.

LAMB

Lamb is an energy-rich, high-quality meat, which contains important
nutrients for immunity and the slowing down of ageing.

MAJOR NUTRIENTS PER 100 G/3½ OZ LAMB

229 kcal	16.97g	8.18g	62.5g	3.5mg	628mg	5.1g	92mg
CALORIES	TOTAL FAT	SATURATED FAT	MONO UN-SATURATED FAT	CARBS	FIBRE	PROTEIN	VITAMIN B2

74mg	0.56 mg	0.34 mg	2.47 mg	1.43 mg	7.5mg	3.67 mg
VITAMIN B3	VITAMIN B5	VITAMIN B6	VITAMIN B12	IRON	SELENIUM	ZINC

Animal, as well as plant sources of food, supply antioxidants that support immunity. Lamb is rich in the antioxidant trace minerals zinc and selenium. These produce liver enzymes that are our most powerful defence against free radicals, the harmful molecules that damage and age all parts of the body, from the skin to the internal organs. Another antioxidant that is present in lamb, coenzyme Q-10, works to protect the heart and to provide energy for the body as a whole. Coenzyme Q-10 has also been shown to reduce the incidence of congestive heart failure, Alzheimer's disease, Parkinson's disease, chronic fatigue, breast cancer and gum disease.

- Quality source of protein, for repairing and rebuilding worn-out cells. A single serving provides around 60 per cent of your daily requirements.
- Contains B-complex vitamins that support vitality in every cell of the body to keep you looking and feeling young.
- Although high in saturated fat, it also contains beneficial levels of heart-healthy monounsaturated fats.

DID YOU KNOW?

Lamb is the meat of a sheep that is under a year old. After a year, the sheep and its meat are known as hogget. Beyond two years, when the sheep develops two permanent incisor teeth, it is classed as mutton.

PRACTICAL TIPS

As a red meat, lamb is generally higher in saturated fat than white. You don't need to eat it often to enjoy its benefits. It's best to be picky about the cuts you choose – chops are the healthiest option. Lamb also makes a delicious burger alternative to beef, and works well with apricots and prunes, as in Middle Eastern tagines.

PISTACHIO-CRUSTED LAMB CHOPS

This is a delicious method of cooking lamb chops, with pistachios and dried cherries. Red stone fruit such as cherries or plums have a lovely depth of flavour that goes particularly well with lamb.

SERVES 4 • PREP TIME: 20 MINS • COOK TIME: 40 MINS

PER SERVING:

			50g	29.4g	11.7g	43.4g	3.5g
859 kcal	47.1g	16.2g	50g	29.4g	11.7g	43.4g	3.5g
CALORIES	FAT	SAT FAT	CARBS	SUGAR	FIBRE	PROTEIN	SALT

INGREDIENTS

2 tbsp olive oil
½ onion, thinly sliced
225 ml/8 fl oz ruby port
140 g/5 oz dried sweet cherries, roughly chopped
225 ml/8 fl oz chicken stock
1 tbsp clear honey
1¾ tsp salt
3 garlic cloves
100 g/3½ oz roasted, unsalted pistachio nuts
8 lamb chops
½ tsp pepper
1 tbsp Dijon mustard mixed with 1 tbsp water

1. Preheat the oven to 220°C/425°F/Gas Mark 7.

2. Heat the oil in a heavy frying pan over a medium–high heat. Add the onion and cook for about 5 minutes, stirring occasionally, until soft. Add the port, cherries, stock, honey and ¾ teaspoon of the salt and bring just to the boil. Reduce the heat to medium–low and simmer for about 20 minutes until the sauce is thick and syrupy.

3. Meanwhile, put the garlic into a processor and pulse until finely chopped. Add the nuts and pulse until finely chopped. Transfer to a plate.

4. Season the lamb chops on all sides with the remaining salt and the pepper, then brush with the mustard mixture. Press each lamb chop into the nut mixture to coat well all over.

5. Transfer the chops to a baking tray and bake in the preheated oven for 6 minutes. Turn over and cook for a further 6 minutes for medium rare, or 7–8 minutes for well done. Remove from the oven and loosely tent with foil. Leave to rest for 5 minutes before serving.

6. Serve hot, with the sauce spooned over the top.

GRASS-FED, FREE-RANGE BEEF

Grass-fed, free-range beef provides fats that help with weight loss
and promote youthful skin, bones and heart.

MAJOR NUTRIENTS PER 100 G/3½ OZ BEEF, GRASS-FED

192 kcal	12.73g	5.34g	4.8g	0mg	19.42g	4.82 mg
CALORIES	TOTAL FAT	SATURATED FAT	MONO UN-SATURATED FAT	FIBRE	PROTEIN	VITAMIN B3

0.58 mg	0.36 mg	1.97 mg	930 mcg	1.99mg	14.2 mcg	4.55 mg
VITAMIN B5	VITAMIN B6	VITAMIN B12	VITAMIN E	IRON	SELENIUM	ZINC

Grass-fed cattle generally get more exercise, making their meat leaner.
For every 85 g/3 oz serving, there is around 6 g/⅛ oz less fat in grass-
fed beef than in its grain-fed counterpart. This is good news for calorie
counters but, more importantly, the quality of fat contained in grass-fed
beef is better. Grass-fed beef contains high levels of omega-3 oils, which
keep the heart, joints, brain and skin appearing youthful. Another fat, CLA
(conjugated linolenic acid), comes direct from the grass, and enables
stored fat to be burned as energy, raising the metabolism and helping
maintain a trim figure. Low levels of CLA in our diet have been partly linked
to the rise of obesity.

- Contains four times more vitamin E than grain-fed beef, to hold back
  wrinkles and prevent age spots.
- Good selenium levels lessen anxiety, depression and fatigue. Low
  levels are associated with heart and bone degeneration.
- Contains the highest level of zinc in any meat, promoting clear skin
  and strong nails.
- Coenzyme Q-10 increases energy in all cells, especially the heart, so
  supporting overall vigour.

DID YOU KNOW?

*Cattle naturally roam and feed on
pasture. Cows were only fed grain
when humans moved on from their
role as hunter-gatherers to become
farmers, around 10,000 BC.*

PRACTICAL TIPS

Ask your butcher for the best source or find a farm shop attached to its
own pasture. Sirloin, fillet and rump steak are the healthiest, leanest cuts.
This is a very nutrient-dense food, so you only need to eat it two to four
times a month to get the benefits.

BEEF STIR-FRY

A quick and healthy meal that comes together in less than half an hour – perfect for a tasty mid-week meal for four.

SERVES 4 • PREP TIME: 10 MINS • COOK TIME: 10–12 MINS

PER SERVING:

167 kcal	3.4g	1.1g	9.3g	5.4g	2.5g	25.8g	0.2g
CALORIES	FAT	SAT FAT	CARBS	SUGAR	FIBRE	PROTEIN	SALT

INGREDIENTS

2–3 sprays olive oil

400 g/14 oz grass-fed free-range steak, such as topside, cut into thin strips (fat removed)

1 orange pepper, deseeded and cut into thin strips

4 spring onions, chopped

1–2 fresh jalapeño peppers, deseeded and chopped

2–3 garlic cloves, chopped

115 g/4 oz mangetout, trimmed and cut in half diagonally

115 g/4 oz large field mushrooms, sliced

1–2 tsp hoisin sauce, or to taste

1 tbsp orange juice

85 g/3 oz rocket or watercress

1. Preheat a wok then spray in the oil and heat for 30 seconds. Add the beef and stir-fry for 1 minute or until browned. Using a slotted spoon, remove and reserve.

2. Add the orange pepper, spring onions, jalapeño peppers and garlic and stir-fry for 2 minutes. Add the mangetout and mushrooms and stir-fry for a further 2 minutes.

3. Return the beef to the wok and add the hoisin sauce and orange juice. Stir-fry for 2–3 minutes, or until the beef is tender and the vegetables are tender but still firm to the bite. Stir in the rocket and stir-fry until it starts to wilt. Serve immediately.

VARIATION
This delicious stir-fry goes well with brown rice or wholewheat noodles to boost fibre.

PORK

Pork has an unfair reputation as a high calorie choice. In fact, if you choose the right cut it is a good lean source of protein and contains an impressive number of nutrients.

MAJOR NUTRIENTS PER 100 G/3½ OZ LEAN PORK FILLET

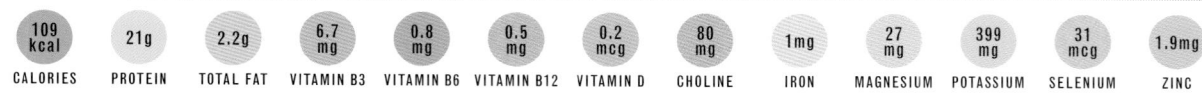

109 kcal	21g	2.2g	6.7 mg	0.8 mg	0.5 mg	0.2 mcg	80 mg	1mg	27 mg	399 mg	31 mcg	1.9mg
CALORIES	PROTEIN	TOTAL FAT	VITAMIN B3	VITAMIN B6	VITAMIN B12	VITAMIN D	CHOLINE	IRON	MAGNESIUM	POTASSIUM	SELENIUM	ZINC

Lean, high-protein pork, such as leg steak, contains vitamin D, which is hard to find in the diet and is vital to help make and maintain our bone density throughout life. Pork is higher than most other meats in healthy monounsaturated fats and is also rich in choline and B vitamins, all of which can protect the arteries from cholesterol damage and therefore help to prevent cardiovascular disease. The meat is very high in potassium to balance sodium in our bodies and act as a natural diuretic, reducing fluid retention and helping control high blood pressure. Eating pork is an excellent way to get your zinc, as well. This antioxidant mineral can help support optimal immune system function, fight infection and heal wounds quickly. There's iron, too, half of which is haem iron – the type that is most easily absorbed by our bodies.

- Very good source of lean high-quality protein.
- Source of bone-building vitamin D.
- Contains several heart-protective nutrients.
- Rich in zinc for immune function, and haem iron for healthy blood.

DID YOU KNOW?

Cured pork products, such as bacon, ham and deli sausage, are high in salt, may be high in fat, and may contain nitrites, which are linked with an increased risk of cancers. The smoking process some cured meats undergo also produces carcinogens. Stick to fresh pork.

PRACTICAL TIPS

Pork fillet or leg can be cubed and used for kebabs, with a yogurt, garlic and cucumber sauce. Or try cooking in a similar way to beefsteak. Thinly sliced, pork makes a good addition to vegetable stir-fries. Lean pork freezes well and will keep for a year. The official recommendation is to eat no more than 70g red meat a day, as very high meat intake is linked with increased risk of bowel cancer.

PORK-STUFFED CABBAGE LEAVES

This is a great way to use the leafiness of the cabbage to make a
healthy wrap for the tasty pork and rice filling.

SERVES 4 • PREP TIME: 45 MINS • COOK TIME: 1 HOUR

PER SERVING:

364 kcal	24.8g	9.1g	 18.8g	6.9g	3.1g	17.5g	2.3g
CALORIES	FAT	SAT FAT	CARBS	SUGAR	FIBRE	PROTEIN	SALT

INGREDIENTS

1 tbsp olive oil
15 g/½ oz butter
400 g/14 oz canned chopped tomatoes
450 ml/15 fl oz chicken stock
1 onion, grated
8 large cabbage leaves, thick stems removed
300 g/10½ oz fresh pork mince
100 g/3½ oz cooked white rice
finely grated rind of 1 lemon
2 tsp paprika
½ tsp dill seeds
1 egg, lightly beaten
¾ tsp salt
¼ tsp pepper
salt and pepper (optional)
1 tsp chopped fresh dill, to garnish

1. Heat the oil and butter in a large frying pan. Add the
tomatoes, stock and all but 2 tablespoons of the grated onion.
Season to taste with salt and pepper, if using. Bring to the boil,
then reduce the heat and simmer gently while you prepare the
cabbage leaves.

2. Bring a large saucepan of water to the boil. Add the cabbage
leaves and blanch for 2 minutes. Drain and rinse under cold
running water, then pat dry.

3. Combine the pork, rice, lemon rind, paprika, dill seeds,
egg and the remaining onion. Add ¾ teaspoon of salt and ¼
teaspoon of pepper and mix well. Divide the stuffing between
the cabbage leaves. Fold over the base and sides of each leaf,
then roll up to make a parcel.

4. Place the parcels seam side down in the sauce. Cover and
simmer over a low heat for 45 minutes until cooked through.

5. Sprinkle with fresh dill and serve immediately.

HINT
*Ask your butcher to mince a lean cut of pork for this dish as fat is
easily camouflaged in pork mince due to its pale colour.*

SALMON

Salmon is an excellent source of omega-3 fats, cancer-fighting selenium and vitamin B12, which helps protect against heart disease and a form of anaemia.

MAJOR NUTRIENTS PER 100 G/3½ OZ SALMON

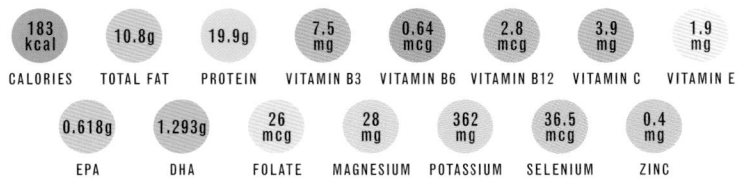

183 kcal	10.8g	19.9g	7.5 mg	0.64 mcg	2.8 mcg	3.9 mg	1.9 mg
CALORIES	TOTAL FAT	PROTEIN	VITAMIN B3	VITAMIN B6	VITAMIN B12	VITAMIN C	VITAMIN E

0.618g	1.293g	26 mcg	28 mg	362 mg	36.5 mcg	0.4 mg
EPA	DHA	FOLATE	MAGNESIUM	POTASSIUM	SELENIUM	ZINC

Much of the salmon that we eat today is farmed rather than wild. Although wild salmon tends to contain less fat and a little more of some of the nutrients, the two kinds are broadly comparable. Salmon is our major source of fish oils, which provide protection against heart disease, blood clots, stroke, high blood pressure, high blood cholesterol, Alzheimer's disease, depression and certain skin conditions. Salmon is also an excellent source of selenium – which protects against cancer – protein, niacin, vitamin B12, magnesium and vitamin B6.

- Protection against cardiovascular diseases and stroke.
- Helps keep the brain healthy and improve insulin resistance.
- May help children's concentration and brain power and protects against childhood asthma.
- Helps keep skin smooth, minimizes sunburn, can help beat eczema and helps prevent dry eyes.
- Helps minimize joint pain and may protect against cancers.

DID YOU KNOW?

Farmed salmon has been found to contain up to twice the fat of wild salmon – the wild fish is leaner.

PRACTICAL TIPS

For optimum omega-3 content, cook salmon lightly and poach or grill rather than pan-fry. Overcooking can oxidize the essential fats and this means that they are no longer beneficial. Frozen salmon retains the beneficial oils, vitamins and minerals, while canned salmon loses a proportion of these valuable nutrients.

GRILLED SALMON WITH CITRUS SALSA

The salsa really makes this dish – citrus fruits and fish have long been recognized as good companions and this zesty accompaniment really proves the case.

SERVES 4 • PREP TIME: 10 MINS • COOK TIME: 10 MINS

PER SERVING:	387 kcal	27.1g	5.2g	9.6g	6.1g	2g	26.7g	0.5g
	CALORIES	FAT	SAT FAT	CARBS	SUGAR	FIBRE	PROTEIN	SALT

INGREDIENTS

4 salmon fillets
1 tbsp olive oil
1 tbsp light soy sauce
pepper (optional)

CITRUS SALSA

1 large orange
1 lime
2 tomatoes, peeled and diced
2 tbsp extra virgin olive oil
2 tbsp chopped fresh coriander
¼ tsp caster sugar
salt and pepper (optional)

1. Preheat the grill to high. To make the salsa, cut all the peel and white pith from the orange and lime and remove the segments, discarding the membranes and reserving the juices.

2. Chop the segments and mix with the reserved juice, the tomatoes, oil and coriander. Add the sugar and season with salt and pepper, if using.

3. Place the salmon fillets on the grill rack. Mix the oil and soy sauce together, brush over the salmon and season with pepper, if using. Place under the preheated grill and cook, turning once, for 8–10 minutes, until the fish is firm and flakes easily.

4. Serve with a spoonful of the citrus salsa on the side.

VARIATION

This citrus salsa would also work well with grilled trout or tuna.

MACKEREL

Relatively inexpensive, mackerel is an excellent source of omega-3 fats and is also rich in minerals and vitamin E. It is also anti-inflammatory which can help ease joint pain.

MAJOR NUTRIENTS PER 100 G/3½ OZ MACKEREL

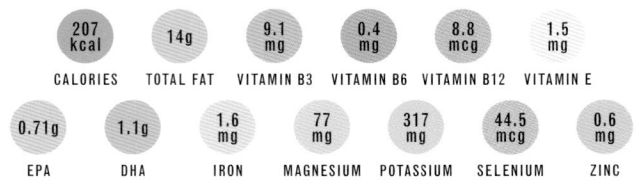

207 kcal	14g	9.1 mg	0.4 mg	8.8 mcg	1.5 mg
CALORIES	TOTAL FAT	VITAMIN B3	VITAMIN B6	VITAMIN B12	VITAMIN E

0.71g	1.1g	1.6 mg	77 mg	317 mg	44.5 mcg	0.6 mg
EPA	DHA	IRON	MAGNESIUM	POTASSIUM	SELENIUM	ZINC

Mackerel is a good choice for anyone seeking their weekly 1–2 portions of oily fish. It is also one of the fish with the highest content of EPA and DHA – the two special omega-3 fats found in significant amounts almost exclusively in oily fish and fish livers. Multiple scientific papers provide the evidence that increased consumption confers many important, and even vital, health benefits. Numerous trials show that a regular intake of fish oils protects us against heart disease and stroke by reducing inflammation and blood pressure and improving the blood fat and cholesterol profile.

- Anti-inflammatory that can ease symptoms of Crohn's disease, joint pain and arthritis.
- Can help prevent heart disease and stroke.
- Rich in selenium, magnesium, iron, potassium and vitamins D and E.

DID YOU KNOW?

The Romans used mackerel to make garum, a fermented fish sauce similar to that used in Thai cooking today.

PRACTICAL TIPS

Look for mackerel with firm, shiny bodies and bright eyes. Fresh mackerel won't droop if held horizontally by the head. Oily fish spoils faster than white fish and mackerel is best eaten within 24 hours of purchase. Baking, grilling, barbecuing or pan-frying are excellent cooking methods and, as it is rich-tasting, instead of creamy sauces, it is best served with sharp or spicy flavours, such as rhubarb sauce, mustard or horseradish.

GRIDDLED MACKEREL ON RYE BREAD

Fresh mackerel is packed with healthy fats and protein
and this hearty lunch is ideal for busy days.

SERVES 4 • PREP TIME: 10 MINS • COOK TIME: 10 MINS

PER SERVING:	458 kcal	26.3g	5.4g	25.5g	2.1g	3.4g	28.4g	1.5g
	CALORIES	FAT	SAT FAT	CARBS	SUGAR	FIBRE	PROTEIN	SALT

INGREDIENTS

4 mackerel fillets,
each weighing 125 g/4½ oz
4 slices dark rye bread,
each weighing 50 g/1¾ oz
1 tbsp chopped fresh flat-leaf parsley, to garnish

ANCHOVY RELISH

4 tbsp chopped fresh flat-leaf parsley
2 tbsp capers from a jar, drained
2 tsp Dijon mustard
6 anchovy fillets in oil, drained
juice of ½ lemon
1 tsp pepper
2 tbsp extra virgin olive oil

1. To make the relish, place the parsley, capers, mustard, anchovy fillets and lemon juice in a blender or food processor and whizz for a few seconds to blend. Alternatively, very finely chop the parsley, capers and anchovies and stir them together with the mustard and lemon juice in a small bowl. Stir the pepper and oil into the relish and set aside.

2. Place a ridged griddle pan over a high heat, then add the mackerel fillets and cook for 2–3 minutes on each side, or until bubbling and cooked through. Meanwhile, toast the rye bread.

3. Place the mackerel on the toasted bread and drizzle over the relish. Garnish with the parsley and serve immediately.

VARIATION

If you can't get rye bread, brown wholemeal bread or granary bread will work just as well with the mackerel.

TUNA

Fresh tuna is an important source of omega-3 fats and antioxidant minerals for arterial and heart health, and is also rich in vitamin E for healthy skin.

MAJOR NUTRIENTS PER 100 G/3½ OZ TUNA

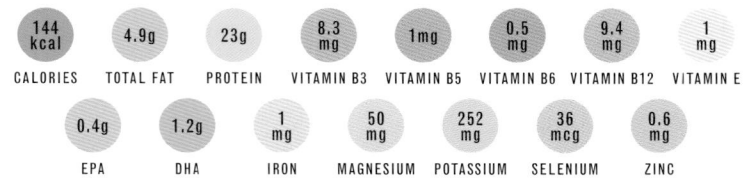

144 kcal	4.9g	23g	8.3 mg	1mg	0.5 mg	9.4 mg	1 mg
CALORIES	TOTAL FAT	PROTEIN	VITAMIN B3	VITAMIN B5	VITAMIN B6	VITAMIN B12	VITAMIN E

0.4g	1.2g	1 mg	50 mg	252 mg	36 mcg	0.6 mg
EPA	DHA	IRON	MAGNESIUM	POTASSIUM	SELENIUM	ZINC

The firm, dense and meaty flavourful flesh of fresh or frozen tuna makes it an ideal choice of fish for non-fish lovers. Quick to cook, it is an excellent source of protein and is especially rich in B vitamins, selenium and magnesium. A small portion will contain around 20 per cent of your daily vitamin E needs. While most types of tuna contain fewer of the essential omega-3 fats than some other oily fishes, there is still a good content of EPA and DHA fats. DHA is particularly effective at keeping our hearts and brains healthy and in good working order. Just one portion of tuna per week can provide the recommended weekly intake of 1.4 g of these fats.

- A good source of omega-3, EPA and DHA fats, which offer protection against a range of diseases.
- High in protein.
- Rich in selenium and magnesium for heart health.
- Extremely rich in vitamin B12 for healthy blood.

DID YOU KNOW?

Research has found that when tuna is canned (whether in oil, water, brine or a sauce) it loses most of its beneficial omega-3 fats, so shouldn't count towards your oily fish intake.

PRACTICAL TIPS

Fresh fish should be odourless and is best cooked and eaten on the day of purchase. To retain all the health benefits of the omega-3 fats, lightly sear tuna in a pan on both sides and cook for as little time as possible. Tuna steaks can also be sliced and stir-fried for one minute with sliced vegetables – unlike many types of fish, it won't disintegrate.

TUNA WITH PAK CHOI & SOBA NOODLES

The addition of ginger and fresh chilli really brings out the flavour of the tuna in this fresh-tasting stir-fry. Don't overcook the pak choi or it will lose its characteristic crunchiness.

SERVES 2 • PREP TIME: 25 MINS • COOK TIME: 20 MINS

PER SERVING:

 717 kcal CALORIES **27.2g** FAT **4.2g** SAT FAT **53.2g** CARBS **7.1g** SUGAR **7.4g** FIBRE **63.8g** PROTEIN **1.8g** SALT

INGREDIENTS

400 g/14 oz pak choi
1–2 tsp salt
115 g/4 oz soba noodles
2 tuna steaks, each weighing about 175 g/6 oz,
and 15 mm/⅝ inch thick
1 tbsp groundnut oil, for brushing
2 tbsp groundnut oil
2 slices fresh ginger, cut into matchsticks
½–1 fresh red chilli, deseeded and thinly sliced
4 spring onions, some green included,
thicky sliced diagonally
140 g/5 oz frozen soya beans, thawed
2 tbsp chicken stock
squeeze of lime juice
3 tbsp chopped fresh coriander
sea salt and pepper (optional)

1. Slice the pak choi stems into bite-sized pieces. Slice the leaves into broad ribbons.

2. Add the salt to a large saucepan of water and bring to the boil. Add the noodles, bring back to the boil and cook for 5–6 minutes, until just tender. Drain, reserving the cooking water. Rinse well and set aside. Return the reserved water to the pan and keep warm over a low heat.

3. Meanwhile, cut the tuna steaks into thirds. Brush with oil and season with sea salt and pepper, if using. Heat a ridged griddle pan over a high heat. Add the tuna and fry for 2–2½ minutes on each side. Transfer to a plate and set aside in a warm place.

4. Heat a wok over a medium–high heat. Add the oil and sizzle the ginger, chilli and spring onions for a few seconds.

5. Add the pak choi stalks, soya beans and stock and stir-fry for 3 minutes. Add the pak choi leaves and stir-fry for a further minute. Add the lime juice and coriander, then season to taste with sea salt and pepper, if using.

6. Reheat the noodles in the cooking water, then drain. Divide the noodles between two plates, add the vegetables and arrange the tuna on top. Serve immediately.

CLAMS

Low in fat and high in protein, clams are an ideal food for dieters and
they are rich in calcium for a healthy heart and bones.

MAJOR NUTRIENTS PER 100 G/3½ OZ SHUCKED CLAMS

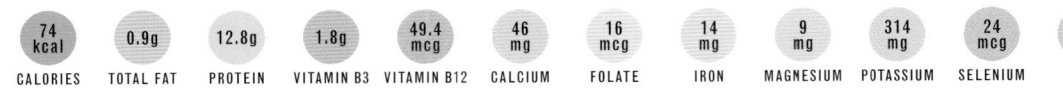

74 kcal	0.9g	12.8g	1.8g	49.4 mcg	46 mg	16 mcg	14 mg	9 mg	314 mg	24 mcg	1.4 mg
CALORIES	TOTAL FAT	PROTEIN	VITAMIN B3	VITAMIN B12	CALCIUM	FOLATE	IRON	MAGNESIUM	POTASSIUM	SELENIUM	ZINC

There are various types of clams, ranging in size and shape. All edible clams are highly nutritious, being low in fat and high in a wide range of minerals and B vitamins. Clams have a particularly high iron content and just 100 g/3½ oz shelled clams provide a whole day's intake. Iron carries oxygen from the lungs to all parts of the body and is vital for our immune system, helping to increase resistance to infection and aid the healing process. For women who are likely to suffer from anaemia due to iron loss during menstruation, eating clams is a great way to replenish iron in the blood.

- High in iron for healthy blood.
- Provide high amounts of calcium for strong bones.
- High in selenium, the anti-cancer mineral.
- Good source of zinc to boost the immune system and fertility.

PRACTICAL TIPS

Care should be taken when 'shucking' clams (removing them from their shells). The clam should be held in a thick cloth and a proper shucking knife used to pry open the shell. Clams in their shells can be cooked like mussels – in a little liquid over a high heat, covered. Any that don't open after 3 minutes should be discarded. Clams go well with spaghetti, or can be used in a seafood chowder soup. Garlic, parsley and tomato are natural culinary companions.

DID YOU KNOW?

Clams are usually found buried in sand or mud. Although native to both salt and fresh water, salt-water clams are considered to have a superior flavour.

CLAMS IN BLACK BEAN SAUCE

Clams cooked in black bean sauce are a popular partnership in Chinese cooking. Traditionally cheap and widely available, clams provide many essential minerals.

SERVES 4 • PREP TIME: 18 MINS • COOK TIME: 10 MINS

PER SERVING:

75 kcal	3.7g	0.6g	3.9g	0.1g	0.7g	5.7g	0.5g
CALORIES	FAT	SAT FAT	CARBS	SUGAR	FIBRE	PROTEIN	SALT

INGREDIENTS

900 g/2 lb small clams
1 tbsp vegetable or groundnut oil
1 tsp finely chopped fresh ginger
1 tsp finely chopped garlic
1 tbsp fermented black beans, rinsed and roughly chopped
2 tsp Chinese rice wine
1 tbsp finely chopped spring onion
salt (optional)

1. Discard any clams with broken shells and any that refuse to close when tapped. Thoroughly wash the remaining clams and leave to soak in clean water until ready to cook.

2. Heat a wok over a medium–high heat and add the oil. Add the ginger and garlic and stir-fry until fragrant. Add the beans and cook for 1 minute.

3. Increase the heat to high, add the clams and rice wine and stir-fry for 2 minutes to combine everything. Cover and cook for a further 3 minutes, or until the clam shells have opened. Discard any that remain closed. Add the spring onion and season to taste with salt, if using. Serve immediately.

ANCHOVIES

Anchovies are a delicious way to combine the benefits of omega-3 oils
with a healthy dose of rejuvenating high-quality protein.

MAJOR NUTRIENTS PER 100 G/3½ OZ ANCHOVIES

131 kcal	4.84g	0mg	0mg	20.35g	14.02 mg	0.65 mg	0.54g	0.91g	147 mg	36.5 mg
CALORIES	TOTAL FAT	CARBS	FIBRE	PROTEIN	VITAMIN B3	VITAMIN B5	OMEGA-3 OILS – EPA	OMEGA-3 OILS – DHA	CALCIUM	SELENIUM

Anchovies contain high levels of essential omega-3 oils and protein, which help the body to repair and renew skin, bone and muscle, and hold back the ravages of time. The protein in anchovies also helps regulate energy levels by reducing sugar cravings, making it an important player in effective metabolism and weight management. As oily fish is high in omega oils and low in saturated fats, it is the perfect alternative to red meat. Anchovies support heart health, and also have a high vitamin B profile. Two portions a week of anchovies, or any oily fish, has been shown to significantly reduce the risk of heart attack, which increases as we grow older.

- The small bones in anchovies provide calcium to keep bones strong and the heart pumping efficiently.
- Selenium helps detoxify heavy metals like mercury and cadmium that have an ageing effect.
- Vitamins B3 and B5 create energy in all cells to keep the body young.

DID YOU KNOW?

The strong flavour of anchovies makes them a common ingredient in many popular condiments, not just fish sauces but also Worcestershire sauce.

PRACTICAL TIPS

Fresh anchovies are hard to find but some anchovies are more healthily preserved than others. Bottled anchovies are preserved in oil rather than salt, and marinated white anchovies (available in most delis and supermarkets) have a less intense flavour than canned ones.

STUFFED TOMATOES

These stuffed tomatoes make an excellent, quick-and-easy summer snack or starter.
Avocado, olives and anchovies add essential nutrients.

MAKES 12 • PREP TIME: 20 MINS • COOK TIME: NONE

PER STUFFED TOMATO:	77 kcal	6.5g	1g	4.1g	1.8g	1.9g	1.5g	0.3g
	CALORIES	FAT	SAT FAT	CARBS	SUGAR	FIBRE	PROTEIN	SALT

INGREDIENTS

12 small ripe tomatoes,
about 4.5 cm/ 1¾ inches in diameter
1 large ripe avocado
1 tbsp lemon juice
4 tbsp mayonnaise
6 canned or bottled anchovy fillets in oil,
drained and finely chopped
8 stoned black olives, finely chopped
pepper (optional)
1 tbsp snipped fresh chives, to garnish

1. Cut a thin slice from the base of each tomato and scoop out the seeds. Place cut side down on several layers of kitchen paper and leave to drain.

2. Meanwhile, halve the avocado and remove the stone. Scoop the flesh into a bowl and mash with the lemon juice. Add the mayonnaise, anchovies and olives. Mix well and season with pepper, if using.

3. Spoon the avocado mixture into the tomatoes. Arrange on a serving plate and sprinkle with the chives.

CRAB

This low-fat, high-protein shellfish contains l-tyrosine for brain power
and high levels of selenium for protection from cancer.

MAJOR NUTRIENTS PER 100 G/3½ OZ CRABMEAT

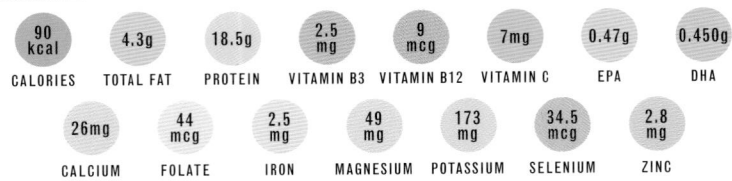

90 kcal	4.3g	18.5g	2.5 mg	9 mcg	7mg	0.47g	0.450g
CALORIES	TOTAL FAT	PROTEIN	VITAMIN B3	VITAMIN B12	VITAMIN C	EPA	DHA

26mg	44 mcg	2.5 mg	49 mg	173 mg	34.5 mcg	2.8 mg
CALCIUM	FOLATE	IRON	MAGNESIUM	POTASSIUM	SELENIUM	ZINC

Like mussels, crabs are low in total fat and saturates and rich in minerals.
Crabmeat is a good source of l-tyrosine, an amino acid that has been
shown to help brain power. It contains as much protein as a similar weight
of lean beef and is therefore ideal for pescatarians. A 100 g/3½ oz portion
of crab provides over half the recommended daily intake of selenium, a
powerful mineral with anti-cancer action, as well as a quarter of a day's
folate. This vitamin helps to protect against birth defects, and is also linked
to a reduction in levels of blood homocysteine, which is a contributing
factor in heart disease.

- Excellent source of low saturated fat protein, which also contains
  omega-3 fats.
- Rich in several important minerals.
- Contributes a range of B vitamins in good amounts.
- Very good choice for people watching their weight.

DID YOU KNOW?

*There are more than 8,000
species of fresh and saltwater crabs.
Every year, over 1 million tons
are eaten.*

PRACTICAL TIPS

You can buy live crabs and boil them at home, but many people prefer to
buy prepared and dressed crabs, or packets of frozen cooked crabmeat.
Unfortunately, canned crab is often high in sodium and has lost much of
its omega-3 fats. The white meat is delicately flavoured, while the brown
meat is rich and strong tasting – both are best served simply with lemon
and black pepper.

LITTLE CURRIED CRAB CAKES WITH AVOCADO SALAD

Once you've done the preparation, these little crab cakes are easy to put together, and are perfectly complemented by the tangy avocado salad.

SERVES 4 • PREP TIME: 20 MINS • COOK TIME: 10 MINS

PER SERVING:

 362 kcal CALORIES

 14g FAT

 2.3g SAT FAT

 40g CARBS

 3.9g SUGAR

 7.7g FIBRE

23.7g PROTEIN

1.3g SALT

INGREDIENTS

300 g/10½ oz white crabmeat
150 g/5½ oz canned sweetcorn kernels, drained
100 g/3½ oz wholemeal panko breadcrumbs
1 large egg, beaten
1½ tbsp light mayonnaise
1½ tbsp fat-free Greek-style yogurt
2 tbsp snipped fresh chives
2 tsp Dijon mustard
1 tsp curry powder and ¼ tsp pepper
10 sprays cooking spray, for oiling
1 large ripe avocado
1 tomato, finely chopped
juice of ½ lime
small bunch of fresh coriander, leaves only
½ fresh red jalapeño chilli, deseeded and chopped
3 spring onions, chopped

1. Mix the crabmeat, sweetcorn, breadcrumbs, egg, mayonnaise, yogurt, chives, mustard, curry powder and pepper together in a bowl.

2. Using your hands, shape the mixture into eight patties. Spray a non-stick frying pan with cooking spray to coat, then heat to just below medium–high and add the patties to the pan. Cook the patties for 4 minutes, without turning or moving them.

3. Meanwhile, make the salad. Stone, peel and slice the avocado, then lightly crush it in a bowl. Add the tomato, lime juice, coriander leaves, chilli and spring onions and stir to combine.

4. Spray the tops of the patties with more cooking spray, then use a metal spatula to turn each one over carefully. Cook for a further 3 minutes, or until the crab cakes are golden and piping hot. Serve immediately with the avocado salad.

HINT
Try serving these mini crab cakes with some more Greek-yogurt lightly drizzled over the top.

SARDINES

Sardines are one of the best sources of omega-3 fats and can protect us against heart disease and Alzheimer's disease. They can also help lower 'bad' blood cholesterol.

MAJOR NUTRIENTS PER 140 G/5 OZ (ABOUT 3) SARDINES

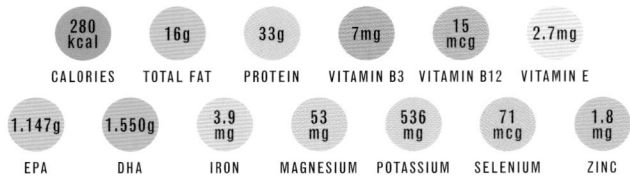

280 kcal	16g	33g	7mg	15 mcg	2.7mg
CALORIES	TOTAL FAT	PROTEIN	VITAMIN B3	VITAMIN B12	VITAMIN E

1.147g	1.550g	3.9 mg	53 mg	536 mg	71 mcg	1.8 mg
EPA	DHA	IRON	MAGNESIUM	POTASSIUM	SELENIUM	ZINC

Sardines are usually eaten canned. They retain most of the nutrients of fresh sardines, but fresh sardines are a healthy treat. They are one of the richest fish in omega-3 fats, DHA and EPA. These fatty acids can help prevent or control diseases including arthritis, cardiovascular disease and Alzheimer's disease, and an adequate intake can help improve depression and enhance cognitive powers. Sardines are one of the few foods rich in vitamin D, which helps form and protect our bones throughout life. They are also very high in other vitamins and minerals and one portion provides about a third of an adult's daily requirement of iron, vitamin E, vitamin B12 and selenium.

- Excellent source of omega-3 fats for disease prevention.
- Ideal food for long-term brain health and cognitive powers.
- Help lower 'bad' blood cholesterol and high blood pressure.
- Regular consumption can give up to 50 per cent reduced risk of stroke.

DID YOU KNOW?

Weight for weight, sardines provide more protein than steak, more potassium than bananas and more iron than cooked spinach.

PRACTICAL TIPS

Fresh sardines can be cleaned (ask your seller to do this) and then grilled and served with lemon juice and bread, or with grilled tomatoes on wholemeal toast. Sardines can also be filleted for people who don't want to deal with the bones, although the bones are edible and are an excellent source of calcium. Filleted fish can be enhanced with a mustard sauce, which cuts through the oily richness.

GRILLED SARDINES STUFFED WITH FETA & PINE NUTS

The delicately herby stuffing brings feta and pine nuts together with raisins and lemon in this Mediterranean-inspired dish. It complements the grilled sardines perfectly.

SERVES 4 • PREP TIME: 30 MINS • COOK TIME: 12 MINS

PER SERVING:

767 kcal	47.7g	10.8g	22.3g	14.7g	2.3g	67.9g	1.8g
CALORIES	FAT	SAT FAT	CARBS	SUGAR	FIBRE	PROTEIN	SALT

INGREDIENTS

12 sardines, gutted and heads removed
100 g/3½ oz pine nuts
85 g/3 oz raisins
100 g/3½ oz feta cheese, crumbled
grated zest of 2 unwaxed lemons
40 g/1½ oz fresh flat-leaf parsley, finely chopped
pinch of sea salt
¼ tsp of pepper
3 tbsp olive oil
1 lemon, cut into wedges, to serve (optional)

1. Butterfly the sardines and remove the backbones.

2. Heat a frying pan over a low heat. Add the pine nuts and toast for 5–6 minutes, or until golden, tossing halfway through. Leave to cool, then grind half the nuts in a pestle and mortar. Transfer them to a bowl, add the raisins, cheese, lemon zest, parsley, whole pine nuts, salt and pepper and mix well.

3. Spoon 2 teaspoons of the filling into the cavity of each butterflied sardine. Close each sardine like a book and secure using a couple of cocktail sticks or a piece of string.

4. Preheat the grill to high. Line a baking tray with foil. Lay the filled sardines on the prepared tray and drizzle over half the oil. Grill for 6 minutes, turning halfway through and drizzling with the remaining oil. Serve hot, with lemon wedges for squeezing over, if using.

HINT
You will need 24 wooden cocktail sticks or some string to prepare the sardines for cooking.

TROUT

Trout provides a package that safeguards the joints, eyes and brain from damage and keeps them working like new. It also helps to increase energy levels.

MAJOR NUTRIENTS PER 100 G/3½ OZ FRESH TROUT

148 kcal	6.61g	0mg	0mg	20.77g	0.35 mg	4.5 mg	7.79 mg	155IU	0.2g	0.53g
CALORIES	TOTAL FAT	CARBS	FIBRE	PROTEIN	VITAMIN B1	VITAMIN B3	VITAMIN B12	VITAMIN D	OMEGA-3 OILS – EPA	OMEGA-3 OILS – DHA

Omega-3 oils are crucial players in mood and behaviour regulation as they affect how we use the stabilizing brain chemicals serotonin and dopamine. Eating oily fish one to three times a week has also been shown to improve brain power and slow down the loss in concentration, memory and mental acuity associated with ageing and stress. Of all the oily fish, trout is one of the least contaminated by mercury toxicity. Mercury is common in larger oily fish like tuna and swordfish, which can spend years accumulating this dangerous and ageing substance.

- Contains pink astaxanthin, which supports good eye health and keeps the brain firing on all cylinders.
- Vitamin D is needed for an agile brain. Low levels are linked to depression and dementia.
- High levels of B vitamins promote youthful vitality and increased energy levels.
- Omega-3 oils lubricate joints to ensure pain-free agility.

DID YOU KNOW?

Trout is a type of salmon that spends its life in freshwater streams and ponds.

PRACTICAL TIPS

Trout can be bought both fresh and smoked. The fresh fish are easy to stuff with herbs and lemon and bake, and the smoked variety makes a good alternative to the stronger-flavoured salmon. This is an excellent choice of oily fish for people who are put off by a strong fishy flavour.

GINGER & SESAME TROUT WITH BRAISED PAK CHOI

Recipes with Asian ingredients have a reputation for being high in salt, but here the salt content has been reduced, while keeping all the delicious flavours.

SERVES 2 • PREP TIME: 10 MINS • COOK TIME: 10 MINS

PER SERVING:

 376 kcal CALORIES
 18.2g FAT
 3g SAT FAT
 12.2g CARBS
 5.6g SUGAR
 2.9g FIBRE
36.5g PROTEIN
0.9g SALT

INGREDIENTS

2 heads of pak choi
½ tbsp groundnut oil
½ tsp Chinese five spice
2 tbsp rice wine
1 small green chilli, deseeded and finely chopped
6 sprays cooking oil spray
4 rainbow trout fillets
1 tbsp sesame oil
2-cm/¾-inch piece fresh ginger, finely grated
1 tbsp low-salt soy sauce
½ tbsp rice vinegar
1 tsp sesame seeds
1 tbsp ketjap manis (Indonesian soy sauce)
4 spring onions, chopped, to garnish

1. Quarter each head of pak choi lengthways, rinse under cold running water and pat dry on kitchen paper. Place a large saucepan over a medium–high heat and add the groundnut oil. Add the pak choi and fry for 3 minutes, or until starting to colour. Stir in the five spice and rice wine and cook for a further minute, then add 1 tablespoon of boiling water and scatter in the chilli. Bring to a simmer, cover, reduce the heat to low and cook for 2–3 minutes, or until the pak choi is just tender.

2. Meanwhile, place a large frying pan over a medium–high heat and spray with 3 sprays of cooking oil spray. Add the trout fillets and cook for 2–3 minutes, then turn over with a spatula. Spray the pan with 3 sprays of cooking spray and cook for a further 2 minutes, or until the fillets are just cooked through. Remove from the pan and keep warm.

3. Reduce the heat to medium, add the sesame oil to the pan and stir in the ginger. Cook for 1 minute, then add the soy sauce, vinegar, sesame seeds and ketjap manis and stir to combine.

4. Serve the trout fillets with the sesame mixture spooned over the top. Garnish with the spring onions and serve with the pak choi mixture on the side.

SCALLOPS

They may be a luxurious treat but scallops can also help boost your vitamin B12
and magnesium intake to protect the arteries and bones.

MAJOR NUTRIENTS PER 100 G/3½ OZ SHUCKED SCALLOPS

88 kcal	0.8g	16.8g	1.5g	24 mg	16 mcg	56 mg	314 mg	22 mcg	0.95 mg
CALORIES	TOTAL FAT	PROTEIN	VITAMIN B12	CALCIUM	FOLATE	MAGNESIUM	POTASSIUM	SELENIUM	ZINC

Scallops are an excellent source of vitamin B12, which is needed by the body to deactivate homocysteine, a chemical that can damage blood vessel walls. High homocysteine levels are also linked to osteoporosis. A recent study found that osteoporosis occurred more frequently among women whose vitamin B12 status was deficient. A high intake of vitamin B12 has also been shown to be protective against colon cancer. Scallops are also a very good source of magnesium and a regular intake helps build bone, release energy, regulate nerves and keep the heart healthy. Deficiency can cause abnormal heart rhythms.

- Low in calories and fat so ideal for dieters.
- Rich in magnesium, which has several roles to play in body maintenance.
- A good source of vitamin B12 for arterial and bone health. Regular intake may help to protect against colon cancer.

DID YOU KNOW?

Scallops are rich in tryptophan, an amino acid that may help cure insomnia and aids the production of mood-enhancing serotonin in our brains.

PRACTICAL TIPS

Fresh scallops should have flesh that is white and firm, have no evidence of browning and be free of odour. Scallops should be cooked for only a few minutes since exposure to too much heat will cause them to become tough. The sweet flavour of scallops goes well with chilli, coriander, garlic and parsley.

CHILLI ORANGE NOODLES WITH SEARED SCALLOPS

Delicate scallops are delicious when paired with a chilli-orange dressing
and the noodles help to make a healthy and satisfying meal.

SERVES 4 • PREP TIME: 10 MINS • COOK TIME: 10 MINS

PER SERVING:

563 kcal	38g	4.9g	54.9g	15.1g	2.8g	13.2g	4g
CALORIES	FAT	SAT FAT	CARBS	SUGAR	FIBRE	PROTEIN	SALT

INGREDIENTS

350 g/12 oz fresh udon noodles
12–16 scallops, corals removed
1 tbsp unsalted butter
1 tbsp olive oil
salt and pepper (optional)
3 spring onions, thinly sliced, to garnish

DRESSING

3 garlic cloves, finely chopped
1 tbsp finely chopped fresh ginger
zest and juice of 1 orange
4 tbsp soy sauce
90 ml/3 fl oz sweet chilli sauce
125 ml/4 fl oz vegetable oil

1. Cook the noodles according to the packet instructions. Drain and set aside.

2. To make the dressing, combine the garlic, ginger, orange zest and juice, soy sauce and sweet chilli sauce in a bowl and whisk to combine. Add the oil and whisk until emulsified.

3. Rinse the scallops, pat them dry, and season with salt and pepper, if using. Heat the butter and oil in a large frying pan over a high heat until the butter is melted. Add the scallops and sear for about 1½ minutes on each side until they have a golden brown crust but are still translucent in the centre.

4. In a large bowl, toss the noodles with most of the dressing. Divide the noodles between four plates. Top each with 3–4 scallops. Drizzle a little more dressing over the scallops and serve immediately, garnished with spring onions.

HINT
To get maximum nutrients from the scallops take care not to overcook them – a searing hot pan is the best cooking method.

MUSSELS

Inexpensive and delicious, mussels are a source of protein, B vitamins
for nerve health, and iodine for thyroid function.

MAJOR NUTRIENTS PER 100 G/3½ OZ SHUCKED MUSSELS

86 kcal	2.2g	11.9g	0.41g	0.16g	8mg	1.6 mcg	12 mcg
CALORIES	TOTAL FAT	PROTEIN	EPA	DHA	VITAMIN C	VITAMIN B3	VITAMIN B12

0.55 mg	26 mg	42mg	3.9 mg	34 mg	320 mg	44.5 mcg	1.6 mg
VITAMIN E	CALCIUM	FOLATE	IRON	MAGNESIUM	POTASSIUM	SELENIUM	ZINC

Mussels are low in saturated fat and high in protein, while also containing
some omega-3 essential fats, a wide range of vitamins and many minerals
in excellent amounts. They are also low in cholesterol. A portion of mussels
will provide around a third of the recommended daily intake of iron for an
adult, and about three quarters of a day's selenium requirement. Mussels
are a very good source of B vitamins, providing over 100 per cent of daily
B12 needs, a quarter of necessary folate and a useful amount of niacin.
Like most shellfish, mussels are also a good source of fluoride for healthy
teeth and iodine for healthy thyroid function.

- A low-calorie, low-fat source of good quality protein.
- Contain useful amounts of omega-3 essential fats.
- Rich in iron and selenium.
- Good source of B vitamins.

DID YOU KNOW?

*A mussel with orange flesh
is female, while a whiter mussel
is usually male. Both are equally
tasty and rich in nutrients.*

PRACTICAL TIPS

Fresh mussels should not smell fishy or of iodine. They should have a
slight briny odour. Farmed mussels are considered safer to eat than wild
mussels, which can harbour toxins from the sea. Discard any live mussels
that don't close tight when tapped and, discard any that have failed to open
during cooking. Mussels go very well with garlic, parsley and white wine
and can be added to fish stews, soups, paella and shellfish salads.

MIXED SEAFOOD CHOWDER

Chowder is a classic American East Coast main-meal soup, often made with clams. This mixed seafood version is equally good and just as nutritious.

SERVES 4 • PREP TIME: 10 MINS • COOK TIME: 30–35 MINS

PER SERVING:
 362 kcal CALORIES
 15.5g FAT
5g SAT FAT
 22.7g CARBS
6.7g SUGAR
 2.3g FIBRE
30.4g PROTEIN
2.7g SALT

INGREDIENTS

1 tbsp vegetable oil
1 large onion, chopped
80 g/2¾ oz pancetta, cubed
1 tbsp plain flour
600 ml/1 pint fish stock, made from 1 fish stock cube
225 g/8 oz small new potatoes, halved
pinch of saffron threads
pinch of cayenne pepper
300 ml/10 fl oz semi-skimmed milk
200 g/7 oz haddock or other white fish fillet, cubed
150 g/5½ oz salmon fillet, cubed
200 g/7 oz cooked shelled mussels
pepper (optional)

1. Heat the oil in a large saucepan over a medium heat, then add the onion and pancetta. Cook for 8–10 minutes, until the onion is soft and the pancetta is cooked. Stir in the flour and cook for a further 2 minutes.

2. Stir in the stock and bring to a gentle simmer. Add the potatoes, then cover and simmer for 10–12 minutes until the potatoes are tender and cooked through.

3. Add the saffron, cayenne pepper and pepper, if using, then stir in the milk. Tip the fish into the pan and gently simmer for 4 minutes.

4. Add the mussels and cook for a further 2 minutes to warm through. Serve immediately.

VARIATION

For a richer, creamier and more luxurious chowder, replace half the milk with single cream.

OYSTERS

Prized for their nutritional qualities, oysters are rich in zinc, which boosts fertility and skin health, and wound-healing and immune-boosting properties.

MAJOR NUTRIENTS PER 6 OYSTERS

50 kcal	1.3g	4.4g	13.6 mcg	37 mg	15 mcg	4.9 mcg	28 mg	53.5 mcg	31.8 mg
CALORIES	TOTAL FAT	PROTEIN	VITAMIN B12	CALCIUM	FOLATE	IRON	MAGNESIUM	SELENIUM	ZINC

Although there is little scientific evidence that oysters are an aphrodisiac, they are one of our best sources of zinc and this mineral is strongly linked with fertility and virility. Zinc is also important for skin health, wound healing and the immune system, and is an antioxidant. Recent research has found that ceramide compounds in oysters inhibit the growth of breast cancer cells. Oysters also contain a reasonable amount of essential omega-3 fats, are rich in selenium for a healthy immune system and contain easily absorbed iron for energy and healthy blood.

- Excellent source of zinc for fertility and virility.
- Contain compounds and minerals that can protect against cancers.
- High iron content for energy, resistance to infection and healthy blood.
- A good source of B vitamins.

DID YOU KNOW?

Traditionally, an oyster is eaten 'all in one go' from the shell, without chewing. You can also cook oysters but some of the beneficial compounds may be lost.

PRACTICAL TIPS

Oysters need to be very fresh and, if eaten raw, they should be alive. It is safest to eat farmed oysters, because in recent years wild oysters have been found to contain toxic levels of contaminants. A healthy way to serve fresh oysters is to top them with chopped shallots, chilli, lime juice and rocket.

OYSTERS VALENTINO

If you prefer your oysters cooked rather than raw, this traditional recipe is probably the best ever created. The hot pepper sauce adds great depth of heat.

SERVES 2 • PREP TIME: 20 MINS • COOK TIME: 5 MINS

PER SERVING: 142 kcal CALORIES | 4.6g FAT |  1.9g SAT FAT | 11.4g CARBS | 1g SUGAR | 0.8g FIBRE | 12.5g PROTEIN | 0.5g SALT

INGREDIENTS

12 unopened fresh oysters
4 tbsp fresh breadcrumbs
2 tbsp diced red pepper
1 tbsp finely chopped spring onion
1 tbsp chopped fresh parsley
zest of 1 lime
hot pepper sauce (optional)
3 tbsp freshly grated Parmesan cheese

1. To open the oysters, hold them flat side up above a sieve set over a bowl to catch the juices. Insert the point of an oyster knife into the hinge and work it around until you can prise off the top shell and discard. Loosen the oyster from the deep shell and strain off and reserve the juice.

2. Crumple a sheet of foil and place in a grill pan. Arrange the shells in the pan. Preheat the grill to hot.

3. In a small bowl, mix the breadcrumbs, red pepper, spring onion, parsley and lime zest together. Add enough of the oyster juice to moisten, a few drops of hot pepper sauce, if using, then divide the mixture between the oysters.

4. Sprinkle each oyster with a little cheese and cook under the preheated grill for 3–4 minutes, or until golden and bubbling. Serve immediately.

HINT
The foil will help the oysters stay flat and ensure that they grill evenly.

CRAYFISH

Low in sodium and rich in vitamin E, crayfish are good for heart health and excellent skin, as well as offering protection against heart disease and some cancers.

MAJOR NUTRIENTS PER 100 G/3½ OZ CRAYFISH TAILS

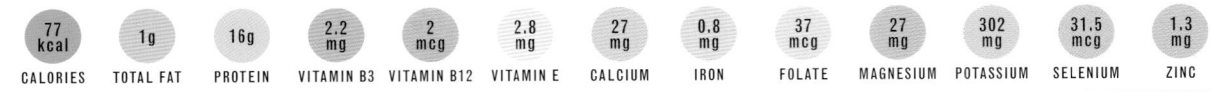

77 kcal	1g	16g	2.2 mg	2 mcg	2.8 mg	27 mg	0.8 mg	37 mcg	27 mg	302 mg	31.5 mcg	1.3 mg
CALORIES	TOTAL FAT	PROTEIN	VITAMIN B3	VITAMIN B12	VITAMIN E	CALCIUM	IRON	FOLATE	MAGNESIUM	POTASSIUM	SELENIUM	ZINC

Crayfish are freshwater crustaceans – you can find them in some fish markets or as prepared tails in the freezer or chiller cabinets. They have a bright pink appearance and a sweet flavour and make a good substitute for prawns in recipes. They are much lower in sodium and cholesterol than prawns and, like most other shellfish, crayfish contain an excellent range of minerals. They are a good source of the antioxidant vitamin E, which is linked with protection from arterial and heart disease and some cancers, and can reduce the pain of arthritis.

- Low in calories and saturated fat.
- Excellent source of vitamin E.
- Rich in a range of vital minerals.
- Reasonably low in sodium and cholesterol.

DID YOU KNOW?

Crayfish are closely related to lobsters, and have a similar, sweet flavour and nutritional profile.

PRACTICAL TIPS

If you buy uncooked crayfish, they should be live. To cook, drop into boiling water for 8–15 minutes, depending on size. Cooked, chilled or frozen crayfish can be eaten at room temperature or added to stir-fries for the last minute of cooking to heat through. Don't overcook or they will be tough. Try serving cooked crayfish tails on wholemeal toast sprinkled with lemon juice and black pepper, garnished with rocket. Crushed crayfish shells make a good base for a seafood stock or sauce.

CRAYFISH CAKES WITH AVOCADO & CHILLI MASH

These tasty crayfish cakes are a very low-fat treat and are excellent
served with the creamy yet spicy avocado and chilli mash.

SERVES 2 • PREP TIME: 15 MINS • COOK TIME: 10 MINS

PER SERVING:

313 kcal	14g	2.1g	22.6g	4.3g	7.4g	23.6g	0.8g
CALORIES	FAT	SAT FAT	CARBS	SUGAR	FIBRE	PROTEIN	SALT

INGREDIENTS

30 g/1 oz wholemeal breadcrumbs
½ tsp pepper
2 tbsp finely chopped fresh flat-leaf parsley
200 g/7 oz peeled and cooked crayfish tails
*50 g/1¾ oz ready-roasted red pepper from a jar,
drained and chopped*
1 tsp medium-hot peri peri sauce
1 tbsp extra-light mayonnaise
1 small egg white, beaten
10 g/¼ oz flour, for dusting
1 ripe avocado, sliced
1 small fresh red chilli, deseeded and chopped
1 spring onion, finely chopped
½ tsp smoked paprika
juice of ¼ lime
6 sprays cooking oil spray

1. Put the breadcrumbs, pepper and parsley into a bowl and stir well to combine.

2. Roughly chop the crayfish tails. In a separate bowl, combine the crayfish tails, red pepper, peri peri sauce and mayonnaise. Stir the breadcrumb mixture into the crayfish mixture.

3. Add the beaten egg and mix to a moderately firm mixture – the cakes will firm up more once they are cooked. Divide into four rough rounds and sprinkle with flour. If you have time, chill for up to 1 hour.

4. To make the mash, place the avocado slices in a bowl and roughly mash with a fork. Stir in the chilli, spring onion, paprika and lime juice.

5. Spray a non-stick frying pan with the cooking oil spray and place over a medium–high heat. Add the crayfish cakes and cook for 2–3 minutes, or until the underside is crisp and golden. Turn and cook for a further 2–3 minutes, or until cooked through. Serve the cakes immediately with the avocado mash.

LOBSTER

Low-fat lobster flesh is an excellent source of minerals, including zinc, potassium, selenium and calcium. Their health benefits mean they are a treat worth indulging in.

MAJOR NUTRIENTS PER 1 SMALL LOBSTER

135 kcal	1.35g	28g	2mg	1.4 mcg	2.2 mg	72 mg	0.45 mg	41 mg	2.4 mg	413 mg	62 mcg	4.5g
CALORIES	TOTAL FAT	PROTEIN	VITAMIN B3	VITAMIN B12	VITAMIN E	CALCIUM	IRON	MAGNESIUM	PANTOTHENIC ACID	POTASSIUM	SELENIUM	ZINC

For most of us lobster is probably an occasional indulgence rather than an everyday food but, despite its luxurious connection, it is a healthy treat. Lobsters, like crayfish and crabs, are rich in minerals, including zinc, potassium and selenium. They are richer in calcium than many other shellfish and one portion provides about one tenth of the recommended daily intake. Calcium can help prevent osteoporosis and is important for heart health and muscle function. Lobster is also a very good source of vitamin E, which acts as an antioxidant and helps to keep arteries healthy.

- One lobster portion provides a whole day's selenium intake.
- Very rich source of zinc, the antioxidant mineral that boosts immunity, protects the skin and is vital for fertility.
- High in pantothenic acid, the B vitamin essential for the conversion of food to energy.

DID YOU KNOW?

Lobsters can live for over 50 years in the wild and are dark blue in appearance. It is only when they are cooked that they become deep pink.

PRACTICAL TIPS

Fresh lobsters are usually sold live because the meat deteriorates quickly after the lobster is killed. They should be frozen for 1 hour and then boiled for 15 minutes, depending on size. Prepared lobster tails can be bought from the freezer or chill cabinet of most supermarkets. A large lobster claw yields a lot of meat so don't discard it – simply crush to remove the meat. Cooked lobster tail can be eaten simply as a salad, with lemon juice.

BEETROOT, LOBSTER & SPINACH RISOTTO

With beetroot and spinach as well as lobster, this unusual and attractive red risotto provides a powerful nutrient boost on a single plate.

SERVES 4 • PREP TIME: 15 MINS • COOK TIME: 30 MINS

PER SERVING:

722 kcal	34.3g	18.7g	71.2g	8.5g	5.5g	29.5g	5.6g
CALORIES	FAT	SAT FAT	CARBS	SUGAR	FIBRE	PROTEIN	SALT

INGREDIENTS

1.6 litres/2¾ pints vegetable stock
30 g/1 oz butter
2 tbsp olive oil
1 small onion, diced
280 g/10 oz risotto rice
100 ml/3½ fl oz dry white wine
5 small raw beetroots, grated
1 tsp grated horseradish
juice of ½ lemon
175 g/6 oz baby leaf spinach
225 g/8 oz ready-to-eat lobster meat
115 g/4 oz freshly grated Parmesan cheese
salt and pepper (optional)
150 ml/5 fl oz crème fraiche, to serve

1. Bring the stock to the boil in a large saucepan, then simmer over a low heat. Meanwhile, heat the butter and oil in a separate large saucepan over a medium heat, add the onion and fry for 3 minutes. Add the rice and stir to coat with the butter and oil. Cook for a further 2 minutes. Add the wine and simmer for 2 minutes, or until absorbed.

2. Add the beetroots and stir well. Add 2 ladles of hot stock to the pan, then cover and cook for 2 minutes, or until absorbed. Stir well and add another ladle of stock. Stir constantly until the stock is absorbed, then add another ladle. Continue adding the stock, one ladle at a time, until it has all been absorbed and the rice is almost cooked.

3. Stir in the horseradish and lemon juice, then add the spinach and season to taste with salt and pepper, if using. Divide between warmed bowls, top with the lobster and cheese and serve immediately, accompanied by the crème fraiche.

VARIATION

If you don't have vegetable stock, or you just prefer the taste, you can use chicken stock instead.

LIVE GREEK YOGURT

Live Greek yogurt contains bacterial cultures that boost the immune
system and keep the digestive system young and robust.

MAJOR NUTRIENTS PER 100 G/3½ OZ LIVE GREEK YOGURT

61 kcal	3.25g	4.66g	3.47g	99IU	0.14 mg	0.39 mg	0.37 mcg	121 mg	15.2 mg	155 mg
CALORIES	TOTAL FAT	CARBS	PROTEIN	VITAMIN A	VITAMIN B2	VITAMIN B5	VITAMIN B12	CALCIUM	CHOLINE	POTASSIUM

Greek yogurt contains less sugar and more protein than other yogurts as it is strained to remove the carbohydrate-rich whey. Its thickness leaves you fuller than more watery versions and the lower level of lactose (milk sugar) it contains makes it easier to digest. Eating live yogurt regularly has been shown to enhance immune responses and our resistance to disease.

- All yogurt helps reduce 'bad' cholesterol/LDL, but only live yogurt raises 'good' cholesterol/HDL levels, ensuring the arteries stay functioning youthfully.
- People who regularly eat yogurt increase their fat-burning capacity, which leads to weight loss – especially around the waist.
- An important B12 source for vegetarians that helps to prevent dry skin and premature ageing, as well as Alzheimer's disease, heart disease and diabetes.

DID YOU KNOW?

People have been making yogurt for around 5,000 years. However, yogurt wasn't commercially produced until 1919, in Barcelona.

PRACTICAL TIPS

Always choose live or bio yogurts as these contain the beneficial live cultures. If possible, buy from local farms via health food shops or farmers' markets: these products will have their own natural bacteria, rather than bacteria that has been added in the production process. Avoid fruit-flavoured yogurt as this contains added sugar, and instead sweeten with fruit or cinnamon. The creamy, fresh taste of Greek yogurt means it works well as an alternative to milk, cream, soured cream or crème fraîche in savoury dishes.

HEALTHY CAESAR DRESSING

Low-fat natural yogurt and reduced-fat mayo combine to provide the perfect
basis for this lighter, healthy alternative to Caesar dressing.

MAKES ABOUT 125 ML/4 FL OZ • PREP TIME: 15 MINS • COOK TIME: NONE

PER 125 ML/4 FL OZ:

147 kcal CALORIES	5.3g FAT	0.7g SAT FAT	10.6g CARBS	5g SUGAR	1.2g FIBRE	15g PROTEIN	1.5g SALT

INGREDIENTS
100 g/3½ oz low-fat Greek-style natural yogurt
3 anchovy fillets, roughly chopped
2 garlic cloves, crushed
grated zest and juice of ½ lemon
30 g/1 oz fresh flat-leaf parsley, roughly chopped
1 tbsp low-fat mayonnaise

1. Place all of the ingredients, except the mayonnaise, in a small bowl and blend with a hand-held blender until the parsley and anchovies have disintegrated. As the parsley breaks down, the dressing will take on a beautiful green colour and become easier to blend.

2. Stir in the mayonnaise. Serve immediately as an alternative to Caesar dressing. This will also keep for three days in a covered container in the refrigerator.

MILK

Milk provides a complete source of easily digested protein and is one of our major sources of calcium for bone health.

MAJOR NUTRIENTS PER 100 ML/3½ FL OZ SEMI-SKIMMED (2% FAT) MILK

52 kcal	2g	4.9g	3.4g	0.55 mcg	124 mg	144 mg	0.49 mg
CALORIES	TOTAL FAT	CARBS	PROTEIN	VITAMIN B12	CALCIUM	POTASSIUM	ZINC

This versatile food is particularly good for vegetarians, who have a limited number of sources of complete protein (which is a protein source containing all nine of the indispensible amino acids – the building blocks of protein) in their diet. Milk is also one of the best sources of the mineral calcium, adequate intake of which is needed to help us build and maintain bone volume and density, and is also vital for muscle, heart and nerve function. Calcium absorption is also helped by essential fatty acids, which is why organic milk is preferable – it contains around 62% more essential omega-3 fats than standard milk. Milk is also a good source of vitamin B12, which can be in shortfall on a vegetarian diet.

- A complete protein source suitable for vegetarians.
- A good source of calcium vital for bone health.
- Organic milk is a source of omega-3 fats which aid calcium absorption.

DID YOU KNOW?

If you do choose organic milk you will also reduce your intake of hormones and antibiotics that are regularly added to the feed of cows on non-organic farms. In order to reap most benefit from the omega-3 fats in organic milk, choose full fat or semi-skimmed varieties. Skimmed milk will contain virtually none.

PRACTICAL TIPS

Coffee and strong tea can interfere with the absorption of calcium, so it is best to drink your milk on its own or as the basis for a smoothie. Or use it to make desserts, pour over breakfast cereal, and so on. Some people have an intolerance to lactose, a type of sugar found in milk, which can give them digestive problems. This should be diagnosed by a doctor.

BEE POLLEN & NECTARINE SMOOTHIE

Nutritious bee pollen adds an intriguing touch to this nifty and nourishing nectarine milkshake. The honey adds natural sweetness too.

SERVES 2 • PREP TIME: 15 MINS • COOK TIME: NONE

PER SERVING:	163 kcal	3.2g	1.8g	28.7g	22.8g	2.6g	7.3g	0.1g
	CALORIES	FAT	SAT FAT	CARBS	SUGAR	FIBRE	PROTEIN	SALT

INGREDIENTS

2 ripe nectarines, quartered
200 ml/7 fl oz semi-skimmed milk
2 tbsp Greek-style natural yogurt
1 tbsp bee pollen
1 tsp clear honey
handful of ice cubes
1 tsp bee pollen, to decorate
2 nectarine slices, to decorate

1. Place the nectarines, milk, yogurt, bee pollen and honey in a blender and whizz until smooth. Add the ice cubes and whizz again until completely blended.

2. Pour the milkshake into chilled glasses and decorate with the bee pollen and a slice of nectarine. Serve immediately.

GOAT'S CHEESE

Goat's cheese is higher in calcium and lower in fat than cheese made from cow's milk,
making it better for bone strength and as a rejuvenating source of protein.

MAJOR NUTRIENTS PER 100 G/3½ OZ GOAT'S CHEESE

364 kcal	29.84g	2.54g	21.58g	1464 IU	0.07 mg	0.68 mg	1.15 mg
CALORIES	TOTAL FAT	CARBS	PROTEIN	VITAMIN A	VITAMIN B1	VITAMIN B2	VITAMIN B3
22IU	706 mg	6098 mg	298 mg	15.4 mg	6.06 mg	375 mg	3.8 mcg
VITAMIN D	OMEGA-6 OILS	OMEGA-9 OILS	CALCIUM	CHOLINE	MANGANESE	PHOSPHORUS	SELENIUM

Cheese is especially valuable for vegetarians as an alternative to meat.
Goat's cheese tends to be more traditionally made than cow's milk
cheeses, so can contain fewer chemical additives and preservatives.
Although it contains the same protein, casein, that is present in cow's
milk and may cause allergies, it takes a different form and is often more
tolerated by people with digestive sensitivities. Goat's cheese provides a
type of saturated fat that is needed for nervous system communication
and that is healthy when eaten in a diet that is also high in omega-3 and
omega-6 oils, such as those found in oily fish, nuts and seeds.

- Contains phosphorus, manganese, vitamin B3 and vitamin A, which all
  help to lock calcium into the bones, keeping them strong.
- The combination of protein with quality saturated fat can help
  prevent the sugar cravings that lead to premature ageing of the skin,
  eyes and organs.
- Goat's milk is higher in vitamins B1 and B3 than cow's milk. These
  B-vitamins make energy to repair cells and boost vitality.

DID YOU KNOW?

*The fat particles in goat's milk
are much smaller than those in
cow's milk, being closer in size
to those in human milk. This is
why goat's milk is easier to digest
and why there is no need for the
homogenization process.*

PRACTICAL TIPS

Choose soft cheeses for less saturated fat, and cheeses from farm shops
or markets for optimum nutritional benefits. Check the labels of well-
known cheeses like feta as they are sometimes made with cow's milk.

COOL WATERMELON, GOAT'S CHEESE & ROCKET SALAD

The creaminess of the goat's cheese in this salad complements the citrus- and chilli-dressed watermelon to make a quick summer salad.

SERVES 4 • PREP TIME: 10–15 MINS • COOK TIME: NONE

PER SERVING:	215 kcal	10.8g	7.1g	21g	14.6g	2.1g	11.1g	0.3g
	CALORIES	FAT	SAT FAT	CARBS	SUGAR	FIBRE	PROTEIN	SALT

INGREDIENTS

800 g/1 lb 12 oz watermelon flesh, cut into large cubes

grated rind and juice of 2 large limes

½–1 red chilli, deseeded and finely chopped

55 g/2 oz fresh coriander, roughly chopped

70 g/2½ oz rocket

115 g/4 oz firm goat's cheese, cut into cubes

salt and pepper (optional)

4 lime wedges, to serve

1. Put the watermelon in a large salad bowl. Sprinkle with the lime rind and juice and the chilli, then season with a little salt and pepper, if using, and gently toss together.

2. Sprinkle over the coriander, rocket and cheese and gently toss together. Serve with lime wedges.

FREE-RANGE EGGS

Eggs are a perfect protein source, containing all of the amino acids
needed for the body to repair itself and stay young-looking.

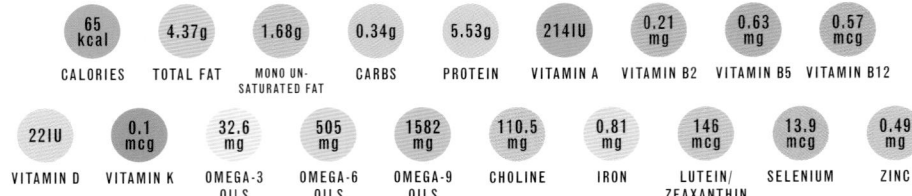

65 kcal	4.37g	1.68g	0.34g	5.53g	214IU	0.21 mg	0.63 mg	0.57 mcg
CALORIES	TOTAL FAT	MONO UN-SATURATED FAT	CARBS	PROTEIN	VITAMIN A	VITAMIN B2	VITAMIN B5	VITAMIN B12

22IU	0.1 mcg	32.6 mg	505 mg	1582 mg	110.5 mg	0.81 mg	146 mcg	13.9 mcg	0.49 mg
VITAMIN D	VITAMIN K	OMEGA-3 OILS	OMEGA-6 OILS	OMEGA-9 OILS	CHOLINE	IRON	LUTEIN/ZEAXANTHIN	SELENIUM	ZINC

Eggs are ideally packaged to support new life, and so contain all the nutrients we need for growth: iron, zinc, vitamin A, vitamin D, the B-vitamins and omega-3 fats. Many people avoid them because of their high cholesterol content, but the body can regulate this if the diet is low in sugar and saturated fat. Many studies show that egg consumption helps prevent chronic age-related conditions like coronary heart disease, loss of muscle mass, eye degeneration, hearing loss and memory loss.

- Contain vitamin B12 to help combat fatigue, depression and lethargy.
- Vitamin A and lutein ensure eye protection and continuing good sight.
- One of the few dietary sources of vitamins K and D, which work together to keep bones strong.
- Contain sulphur and lecithin, substances that help the liver with digestion and detoxification.

DID YOU KNOW?

You can now buy eggs that are 'omega-3 rich'. These come from chickens whose food is enriched with these important brain-fuelling oils.

PRACTICAL TIPS

Eggs are a truly useful storecupboard food. They can be cooked in many different ways, including poaching, scrambling and boiling. Omelettes or frittatas, loaded with healthy vegetables, can also be eaten cold as a snack at any time. Buy organic free-range eggs, as the chicken feed gives these eggs a higher nutritional value, indicated by their deeper yellow yolk and richer taste.

POACHED EGGS & KALE WITH WHOLEMEAL SOURDOUGH

Kale adds valuable nutrients and vivid green colour to these
poached eggs served on sensational sourdough toast.

SERVES 4 • PREP TIME: 20 MINS • COOK TIME: 15–17 MINS

PER SERVING:

 324 Kcal CALORIES

 15.1g FAT

 3g SAT FAT

 36.3g CARBS

2.6g SUGAR

4.4g FIBRE

 12.6g PROTEIN

 1g SALT

INGREDIENTS

4 eggs
100 g/3½ oz kale, chopped
4 large slices of wholemeal sourdough bread
2 garlic cloves, halved
2 tbsp olive oil
1 tsp dried red chilli flakes
salt and pepper (optional)

1. Bring a shallow saucepan of water to a gentle simmer. Crack an egg into a small bowl or ramekin, then slide the egg into the water, lowering the bowl as close to the water as possible. Using a large spoon, gently fold any stray strands of white around the yolk. Repeat with the other eggs.

2. Cook for 2–3 minutes, or until set to your liking, then remove with a slotted spoon. Place the eggs in a small bowl of warm water and set aside until needed.

3. Bring a saucepan of water to the boil and add the kale. Simmer for 3–4 minutes, or until the kale is just cooked but still retains a little crunch. Drain, season with salt and pepper, if using, and set aside.

4. Meanwhile, toast the bread. Place the toast on four plates, then rub each slice with the garlic and drizzle with the oil. Top with some kale and a poached egg, sprinkle over the chilli flakes and serve immediately.

HINT
For best results try and use really fresh eggs for this recipe as they make the best poached eggs.

QUAIL EGGS

Weight for weight, quail eggs contain even more nutrients and accessible protein than hen eggs, helping to repair and renew skin, bones and muscles.

MAJOR NUTRIENTS PER 4 QUAIL EGGS

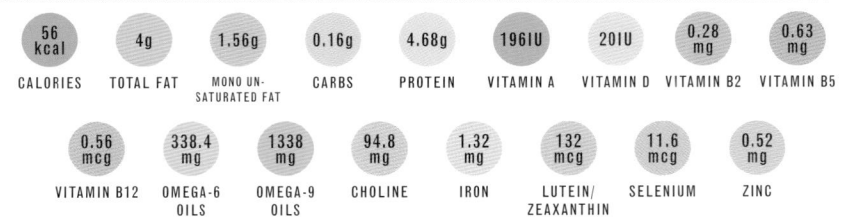

56 kcal	4g	1.56g	0.16g	4.68g	196IU	20IU	0.28 mg	0.63 mg
CALORIES	TOTAL FAT	MONO UN-SATURATED FAT	CARBS	PROTEIN	VITAMIN A	VITAMIN D	VITAMIN B2	VITAMIN B5

0.56 mcg	338.4 mg	1338 mg	94.8 mg	1.32 mg	132 mcg	11.6 mcg	0.52 mg
VITAMIN B12	OMEGA-6 OILS	OMEGA-9 OILS	CHOLINE	IRON	LUTEIN/ZEAXANTHIN	SELENIUM	ZINC

Quail eggs have a higher yolk-to-white ratio than hen eggs. This means that for their size you get a good dose of the yellow carotenoid lutein, which helps prevent damage to fats in your body. The brain, heart, skin, eyes and liver are just a few of these fatty areas and they are very susceptible to damage, so protecting them from the ageing effects of toxins is crucial to staying young. Quail eggs have been used for hundreds of years in traditional Chinese medicine to help combat immune-compromising allergies like hay fever and asthma, and ageing skin conditions like acne, psoriasis and eczema.

- Vitamin D helps revitalize bone and brain, so a dietary source is especially important when we can't get it from sunlight in the winter.
- Choline helps brain function, keeping memory and concentration performing youthfully.
- High selenium, zinc and vitamin A content provides antioxidant protection, preventing ageing and supporting new skin growth.

DID YOU KNOW?

In Romania, quail eggs are traditionally eaten to treat minor ailments as part of a '120-egg cure' (over 25 days). For more serious problems, there is the '240-egg cure' (over 45 days).

PRACTICAL TIPS

Quail eggs can replace hen eggs in any dish, but their beauty lies in their miniature yolk and white, so simply boiling and slicing into a salad is the best option. They fall apart less easily than hen eggs and have a slightly richer, gamier flavour.

TUNA & ASPARAGUS SALAD WITH QUAIL EGGS

This quick and tasty salad combines healthy quinoa with quail eggs
for a protein-packed lunch or light supper.

SERVES 4 • PREP TIME: 10 MINS • COOK TIME: 20 MINS

PER SERVING:

							0.9g
392 kcal	12.5g	1.9g	34.1g	3.3g	5.7g	35.4g	0.9g
CALORIES	FAT	SAT FAT	CARBS	SUGAR	FIBRE	PROTEIN	SALT

INGREDIENTS

175 g/6 oz quinoa, rinsed
8 quail eggs
6 sprays cooking oil spray
24 asparagus spears, woody stems discarded
4 tuna steaks, each weighing 100 g/3½ oz
2 tbsp olive oil
½ tbsp white wine vinegar
½ tsp Dijon mustard
½ tsp sugar
½ tsp salt
½ tsp pepper
12 cherry tomatoes
4 small spring onions, finely chopped, to garnish

1. Bring a saucepan of water to the boil and add the quinoa.
Cook for 15–18 minutes, or until just tender. Drain and set aside.

2. Meanwhile, bring a separate saucepan of water to the boil
and add the eggs. Cook for 3 minutes, then drain and rinse in
cold water to cool. Peel the shells from the eggs.

3. Place a ridged griddle pan over a high heat and spray with
2 sprays of cooking spray. Add the asparagus spears and cook,
turning once, for 4 minutes until slightly charred and just tender.

4. Spray the tuna steaks with the remaining cooking oil spray
and cook in the pan for 1½ minutes. Turn and cook for a further
minute, or until ccoked to your liking. Transfer to a plate and
leave to rest for 2 minutes.

5. Beat together the olive oil, vinegar, mustard, sugar, salt and
pepper in a small bowl. Stir two thirds of this oil mixture into the
cooked quinoa.

6. Cut each tuna steak into three pieces. Divide the quinoa
between four serving plates and top evenly with the tuna
pieces, asparagus, eggs and tomatoes. Drizzle the remaining
dressing over the top and garnish with the spring onions.

GRAINS, PULSES, NUTS & SEEDS

QUINOA

The best source of complete protein in the plant kingdom, quinoa provides all the necessary building blocks for age-defying skin, and bone and brain regeneration.

MAJOR NUTRIENTS PER 100 G/3½ OZ UNCOOKED QUINOA

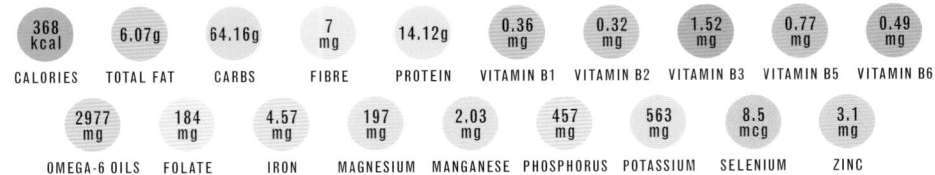

368 kcal	6.07g	64.16g	7 mg	14.12g	0.36 mg	0.32 mg	1.52 mg	0.77 mg	0.49 mg
CALORIES	TOTAL FAT	CARBS	FIBRE	PROTEIN	VITAMIN B1	VITAMIN B2	VITAMIN B3	VITAMIN B5	VITAMIN B6

2977 mg	184 mg	4.57 mg	197 mg	2.03 mg	457 mg	563 mg	8.5 mcg	3.1 mg
OMEGA-6 OILS	FOLATE	IRON	MAGNESIUM	MANGANESE	PHOSPHORUS	POTASSIUM	SELENIUM	ZINC

Most plant foods are lacking in one or more essential amino acid, meaning that vegetarians and vegans need to consider carefully what range of foods they eat in order to get the right spread for youthful health. Quinoa is an easy one-food solution, containing all the essential amino acids, and it also provides a good range of minerals and B vitamins. These enable the protein content of quinoa to be used effectively, so that it can provide the vast amount of energy needed for the constant renewal of skin, hair, nails, teeth, bone and organs. Quinoa is actually a seed, not a grain. As such, it is high in anti-inflammatory omega-6 oils and is ideal for those people who cannot tolerate wheat or gluten.

- Contains phosphorus to make phospholipids in the brain and nervous system, which enable you to move and think youthfully.
- Potassium balances out the sodium in your diet, reducing bloating, puffiness and high blood pressure.
- Zinc and selenium offer potent antioxidant protection from ageing elements in your life, such as pollution, sunlight and chemicals.

DID YOU KNOW?

Quinoa is a seed from South America that the Incas called the 'mother grain'. It was traditionally offered to the sun god Inti, and the first crop of the season was dug up with a golden spade.

PRACTICAL TIPS

Quinoa cooks in a similar way to rice. It has a pleasant, nutty flavour, and is delicious in Mexican and Indian meals. You can also make a great quinoa porridge, either from flakes or from the grain itself. Quinoa is versatile enough to be cooked in both sweet and savoury dishes.

SMASHED AVOCADO
& QUINOA WRAP

Brimming with nourishing, natural goodness, fresh avocado and spinach combine with colourful, crunchy raw red cabbage to create these really appealing quinoa-topped wraps.

SERVES 4 • PREP TIME: 20 MINS • COOK TIME: 15–18 MINS

PER SERVING:

386 kcal	13.2g	2.8g	56.8g	3.6g	10.4g	11.8g	1.4g
CALORIES	FAT	SAT FAT	CARBS	SUGAR	FIBRE	PROTEIN	SALT

INGREDIENTS

175 g/6 oz quinoa
400 ml/14 fl oz vegetable stock
1 large ripe avocado, stoned and peeled
½ tsp smoked paprika
2 garlic cloves, crushed
finely grated zest and juice of 1 lemon
4 wholemeal tortillas
50 g/1¾ oz baby spinach
150 g/5½ oz red cabbage, finely sliced
salt and pepper (optional)

1. Place the quinoa and stock in a small saucepan and bring to a simmer. Simmer, covered, for 15–18 minutes, or until the stock has been fully absorbed. Set aside to cool.

2. Meanwhile, gently mash the avocado with the paprika, garlic, lemon zest and just enough lemon juice to achieve a thick consistency.

3. Spread the mashed avocado down the centre of each wrap and then top with the warm quinoa, spinach and red cabbage. Season with salt and pepper, if using. Tuck in the ends and tightly fold or roll into a wrap and serve immediately.

RYE

Rye has many health benefits that make it an excellent food to incorporate into your diet – most notably the good levels of protein and fibre.

MAJOR NUTRIENTS PER 100 G/3½ OZ RYE FLOUR

325 kcal	2.22g	15.91g	23.8 mg	15.91 mg	0.32 mg	0.25 mg	4.27 mg	1.46 mg
CALORIES	TOTAL FAT	CARBS	FIBRE	PROTEIN	VITAMIN B1	VITAMIN B2	VITAMIN B3	VITAMIN B5

0.44 mg	958 mg	4.97 mg	210 mcg	160 mg	6.06 mg	18 mcg	5.04 mg
VITAMIN B6	OMEGA-6 OILS	IRON	LUTEIN/ ZEAXANTHIN	MAGNESIUM	MANGANESE	SELENIUM	ZINC

Rye contains generous amounts of minerals and fibre, both of which help the body to clear out damaging toxins and harmful cholesterol. It also provides approximately 20 per cent of its calories from protein and a good mix of the amino acids necessary to rebuild and repair all our body structures, from skin to teeth. The levels of protein and fibre in rye ensure that it has a very low glycaemic index score of 26, meaning it releases its sugars very slowly into the bloodstream, which gives us energy over a long period without wanting to eat more. Good levels of magnesium, vitamin B6 and zinc support this action by helping the body to produce the hormone insulin and use sugars efficiently.

- Lutein and zeaxanthin offer carotenoid antioxidant protection from damage to our brains, hearts, liver and skin.
- High magnesium content helps us to make the body proteins we need, and so build skin and bone like new.
- Vitamin B5 holds back the ageing effects of stress.

DID YOU KNOW?

In many countries, including Poland, Finland and Russia, rye is a more popular bread flour than wheat. It is often sold with the addition of flavourings, such as fennel, coriander, molasses or cardamom.

PRACTICAL TIPS

Dark rye is denser and more nutritious than medium and light types. The average supermarket loaf uses medium rye, which is often mixed with wheat to make the bread fluffier, so check labels. Pumpernickel is a dark rye flour and is used to make the pure rye bread of the same name.

PANCAKES WITH CREAMY CITRUS FILLING

This breakfast or dessert has a great balance of protein, carbohydrates and fat.
The rye and spelt flours give the pancakes a nutty, slightly sweet taste.

SERVES 4 • PREP TIME: 20 MINS • COOK TIME: 10 MINS

PER SERVING:

 316 kcal CALORIES **10.7g** FAT **4.3g** SAT FAT **35.8g** CARBS **9.1g** SUGAR **3.4g** FIBRE **19.7g** PROTEIN **1.6g** SALT

INGREDIENTS

250 g/9 oz ricotta cheese
200 g/7 oz fat-free Greek-style yogurt
1 tbsp grated orange rind
2 tbsp orange juice
1–2 tsp stevia granules
40 g/1½ oz rye flour
40 g/1½ oz spelt flour or wholemeal flour
40 g/1½ oz plain flour
1 tsp salt
2 small eggs
1 tbsp groundnut oil
150 ml/5 fl oz skimmed milk
100 ml/3½ fl oz water
8 sprays cooking spray, for oiling
1 orange, peeled, segmented and chopped
2 tsp icing sugar, for dusting

1. In a bowl, combine the ricotta cheese, yogurt, orange rind, orange juice and stevia granules. Set aside in the refrigerator until ready to serve.

2. In a mixing bowl, stir together the rye flour, spelt flour, plain flour and salt, then whisk in the eggs, oil, milk and water until completely smooth.

3. Heat a small, non-stick frying pan over a medium–high heat and coat with cooking spray.

4. When the pan is hot, pour in a quarter of the batter and swirl it around to coat the pan. Cook for 1 minute, or until the underside is golden, then flip the pancake over with a spatula and cook for 1 minute on the other side. Transfer the cooked pancake to a warmed plate while you cook the remaining batter.

5. Repeat to make three more pancakes, spraying the pan between each addition. (You could make eight mini pancakes, if you prefer.)

6. Place the pancakes on serving plates, then fill with the ricotta mixture and a little of the chopped orange and fold over. Decorate with the remaining chopped orange and dust with the icing sugar.

POT BARLEY

This extremely nutritious starchy grain contains soluble fibre that helps to lower 'bad' blood cholesterol and protect us from hormonal cancers and heart disease.

MAJOR NUTRIENTS PER 60 G/2¼ OZ RAW POT BARLEY

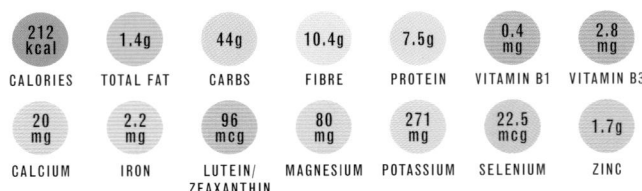

212 kcal	1.4g	44g	10.4g	7.5g	0.4 mg	2.8 mg
CALORIES	TOTAL FAT	CARBS	FIBRE	PROTEIN	VITAMIN B1	VITAMIN B3
20 mg	2.2 mg	96 mcg	80 mg	271 mg	22.5 mcg	1.7g
CALCIUM	IRON	LUTEIN/ ZEAXANTHIN	MAGNESIUM	POTASSIUM	SELENIUM	ZINC

Pot barley is a grain with a rich, slightly nutty flavour and a chewy texture. Most barley that is sold is pearl barley, which has had almost all of the nutrients and fibre removed by processing, whereas pot or hulled barley, has had minimal processing and is therefore a good source of nutrients. These include a very high level of fibre, including soluble fibre and a fibre-like compound called lignan, which may protect against breast and other hormone-dependent cancers, as well as heart disease. Unusually for a grain, barley contains lutein and zeaxanthin, which help to protect eyesight and eye health.

- Whole grain that protects against cancers and heart disease.
- A good source of minerals and B vitamins.
- High in fibre to keep the colon healthy and soluble fibre to lower blood cholesterol.
- Helps to keep eyes healthy.

DID YOU KNOW?

Barley water, made by steeping the grains in water, has long been considered a health drink for its diuretic and kidney-supporting effect.

PRACTICAL TIPS

Pot barley needs up to two hours' simmering in water, but presoaking it for several hours will shorten the cooking time. Add it to soups and casseroles for extra nutrition and fibre. The fats in barley can make it go rancid after a short time, especially if kept in warm, light conditions, so store in a cool, dry, dark place in an airtight container and use within two to three months.

HEARTY BARLEY VEGETABLE SOUP

This is a warming winter soup full of delicious vegetables. The addition of barley gives it good body, as well as lots of fibre and essential minerals and vitamins.

SERVES 6 • PREP TIME: 20-25 MINS • COOK TIME: 1 HOUR 20 MINS–1 HOUR 50 MINS

PER SERVING:

 153 kcal CALORIES   6.7g FAT   4g SAT FAT   22.2g CARBS   6.4g SUGAR   5.7g FIBRE 4.5g PROTEIN 2.5g SALT

INGREDIENTS

2 tbsp sunflower oil
1 onion, finely chopped
1 celery stick, finely chopped
1 garlic clove, crushed
1.5 litres/2 ½ pints vegetable stock or water
85 g/3 oz pot barley, rinsed
1 bouquet garni, made with 1 bay leaf, fresh thyme sprigs and fresh parsley sprigs
2 carrots, diced
400 g/14 oz canned chopped tomatoes
pinch of sugar
½ head of Savoy cabbage, cored and shredded
salt and pepper (optional)
fresh crusty bread, to serve (optional)

1. Heat the oil in a large saucepan. Add the onion, celery and garlic and cook over a medium heat for 5–7 minutes, until soft.

2. Pour in the stock and bring to the boil, skimming off any foam that rises to the surface with a slotted spoon. Add the barley and bouquet garni, reduce the heat to low, cover and simmer for 30 minutes–1 hour until the grains are just beginning to soften.

3. Add the carrots, tomatoes with their can juices, and the sugar to the pan. Bring the liquid back to the boil, then reduce the heat to low, cover and simmer for a further 30 minutes, or until the barley and carrots are tender.

4. Just before serving, remove the bouquet garni, stir in the cabbage and season with salt and pepper to taste, if using.

5. Continue simmering until the cabbage wilts, then ladle into warmed soup bowls and serve with the bread, if using.

VARIATION

Try serving this soup with some freshly grated Parmesan cheese over the top.

BROWN RICE

The fibre in brown rice can help to lower blood cholesterol levels
and keep blood sugar levels even.

MAJOR NUTRIENTS PER 60 G/2¼ OZ RAW BROWN RICE

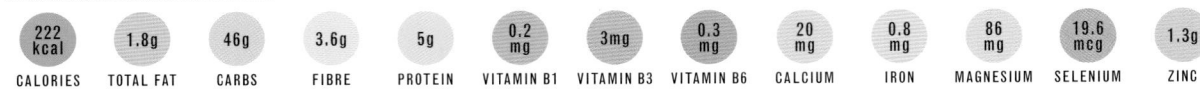

222 kcal	1.8g	46g	3.6g	5g	0.2 mg	3mg	0.3 mg	20 mg	0.8 mg	86 mg	19.6 mcg	1.3g
CALORIES	TOTAL FAT	CARBS	FIBRE	PROTEIN	VITAMIN B1	VITAMIN B3	VITAMIN B6	CALCIUM	IRON	MAGNESIUM	SELENIUM	ZINC

While white rice contains few nutrients other than starch, brown rice has several nutritional benefits. Regular consumption of brown rice and other whole grains has been shown to help prevent heart disease, diabetes and some cancers. It is a good source of fibre, which can help reduce cholesterol levels in the blood and keep blood sugar levels even. Brown rice also contains some protein, and is a good source of several B vitamins and minerals, particularly selenium and magnesium.

- One of the least allergenic foods.
- A reasonably low glycaemic index food that can help control blood sugar levels and may be helpful for diabetics.
- Useful B vitamin content to help convert food into energy and keep the nervous system healthy.
- High selenium content may help protect against cancers; high magnesium content for a healthy heart.

DID YOU KNOW?

Ninety per cent of all rice is still grown and consumed in Asia, where it has been eaten for over 6,000 years.

PRACTICAL TIPS

Store rice in a cool, dark cupboard and use within a few months. Brown rice tends not to keep as well as white rice as it contains small amounts of fat, which can go rancid over time. The longer you store raw rice, the longer it may take to cook. Leftover cooked rice can be kept for a day or two in the refrigerator if you cool it quickly, but it must be reheated until piping hot before serving.

PROTEIN RICE BOWL

Brown rice adds important fibre and fresh chilli supplies some heat to this protein-rich vegetarian lunch for two.

SERVES 2 • PREP TIME: 25 MINS • COOK TIME: 30 MINS

PER SERVING:

653 kcal	33.9g	5.9g	71.1g	4g	8.7g	19.1g	0.3g
CALORIES	FAT	SAT FAT	CARBS	SUGAR	FIBRE	PROTEIN	SALT

INGREDIENTS

150 g/5½ oz brown rice
2 large eggs
70 g/2½ oz spinach
4 spring onions, finely chopped
1 red chilli, deseeded and finely sliced
½ ripe avocado, sliced
2 tbsp roasted peanuts

VINAIGRETTE

2 tbsp olive oil
1 tsp Dijon mustard
1 tbsp cider vinegar
juice of ½ lemon

1. Place the rice in a large saucepan and cover with twice the volume of water. Bring to the boil, then reduce the heat and simmer for 25 minutes, or until the rice is tender and the liquid has nearly all disappeared. Continue to simmer for a further few minutes if any liquid remains.

2. Meanwhile, bring a small saucepan of water to the boil. Carefully add the eggs to the pan and boil for 7 minutes – the whites will be cooked and the yolks should still be very slightly soft. Drain the eggs and pour cold water over them to stop them cooking. When cool enough to handle, tap them on the work surface to crack the shells and peel them. Cut the eggs into quarters.

3. Stir the spinach, half of the spring onions and a little of the chilli into the cooked rice.

4. To make the vinaigrette, whisk the oil, mustard, vinegar and lemon juice together. Pour the dressing over the warm rice and mix to combine.

5. Divide the rice between two bowls and top each with the remaining spring onions, the avocado, the remaining red chilli, the peanuts and egg quarters.

OATS

Economical oats are high in soluble fibre and a source of healthy fats. They can keep hunger at bay, lower 'bad' cholesterol and keep blood sugar levels even.

MAJOR NUTRIENTS PER 60 G/2¼ OZ OATS

233 kcal	4g	40g	6.4g	10g	0.5 mg	0.6 mg
CALORIES	TOTAL FAT	CARBS	FIBRE	PROTEIN	VITAMIN B1	VITAMIN B3

1.5 mg	32 mg	34 mcg	2.8 mg	106 mg	257 mg	2.4g
VITAMIN E	CALCIUM	FOLATE	IRON	MAGNESIUM	POTASSIUM	ZINC

Oats have several health-giving properties. They are rich in the soluble fibre beta-glucan and have been proven to help lower 'bad' cholesterol, boost 'good' cholesterol, maintain a healthy circulatory system and help prevent heart attacks. Oats also contain a range of antioxidants and plant chemicals to help keep heart and arteries healthy, such as avenanthramides (a phytoalexin plant chemical with antibiotic properties), saponins and vitamin E. They also contain polyphenols, plant compounds that can suppress tumour growth. They are also relatively low on the glycaemic index, which means they are particularly suitable for dieters, people with insulin resistance and diabetics.

- One of the best grains to keep the heart and arteries healthy.
- Contain plant chemicals to help reduce the risk of cancers.
- Lower on the glycaemic index than many cereals.
- A good source of a wide range of vitamins and minerals, including B vitamins, vitamin E, magnesium, calcium and iron.

DID YOU KNOW?

Although oats do contain small amounts of gluten, people with gluten intolerance (coeliac disease) often find they can tolerate oats in their diet, especially if limited to no more than 115 g/4 oz a day. Coeliac sufferers should check with their doctor before eating oats.

PRACTICAL TIPS

The fat content of oats means that they don't store well for long, so keep them in an airtight container in a cool, dry, dark place and use within 2–3 weeks. Use oat flakes to make your own home-made muesli. Oat flakes can be used for making cookies and crumble toppings, and oat flour can replace wheat flour.

CREAMY PORRIDGE WITH BLACKBERRIES

Oats are a complex carbohydrate, providing slow-release
energy to keep you sustained throughout the morning.

SERVES 2 • PREP TIME: 5 MINS • COOK TIME: 8 MINS

PER SERVING:	268 kcal	9g	2.9g	38g	1.5g	7.2g	11g	0.7g
	CALORIES	FAT	SAT FAT	CARBS	SUGAR	FIBRE	PROTEIN	SALT

INGREDIENTS

100 g/3½ oz large rolled oats
small pinch of sea salt
600 ml/1 pint cold water
3½ tbsp double cream
1 tbsp stevia
1 tbsp pumpkin seeds
6 large blackberries, quartered

1. Put the oats and salt in a medium-sized saucepan and
pour over the water. Bring to the boil, then reduce the heat to
medium–low and simmer, stirring regularly, for 5–6 minutes, or
until the oats are thick but have a dense pouring consistency.

2. Stir in the cream and stevia. Spoon the porridge into two
bowls, top with the pumpkin seeds and blackberries, and serve
immediately.

BUCKWHEAT

Buckwheat contains a rich supply of youth-enhancing flavonoids, particularly rutin.
These help to keep your circulation flowing freely and prevent varicose veins.

MAJOR NUTRIENTS PER 100 G/3½ OZ BUCKWHEAT

343 kcal	3.4g	71.5g	10 mg	13.25g	0.43 mg	7.02 mg	1.23 mg
CALORIES	TOTAL FAT	CARBS	FIBRE	PROTEIN	VITAMIN B2	VITAMIN B3	VITAMIN B5
0.21 mg	1052 mg	30 mcg	231 mg	1.33 mg	460 mg	8.3 mcg	2.4 mcg
VITAMIN B6	OMEGA-6 OILS	FOLATE	MAGNESIUM	MANGANESE	POTASSIUM	SELENIUM	ZINC

Buckwheat is technically a seed, not a grain, so it is an excellent source of fibre and energy for people who are intolerant to wheat and gluten. Whether you have an intolerance or not, reducing your wheat intake will take pressure off the body. Buckwheat is not only easier to digest than wheat but also more alkalizing, meaning that it helps all physical processes work as efficiently as possible, whatever your time of life. It is a particularly sustaining energy source and is recommended for diabetics as it releases its sugars slowly into the bloodstream. Buckwheat, like millet, also contains substances called nitrilosides that are essential in detoxification processes, helping rid the body of harmful, ageing toxins.

- Contains lecithin, which helps break down fats in the liver and in the food that you eat, aiding detoxification and reducing cravings for fatty foods.
- Magnesium and potassium work together to ensure a healthy heart and strong bones for youthful mobility.
- Selenium produces both of the rejuvenating antioxidants glutathione and coenzyme Q-10.

DID YOU KNOW?

Buckwheat is not related to wheat. It isn't even a grain, but a fruit seed, in the same family as rhubarb and sorrel.

PRACTICAL TIPS

Buckwheat may be used as an alternative to rice. It can also be bought in flakes and made into porridge. Buckwheat flour makes excellent gluten-free pancakes, which are traditional in Poland and Russia, and are also eaten in France.

BUCKWHEAT BREAKFAST BOWL

Buckwheat makes a tasty cereal and, being a source of complex carbohydrates, provides an excellent boost of energy. You'll need to allow time for the buckwheat to sprout, about 36 hours.

SERVES 4 • PREP TIME: 20—25 MINS, PLUS STANDING & SPROUTING • COOK TIME: NONE

PER SERVING:

452 kcal	22.4g	17.5g	58g	22.8g	9.8g	10.1g	0.1g
CALORIES	FAT	SAT FAT	CARBS	SUGAR	FIBRE	PROTEIN	SALT

INGREDIENTS

150 g/5½ oz buckwheat
500 ml/17 fl oz cold water
400 g/14 oz coconut yogurt
grated zest and juice of 1 orange
3 tbsp goji berries
100 g/3½ oz raspberries
1 Granny Smith apple, cored and diced
1 tbsp pumpkin seeds
2 passion fruit, pulp only
2 tsp ground cinnamon
½ tsp ground turmeric
seeds of 1 pomegranate
2 tbsp agave syrup

1. Rinse the buckwheat three times in fresh water to clean the groats. Place in a bowl with the cold water. Leave to stand for 30 minutes.

2. Drain and rinse the buckwheat, and leave to stand at room temperature – in either a sprouting tray or a sieve with a bowl beneath – for 36 hours. Rinse the buckwheat if the groats look sticky, and then once more before using.

3. Rinse, drain and divide the buckwheat between four bowls. Divide the yogurt between the bowls, sprinkle over the remaining ingredients and serve.

VARIATION

Add your favourite berries and seeds to the buckwheat in place of the raspberries and pumpkin seeds.

MILLET

This underrated non-gluten grain provides high levels of
hormone-balancing and skin-plumping omega-6 oils.

MAJOR NUTRIENTS PER 100 G/3½ OZ UNCOOKED MILLET

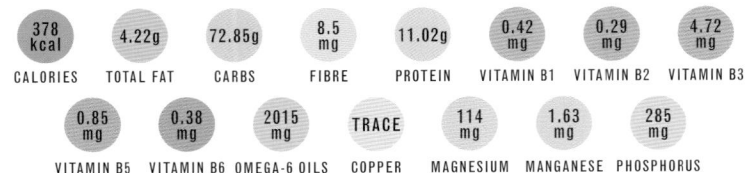

378 kcal	4.22g	72.85g	8.5 mg	11.02g	0.42 mg	0.29 mg	4.72 mg
CALORIES	TOTAL FAT	CARBS	FIBRE	PROTEIN	VITAMIN B1	VITAMIN B2	VITAMIN B3

0.85 mg	0.38 mg	2015 mg	TRACE	114 mg	1.63 mg	285 mg
VITAMIN B5	VITAMIN B6	OMEGA-6 OILS	COPPER	MAGNESIUM	MANGANESE	PHOSPHORUS

Millet contains none of the sticky gluten found in wheat, oats, rye and
barley that can swamp our diets. This makes it easier to digest and
less likely to set off inflammatory tendencies that cause conditions like
eczema, asthma, acne, arthritis, osteoporosis and IBS. The omega-6
oils present in millet also help to soothe and lessen these aggravating
conditions. Omega-6 oils are also vitally important for digestion, immunity,
detoxification and metabolism. Eating them stops us craving more
unhealthy and ageing oils, fats and sugars, and helps maintain healthy,
youthful-looking skin, hair and nails.

- B-vitamins and magnesium support the adrenal glands and help to
  prevent stress ageing the body prematurely.
- B3 lowers high cholesterol and keeps the brain functioning positively.
- Both copper and manganese are needed to make the large amounts of
  the detoxifying enzyme superoxide dismutase, which keeps the system
  youthful.
- Phosphorus plays a part in energy production in every cell; this
  enables new bone to form and fuels the DNA that drives renewal
  throughout the body.

DID YOU KNOW?

*Millet was one of the first grains
to be eaten, meaning that we are
much more likely to be able to
digest it and suffer less intolerance.*

PRACTICAL TIPS

The most common type of millet sold is the pearl, hulled type, but a millet
couscous made from the cracked grain is also available from good health
food shops. Millet flakes can be made into porridge or added to muesli.

SALMON PARCELS WITH MILLET & SPINACH

Salmon is always an excellent pairing with any kind of grain. This delicious lunch or dinner dish provides essential omega-3 and omega-6 oils, together with valuable iron.

SERVES 4 • PREP TIME: 20 MINS • COOK TIME: 30 MINS

PER SERVING:

687 kcal	42.5g	16.5g	33.1g	1.7g	5.2g	41.9g	1.1g
CALORIES	FAT	SAT FAT	CARBS	SUGAR	FIBRE	PROTEIN	SALT

INGREDIENTS

150 g/5½ oz millet, rinsed
½ tsp salt
4 salmon fillets,
each about 175 g/6 oz and 3 cm/1¼ inches thick
15-cm/6-inch piece leek, cut into matchsticks
1 carrot, cut into matchsticks
1 celery stick, cut into matchsticks
1 tbsp snipped fresh chives
85 g/3 oz butter
200 g/7 oz baby spinach
salt and pepper (optional)

1. Preheat the oven to 220°C/425°F/Gas Mark 7 and place a baking tray inside to heat. Cut out four 33-cm/13-inch squares of baking paper.

2. Bring a saucepan of water to the boil. Add the millet and ½ teaspoon of salt. Bring back to the boil, then reduce the heat and simmer briskly for 10 minutes. Drain and set aside.

3. Place a salmon fillet in the centre of each paper square. Arrange the leek, carrot and celery on top and sprinkle with the chives. Season to taste with salt and pepper, if using, and dot with half the butter. Roll up the edges of the paper securely, leaving room in the parcel for steam to circulate.

4. Place the parcels on the preheated baking tray and bake in the preheated oven for 12 minutes.

5. Meanwhile, heat the remaining butter in a frying pan over a medium–high heat. Stir in the reserved millet and the spinach and heat until the spinach has just wilted. Season to taste with salt and pepper, if using.

6. Divide the millet and spinach between four warmed plates and arrange the contents of one of the parcels on top of each. Serve immediately.

SPELT

The rich fibre content of spelt can help to manage weight fluctuations
and keep you trim and active as you get older.

MAJOR NUTRIENTS PER 100 G/3½ OZ SPELT

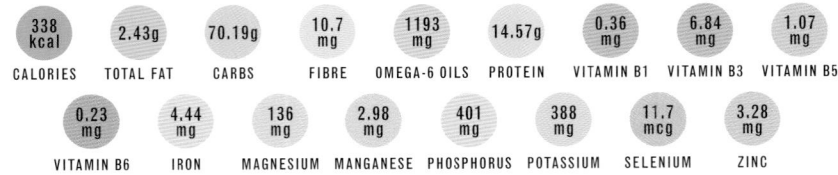

338 kcal	2.43g	70.19g	10.7 mg	1193 mg	14.57g	0.36 mg	6.84 mg	1.07 mg
CALORIES	TOTAL FAT	CARBS	FIBRE	OMEGA-6 OILS	PROTEIN	VITAMIN B1	VITAMIN B3	VITAMIN B5

0.23 mg	4.44 mg	136 mg	2.98 mg	401 mg	388 mg	11.7 mcg	3.28 mg
VITAMIN B6	IRON	MAGNESIUM	MANGANESE	PHOSPHORUS	POTASSIUM	SELENIUM	ZINC

An ancient grain, spelt has not been put through the selective breeding undergone by its modern counterpart, wheat. This makes it lower in the potentially inflammatory and difficult-to-digest gluten that causes intolerances in so many people. Spelt is also higher in iron and vitamin K, both needed to ensure the health of our blood, the life force that carries oxygen and nutrients around the body to vitalize every single cell. It has higher levels of omega-6 oils, too, which keep our cells flexible and are an important contribution to youthful skin. Omega 6 also supports the nervous system to ensure quick brain and muscle reactions.

- Selenium activates the thyroid hormones that keep you burning energy and calories to help you retain a slim and youthful figure.
- Fibre slows the rate at which you break down food, so stabilizing blood sugar levels and helping you resist quick-fix foods that pile on weight.
- Manganese and vitamin B3 help to produce insulin, another vital ingredient in the management of blood sugar levels.

DID YOU KNOW?

Spelt is an ancient cousin of wheat. It was one of the first grains used to make bread and was also popular in ancient Greece and Rome.

PRACTICAL TIPS

Many spelt breads and crackers are now available in health food shops, and spelt can be used as a substitute for rice or potatoes. If you have a severe intolerance to wheat, however, it is advisable to avoid spelt, because the proteins in spelt are similar and may provoke the same reaction.

SPELT & CARROT SALAD

As with most salads, it's the dressing that makes all the difference. Here the grains and crunchy nuts and vegetables are brought to life with the citrussy ginger dressing.

SERVES 4 • PREP TIME: 25 MINS, PLUS STANDING • COOK TIME: 15 MINS

PER SERVING:

462 kcal	27.9g	3.4g	47.5g	5.3g	5.4g	8.3g	1.2g
CALORIES	FAT	SAT FAT	CARBS	SUGAR	FIBRE	PROTEIN	SALT

INGREDIENTS

225 g/8 oz pearled spelt, rinsed
½ tsp salt
2 tbsp fresh thyme leaves
40 g/1½ oz toasted pine nuts
5 spring onions, thinly sliced
4 carrots
3 tbsp salad cress, to serve

DRESSING

2 tbsp orange juice
1 tbsp lemon juice
2-cm/¾-inch piece fresh ginger, squeezed in a garlic press
2 tsp soy sauce
6 tbsp extra virgin olive oil
salt and pepper (optional)

1. Put the spelt and salt into a saucepan with plenty of water to cover. Bring to the boil, then reduce the heat, cover and simmer for 10 minutes, until tender but still chewy. Drain, then spread out on a tray to cool slightly. Tip into a serving bowl while warm.

2. To make the dressing, combine the orange juice, lemon juice and ginger in a small bowl. Add the soy sauce. Season to taste with salt and pepper, if using. Whisk in the oil.

3. Pour the dressing over the spelt, gently mixing with a fork. Stir in the thyme, pine nuts and spring onions.

4. Using a vegetable peeler, shave the carrots into thin ribbons, discarding the woody core. Add to the spelt mixture.

5. Leave to stand at room temperature for 30 minutes. Sprinkle with the cress just before serving.

HINT

Leaving this salad to stand before serving really helps allow the flavours to develop.

MISO

Miso is one of the traditional foods of Japan, where it is associated with long life and good health.

MAJOR NUTRIENTS PER 15 ML/1 TBSP MISO

34 kcal	**1.03g**	**4.55g**	**0.93g**	**2.01g**	**0.02 mg**	**0.04 mg**	**0.16 mg**
CALORIES	TOTAL FAT	CARBS	FIBRE	PROTEIN	VITAMIN B1	VITAMIN B2	VITAMIN B3
0.06 mg	**0.03 mg**	**0.43 mcg**	**8.53 mcg**	**0.43 mg**	**0.3 mg**	**1.2 mcg**	**0.44 mg**
VITAMIN B5	VITAMIN B6	VITAMIN B12	VITAMIN K	IRON	MANGANESE	SELENIUM	ZINC

Like sauerkraut, yogurt and kefir, miso is fermented food associated with good gut health because it feeds the beneficial probiotic bacteria present in the body. This supports toxin elimination and the absorption of nutrients to keep you looking and feeling young and healthy. Fermented foods also help the immune system, keeping in check overreactions that can lead to multiple sensitivities and inflammation, as seen in hayfever and skin problems. The soya variety of miso is a useful vegetarian protein source.

- Contains tryptophan, needed for serotonin production, which encourages good mood and restorative sleep.
- Manganese makes the detoxifying antioxidant enzyme superoxide dismutase, which helps slow down the ageing process.
- Vitamin K transports calcium around the body in support of good bone health and efficient blood clotting.
- Zinc-rich food that promotes optimal immune function and rapid healing, helping your skin look more youthful.

DID YOU KNOW?

Most miso is the hatcho form made from soya beans, but it can also be produced from rice, barley or wheat by adding a koji yeast mould that stimulates fermentation.

PRACTICAL TIPS

Miso is salty, but a little goes a long way in terms of taste and mineral content. The paste is superior to the powdered form and can be used just as easily to make an instant, simple soup when mixed with boiling water. Add miso to boiled vegetables and ginger to make a heartier broth, which you can supplement with prawns, chicken or tofu.

TURKEY MISO SOUP

This soup is just the thing to warm you up on a cold winter's day. The tryptophan content of both the turkey and miso will aid your mood and encourage good sleeping patterns.

SERVES 4 • PREP TIME: 5 MINS • COOK TIME: 25 MINS

PER SERVING:	369 kcal	9.8g	2.1g	32.9g	7.1g	7.9g	35.7g	3g
	CALORIES	FAT	SAT FAT	CARBS	SUGAR	FIBRE	PROTEIN	SALT

INGREDIENTS

225 g/8 oz fresh udon noodles

1 tbsp vegetable oil

1 small leek, halved lengthways and thinly sliced

2 litres/3¾ pints turkey stock

3 carrots, sliced

1 tsp white pepper

225 g/8 oz sugar snap peas, halved

280 g/10 oz cooked turkey meat, shredded or chopped

4 tbsp white miso paste

1. Cook the noodles according to the packet instructions.

2. Heat the oil in a medium-sized saucepan over a medium–high heat. Add the leek and cook, stirring frequently, for 3 minutes, or until it begins to soften. Add the stock, carrots and pepper and bring to the boil. Reduce the heat to low and simmer for 15 minutes, or until the carrots are just tender.

3. Add the sugar snap peas, turkey and cooked noodles and simmer for 2–3 minutes until heated through. Stir in the miso paste until it is dissolved.

4. Transfer the soup to warmed bowls and serve immediately.

CHICKPEAS

Pale, golden chickpeas, sometimes called garbanzo beans, are an excellent, low-cost source of protein, and are rich in fibre, protective plant chemicals and vitamin E.

MAJOR NUTRIENTS PER 60 G/2¼ OZ DRIED CHICKPEAS

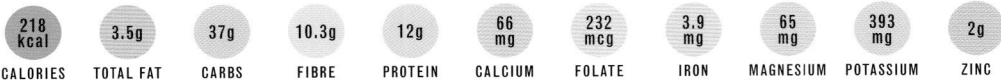

218 kcal	3.5g	37g	10.3g	12g	66 mg	232 mcg	3.9 mg	65 mg	393 mg	2g
CALORIES	TOTAL FAT	CARBS	FIBRE	PROTEIN	CALCIUM	FOLATE	IRON	MAGNESIUM	POTASSIUM	ZINC

Chickpeas are a delicious protein food for vegetarians and a very good source of fibre. Their insoluble fibre, which binds to cholesterol and removes it from the body, not only helps to increase stool bulk and prevent constipation but also helps prevent digestive disorders such as irritable bowel syndrome and diverticulosis. Its soluble fibre controls and lowers blood cholesterol, and helps prevent strokes and heart disease. Chickpeas are extremely high in folate and this helps lower levels of blood homocysteine, which is a risk factor for cardiovascular disease. They are also rich in magnesium, which helps to relax the arteries and helps protect against heart attacks.

- Very high in folate and magnesium.
- A good source of minerals, including iron, zinc and calcium.
- High in potassium to help balance body fluids and protect against fluid retention.
- Rich in plant chemicals to fight heart disease and cancer.

DID YOU KNOW?

Cooked chickpeas are ground into flour, which is used widely in Middle Eastern and Indian cooking. It is an alternative to wheat flour in many recipes, including batters, breads and soups.

PRACTICAL TIPS

Chickpeas need to be soaked for several hours, then boiled for at least 1½ hours. Chickpeas bought prepared in cans are excellent and still contain the important nutrients. Chickpeas are often eaten in the form of hummus, a Middle-Eastern dip, but they can also be used to replace meat or poultry in soups, stews and casseroles.

SMOKY PAPRIKA
ROASTED CHICKPEAS

Chickpeas are made up of complex carbohydrates, which take longer
for the body to digest and so give a slower release of energy.

SERVES 4 • PREP TIME: 15 MINS, PLUS COOLING • COOK TIME: 20–25 MINS

PER SERVING:

235 kcal	8.3g	1g	36g	6.5g	5.7g	7.2g	0.8g
CALORIES	FAT	SAT FAT	CARBS	SUGAR	FIBRE	PROTEIN	SALT

INGREDIENTS

2 tbsp olive oil
1 tsp cumin seeds, roughly crushed
1 tsp smoked mild paprika
¼ tsp ground allspice
¼ tsp ground cinnamon
½ tsp sea salt
800 g/1 lb 12 oz canned chickpeas in water, drained
2 tbsp date syrup

1. Preheat the oven to 200°C/400°F/Gas Mark 6. Add the oil to a roasting tin and place in the oven to heat for 3–4 minutes.

2. Add the cumin seeds, paprika, allspice, cinnamon and salt to a small bowl, and mix together well.

3. Add the chickpeas to the roasting tin, drizzle over the date syrup, sprinkle with the spice mix and stir together. Roast in the preheated oven for 15–20 minutes, stirring once, until brown and crusty.

4. Spoon into a bowl and leave to cool before eating. Store any leftovers in a plastic container in the refrigerator.

SOYA BEANS

A valuable bean, rich in minerals and disease-preventing plant chemicals, soya beans
are a complete source of protein and an ideal food for vegetarians.

MAJOR NUTRIENTS PER 60 G/2¼ OZ DRIED SOYA BEANS

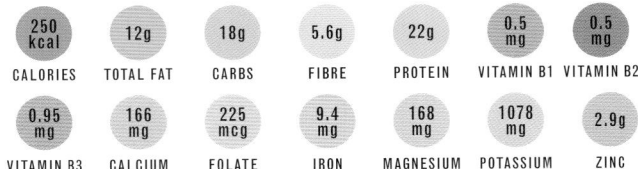

250 kcal	12g	18g	5.6g	22g	0.5 mg	0.5 mg
CALORIES	TOTAL FAT	CARBS	FIBRE	PROTEIN	VITAMIN B1	VITAMIN B2

0.95 mg	166 mg	225 mcg	9.4 mg	168 mg	1078 mg	2.9g
VITAMIN B3	CALCIUM	FOLATE	IRON	MAGNESIUM	POTASSIUM	ZINC

Soya beans have been cultivated in China for over 10,000 years and
are among the few plant sources of complete protein, containing all
eight essential amino acids needed in our diet. Soya is also an excellent
source of calcium, B vitamins, potassium, zinc and magnesium. It is a
very rich source of iron, although this may only be absorbed by the body
if consumed with vitamin C-rich foods. Soya is rich in plant chemicals
that offer protection from diseases, including breast cancer, prostate
cancer and heart disease. A regular intake of soya beans can also reduce
menopausal symptoms.

- Complete source of low saturated-fat protein.
- Rich in plant compounds, which may help protect against hormone-
  based cancers.
- Help lower 'bad' cholesterol and protect against heart disease.
- Can reduce symptoms of the menopause, including hot flushes.

DID YOU KNOW?

*Edamame is the name for fresh
soya beans, which you can find
ready podded, frozen or, sometimes,
fresh in delis and markets. Cook
and use them as you would broad
beans and other fresh legumes.*

PRACTICAL TIPS

Canned soya beans are a quick and easy alternative to dried beans and
contain a similar nutritional profile. Use in soups and casseroles, mash for
a dip or add to vegetable burgers. Tofu is made from processed soya beans
and is a good low-fat, low-sodium alternative to meat. Some of the wheat
flour in baking recipes can be replaced with soya flour to increase nutrient
content.

GREEN BEAN PROTEIN BURST

This spicy bean dish is perfect when there is a surplus of summer beans –
served with spiced tofu it will boost your intake of protein and fibre.

SERVES 4 • PREP TIME: 12 MINS • COOK TIME: 15 MINS

PER SERVING:

516 kcal	37.9g	23.7g	21.9g	8g	9.5g	27.9g	1.2g
CALORIES	FAT	SAT FAT	CARBS	SUGAR	FIBRE	PROTEIN	SALT

INGREDIENTS

400 g/14 oz tofu, drained
2 tbsp soy sauce
2 garlic cloves, crushed
3-cm/1¼-inch piece fresh ginger, grated
½ tsp chilli flakes
300 g/10½ oz runner beans
200 g/7 oz fresh or frozen broad beans
1 tbsp coconut oil
1 red pepper, deseeded and chopped
1 tsp garam masala
1 tsp tomato purée
400 ml/14 fl oz canned coconut milk
100 g/3½ oz frozen soya beans, thawed
1 tbsp lime juice
2 tbsp salted cashew nuts
small handful of fresh coriander

1. Cut the tofu into cubes and place in a non-metallic bowl.

2. Mix the soy sauce, garlic, ginger and chilli flakes together and pour over the tofu.

3. Meanwhile, trim and slice the runner beans diagonally. Bring a large saucepan of water to the boil, add the broad beans and runner beans and blanch for 4 minutes. Drain.

4. Heat the oil in a wok or large frying pan, add the red pepper and stir-fry for 2–3 minutes.

5. Add the garam masala and tomato purée and cook for 1 minute, then pour in the coconut milk. Bring to the boil, then add the broad beans, runner beans and soya beans and simmer for 4–5 minutes until the beans are tender.

6. Add the tofu and lime juice and cook for a further 2–3 minutes until the tofu is heated through.

7. Serve in four warmed bowls, sprinkled with the cashew nuts and coriander.

KIDNEY BEANS

Iron-rich kidney beans are an excellent source of good-quality protein, zinc and fibre, and contain compounds to help prevent blood clots.

MAJOR NUTRIENTS PER 60 G/2¼ OZ DRIED RED KIDNEY BEANS

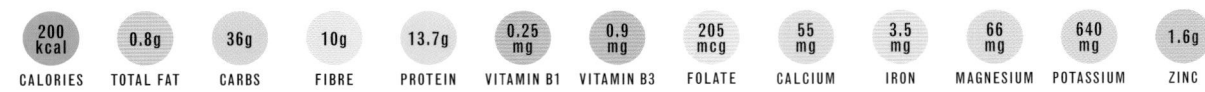

200 kcal	0.8g	36g	10g	13.7g	0.25 mg	0.9 mg	205 mcg	55 mg	3.5 mg	66 mg	640 mg	1.6g
CALORIES	TOTAL FAT	CARBS	FIBRE	PROTEIN	VITAMIN B1	VITAMIN B3	FOLATE	CALCIUM	IRON	MAGNESIUM	POTASSIUM	ZINC

Kidney beans are invaluable for vegetarians as they are high in good-quality protein and minerals. An average portion of kidney beans contains at least a quarter of our day's iron needs to help prevent anaemia and increase energy levels, while their zinc content helps boost the immune system and maintain fertility. The high degree of insoluble fibre in kidney beans helps prevent colon cancer, while for diabetics and people with insulin resistance, the total fibre content helps regulate blood sugar levels.

- Excellent source of protein, iron and calcium for vegetarians.
- Very high fibre content helps regulate release of insulin and helps to prevent hunger – a good choice for dieters.
- Protects against colon cancer.
- Extremely high in potassium, which can minimize fluid retention and may help control high blood pressure.

DID YOU KNOW?

Raw kidney beans can contain high levels of potentially toxic substances, which can cause an upset stomach, vomiting and diarrhoea. In order to remove this risk, the beans must be rapidly boiled for at least 10 minutes before cooking.

PRACTICAL TIPS

There is little nutritional difference between cooked dried kidney beans and canned kidney beans so, if you are short of time, use the canned variety. Red kidney beans are often added to meat dishes such as chilli con carne, or used in three-bean salad and, when mashed with oil and lemon juice, make a good sandwich filling or dip.

MEXICAN BEEF & BEAN BOWL

Chilli con carne with extra beans for protein and fibre, plus red peppers for their great flavour and antioxidant content – a perfect dish to make in advance as the flavours improve over time.

SERVES 4 • PREP TIME: 10 MINS • COOK TIME: 20–25 MINS

PER SERVING:

 682 kcal CALORIES

 25.4g FAT

 8.7g SAT FAT

 69.6g CARBS

 8.7g SUGAR

 11.3g FIBRE

37.9g PROTEIN

0.5g SALT

INGREDIENTS

1 tbsp olive oil
500 g/1 lb 2 oz fresh beef mince
1 onion, chopped
2 red peppers, deseeded and sliced
2½ tsp chilli powder
400 g/14 oz canned red kidney beans, drained
400 g/14 oz canned cannellini beans, drained
400 g/14 oz canned chopped tomatoes
1 tbsp tomato purée
100 ml/3½ fl oz vegetable stock
200 g/7 oz basmati rice
2 tbsp chopped fresh coriander
2 tbsp soured cream
¼ tsp smoked paprika
salt and pepper (optional)

1. Heat the oil in a large frying pan, add the mince and cook for 2–3 minutes until brown all over.

2. Add the onion and red peppers and cook, stirring occasionally, for 3–4 minutes.

3. Stir in the chilli powder and cook for 1 minute, then add the kidney beans, cannellini beans, tomatoes, tomato purée and stock. Bring to a simmer and simmer for 12–15 minutes. Season to taste with salt and pepper, if using.

4. Meanwhile, cook the rice according to the packet instructions.

5. Stir the coriander into the chilli and serve in warmed bowls with the rice, topped with a dollop of soured cream and a sprinkling of smoked paprika.

VARIATION

If you are trying to cut down on red meat, use fresh turkey mince in place of the beef mince – lighter and equally delicious.

LENTILS

Small, lens-shaped dried lentils are one of the pulses richest in cancer-blocking fibres called isoflavones and lignan, and are low in fat and saturates.

MAJOR NUTRIENTS PER 60 G/2¼ OZ DRIED GREEN OR BROWN LENTILS

212 kcal	0.6g	36g	18g	15.5g	0.5 mg	1.6mg
CALORIES	TOTAL FAT	CARBS	FIBRE	PROTEIN	VITAMIN B1	VITAMIN B3

0.3 mg	34 mg	287 mcg	4.5 mg	73 mg	573 mg	2.9g
VITAMIN B6	CALCIUM	FOLATE	IRON	MAGNESIUM	POTASSIUM	ZINC

Lentils come in a variety of colours and include green, brown and red. The green and brown tend to contain the highest levels of nutrients and fibre. Lentils are a very rich source of fibre, both insoluble and soluble, which helps protect us against cancer and cardiovascular disease. They also contain plant chemicals called isoflavones, which may offer protection from cancer and coronary heart disease, and lignan, which has a mild oestrogen-like effect that may lower the risk of cancer, minimize premenstrual syndrome and protect against osteoporosis. Lentils are also rich in B vitamins, folate and all major minerals, particularly iron and zinc.

- Rich in fibre for protection from cardiovascular disease and cancers.
- High iron content for healthy blood and energy levels.
- Contain plant chemicals to help premenstrual syndrome and bone health.
- High zinc content to boost the immune system.

DID YOU KNOW?
Lentils are thought to be one of the earliest foods to have been cultivated, with 8,000-year-old seeds found at sites in the Middle East.

PRACTICAL TIPS

Lentils are one of the few pulses that don't need soaking before cooking. They are also quick to cook by simmering in water for about 30 minutes. Dried lentils cooked in stock with carrots, celery and onion makes a quick soup. Canned lentils contain almost as many nutrients as dried ones.

LENTIL & CHARD SOUP

This vibrant soup is full of fibre for a healthy digestive system and it also contains vital nutrients for good bones and a healthy heart.

SERVES 6 • PREP TIME: 20 MINS • COOK TIME: 55 MINS

PER SERVING:

 229 kcal CALORIES

 2.3g FAT

 0.8g SAT FAT

 41.7g CARBS

 6.5g SUGAR

 7.2g FIBRE

13g PROTEIN

2.2g SALT

INGREDIENTS

150 g/5½ oz brown lentils
1 onion, finely diced
400 ml/14 fl oz passata
600–750 ml/1–1¼ pints chicken stock or vegetable stock
½ tsp cumin seeds, lightly crushed
½ tsp salt
350 g/12 oz chard
175 g/6 oz potatoes, cut into 1-cm/½-inch cubes
6 tbsp chopped fresh mint
2 wholemeal pittas
6 tbsp Greek-style yogurt
salt and pepper (optional)
¼ tsp cumin seeds, to garnish
6 lemon wedges, to garnish

1. Put the lentils in a large saucepan with the onion, passata, 600 ml/1 pint of the stock, cumin seeds and ½ teaspoon salt. Bring to the boil, then cover and simmer over a low heat for 20 minutes, until the lentils are just tender.

2. Remove the stems from the chard and thinly slice. Slice the leaves crossways into ribbons.

3. Add the chard stems and potatoes to the lentils and cook for 10 minutes.

4. Add the chard leaves and cook for a further 15 minutes. If necessary, add the remaining stock to thin the soup – but it should still be quite thick. Stir in 4 tablespoons of the mint and season to taste with salt and pepper, if using.

5. Meanwhile, preheat the grill to medium. Open out the pittas and toast under the preheated grill for 3 minutes, until crisp. Break into bite-sized pieces and arrange around the edge of six warmed soup plates.

6. Ladle the soup into the plates. Add 1 tablespoon of yogurt to each and sprinkle with the remaining mint and some cumin seeds. Garnish with the lemon wedges and serve immediately.

HARICOT BEANS

High-protein haricot beans are often used in canned baked beans and
are very high in fibre, minerals and B vitamins.

MAJOR NUTRIENTS PER 60 G/2¼ OZ DRIED HARICOT BEANS

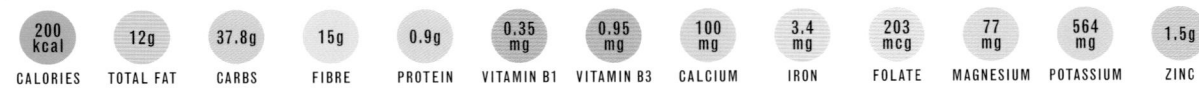

200 kcal	12g	37.8g	15g	0.9g	0.35 mg	0.95 mg	100 mg	3.4 mg	203 mcg	77 mg	564 mg	1.5g
CALORIES	TOTAL FAT	CARBS	FIBRE	PROTEIN	VITAMIN B1	VITAMIN B3	CALCIUM	IRON	FOLATE	MAGNESIUM	POTASSIUM	ZINC

The soluble fibre in haricot beans helps to lower cholesterol and prevent
blood sugar levels from rising too rapidly after a meal, making these
beans a good choice for dieters as well as people with diabetes, insulin
resistance and hypoglycaemia. Their insoluble fibre helps to prevent
constipation and reduce the severity and symptoms of digestive disorders
such as irritable bowel syndrome and diverticulosis. Haricot beans are also
a good source of protein and one of the best beans for supplying calcium.
One portion provides a seventh of the daily recommended intake. They are
also very rich in magnesium, potassium, iron and zinc and are a very good
source of B vitamins and folate.

- Rich in soluble fibre to help lower blood cholesterol and protect from
  cardiovascular disease.
- Insoluble fibre helps the digestive system and bowels.
- A good source of calcium for a healthy heart and strong bones.
- Rich in antioxidant minerals such as zinc to help prevent disease.

DID YOU KNOW?

*Early in the twentieth century
haricot beans were also called
navy beans because they were
a staple food for the US Navy.*

PRACTICAL TIPS

To prepare, soak the beans overnight, then replace the water and boil
rapidly for 10 minutes before simmering for about 1½ hours until tender.
Do not add salt to beans before they are cooked, as the salt will make them
tough. Cooked beans can be puréed with olive oil, salt and pepper as an
alternative to mashed potato.

VEGETABLE COCIDO

Quick and easy to make, this comforting Spanish-inspired stew is
flavoured with smoked paprika for a lovely, deep spicy flavour.

SERVES 4 • PREP TIME: 20 MINS • COOK TIME: 50 MINS

PER SERVING:	525 kcal	26.1g	12.66g	62.3g	14.8g	18.5g	14.6g	1.8g
	CALORIES	FAT	SAT FAT	CARBS	SUGAR	FIBRE	PROTEIN	SALT

INGREDIENTS

2 tbsp virgin olive oil
1 onion, roughly chopped
1 aubergine, roughly chopped
½ tsp smoked hot paprika
2 garlic cloves, finely chopped
1 large red pepper, deseeded and roughly chopped
250 g/9 oz baby new potatoes, unpeeled, and any larger ones halved
450 g/1 lb plum tomatoes, peeled and roughly chopped
410 g/14½ oz canned haricot beans in water, drained
150 ml/5 fl oz home-made vegetable stock
2 fresh rosemary sprigs
2 courgettes, roughly chopped
sea salt and pepper (optional)

1. Heat 1 tablespoon of the oil in a saucepan over a medium heat. Add the onion and fry for 5 minutes, or until soft. Add the remaining oil, then add the aubergine, and fry, stirring, for 5 minutes, or until just beginning to soften and brown.

2. Stir in the paprika and garlic, then the red pepper, potatoes and tomatoes. Add the beans, stock and rosemary, then season with salt and pepper, if using. Bring to the boil, cover, reduce the heat to medium–low and simmer for 30 minutes, stirring occasionally.

3. Stir the courgettes into the stew, then cook, uncovered, for 10 minutes, or until all the vegetables are tender and the sauce has reduced slightly.

4. Ladle the stew into shallow bowls, discard the rosemary sprigs and serve.

VARIATION

*Stews are easy to vary depending on what ingredients you have
to hand. Try replacing the aubergine with mushrooms.*

TOFU

Tofu, or bean curd, is made from soya beans and is widely used in Asian cooking. It is one of the factors associated with Asians' better health in old age.

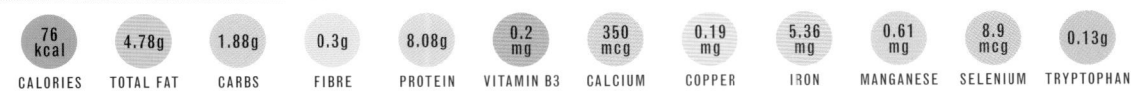

76 kcal	4.78g	1.88g	0.3g	8.08g	0.2 mg	350 mcg	0.19 mg	5.36 mg	0.61 mg	8.9 mcg	0.13g
CALORIES	TOTAL FAT	CARBS	FIBRE	PROTEIN	VITAMIN B3	CALCIUM	COPPER	IRON	MANGANESE	SELENIUM	TRYPTOPHAN

Soya protein is one of the few plant sources of complete protein, which means that it contains all of the essential amino acids that you can't make in the body and must obtain through your diet. This includes the amino acid tryptophan, which is necessary for good mood and sleep, and crucial in combating the ageing effects of daily stress. Soya is also a rich source of saponins and fibre and is therefore often recommended as part of a diet intended to lower cholesterol. Lignins in soy proteins have been found to stop the growth and spread of prostate cancer cells. They also contain phytoestrogens, specifically the isoflavones genistein and daidzein. These have been shown to reduce the incidence of hormone-related prostate and breast cancers and the rate of osteoporosis.

- Enriched with calcium for strong bones and a robust heart.
- Contains iron and copper, which is used by red blood cells to transport oxygen and renew worn-out cells.
- Copper is needed to make collagen and elastin from the enzyme lysyl oxidase, ensuring firm and flexible blood vessels, bones and joints.

DID YOU KNOW?

Tofu was first made 2,000 years ago, in China. It was first written about in a poem called 'Ode to Tofu' by Su Ping in AD 1500.

PRACTICAL TIPS

Tofu is available in three varieties: firm, soft and silken. Each has a different texture and usage. Tofu can seem bland when first tried but it soaks up flavours beautifully. Silken tofu also makes a good protein addition to smoothies.

TOFU PARCELS

Served with fresh crusty bread, these little parcels of flavour and goodness
provide a complete and properly balanced vegetarian meal.

SERVES 4 • PREP TIME: 10 MINS • COOK TIME: 10–15 MINS

PER SERVING:

 169 kcal CALORIES **12.3g** FAT  **1.7g** SAT FAT **5.8g** CARBS  **2.3g** SUGAR **2.5g** FIBRE **11.6g** PROTEIN **TRACE** SALT

INGREDIENTS

2 tbsp olive oil
1 garlic clove, crushed
250 g/9 oz firm tofu, cut into chunks
250 g/9 oz cherry tomatoes, halved
1 small red onion, thinly sliced
handful of fresh basil leaves
salt and pepper (optional)

1. Preheat the oven to 220°C/425°F/Gas Mark 7. Brush four 30-cm/12-inch squares of double-thickness foil with oil. Mix the remaining oil with the garlic.

2. Divide the tofu, tomatoes, onion and basil between the foil squares, sprinkle with salt and pepper, if using, and spoon over the garlic-flavoured oil.

3. Fold over the foil to enclose the filling and seal firmly. Place on a baking sheet in the preheated oven and cook for 10–15 minutes, until heated through.

4. Carefully open the parcels and serve.

BLACK BEANS

Shiny, oval black beans are an ideal and inexpensive addition to the diet, being rich in nutrients and cholesterol-lowering fibre and very low in fat and saturates.

MAJOR NUTRIENTS PER 60 G/2¼ OZ DRIED BLACK BEANS

205 kcal	0.8g	36.7g	13.5g	13.7g	0.4 mg	42 mg	231 mcg	109 mg	550 mg	1.7g
CALORIES	TOTAL FAT	CARBS	FIBRE	PROTEIN	VITAMIN B1	CALCIUM	FOLATE	MAGNESIUM	POTASSIUM	ZINC

Black beans are a delicious addition to the diet. Nutritionally, they are high in the indigestible portion of the plant known as insoluble fibre, which can reduce cholesterol. Their extremely high magnesium content means that they are an excellent food for people at risk of developing or suffering from heart disease – an optimum intake of magnesium is linked with a reduced risk of various heart problems. Black beans are also rich in antioxidant compounds called anthocyanins, flavonoids that can help prevent cancer and blood clots. The darker the bean's seed coat, the higher its level of antioxidant activity. In addition, black beans are an excellent source of minerals and folate.

- High-fibre food to help beat some cancers and reduce cholesterol.
- Rich in anthocyanins to block cancer cells.
- Contain folate for healthy blood and development.
- A very good source of vegetable protein.

DID YOU KNOW?

Black beans were native to South America, but since the fifteenth century, when they were introduced into Europe by Spanish explorers, they have been popular throughout Europe, Africa and Asia as well as the United States.

PRACTICAL TIPS

Buy the beans dried for long storage or cooked in cans. Be sure to rinse canned beans packed in brine thoroughly before use. Presoaking beans reduces the raffinose-type oligosaccharides they contain – these are the sugars associated with flatulence. Black beans can be used in a range of dishes, from soups and stews to rice dishes and crêpe fillings.

BRAZILIAN GREENS WITH BLACK BEANS & ORANGES

Kale and black beans play the starring role in this lively Brazilian-style dish. The beans are a good match for kale's full-bodied flavour, enhanced with orange, chilli, garlic and coriander.

SERVES 4 • PREP TIME: 25 MINS • COOK TIME: 25 MINS

PER SERVING:
 284 kcal CALORIES
 15.7g FAT
 2.1g SAT FAT
 26.6g CARBS
 9g SUGAR
 13.3g FIBRE
11.8g PROTEIN
0.4g SALT

INGREDIENTS

1 large orange
3 tbsp olive oil
1 small onion, finely chopped
1 garlic clove, finely chopped
1 fresh green chilli, deseeded and finely chopped
600 g/1 lb 5 oz kale, thick stalks removed and leaves sliced crossways
6–8 tbsp vegetable stock or chicken stock
400 g/14 oz canned black beans, drained and rinsed
6 tbsp chopped fresh coriander
1 tbsp olive oil, for drizzling
salt and pepper (optional)

1. Using a sharp knife, cut a slice from the top and bottom of the orange. Remove the peel and white pith by cutting downwards, following the shape of the fruit as closely as possible.

2. Working over a bowl, cut between the flesh and membrane of each segment and ease out the flesh. Slice each segment in half. Squeeze the membrane over the bowl to extract the juice.

3. Heat the oil in a large frying pan over a medium heat. Add the onion and fry for 5 minutes until soft. Add the garlic and chilli and fry for a further 2 minutes.

4. Gradually stir in the kale. Add a splash of stock, then cover and cook for 5–6 minutes, or until just wilted. Add more stock if the leaves start to look dry.

5. Stir in the orange juice and any remaining stock. Season to taste with salt and pepper, if using, then cover and cook for 5 minutes until tender.

6. Stir in the beans and the orange segments. Simmer, uncovered, for a few minutes to heat through. Stir in the coriander, drizzle with a little oil and serve immediately.

WALNUTS

Known for their unusually high content of omega-3 fat, walnuts can help prevent heart disease, cancers, arthritis, skin complaints and nervous system disorders.

MAJOR NUTRIENTS PER 30 G/1 OZ WALNUTS

196 kcal	19.5g	4g	2g	4.5g	0.3 mg	0.16 mg	29 mg	0.9 mg	47 mg	132 mg	0.9 mg
CALORIES	TOTAL FAT	CARBS	FIBRE	PROTEIN	VITAMIN B3	VITAMIN B6	CALCIUM	IRON	MAGNESIUM	POTASSIUM	ZINC

Unlike most nuts, walnuts are much richer in polyunsaturated fats than in monounsaturates. The type of polyunsaturates that walnuts contain are mostly the essential omega-3 fats, in the form of alpha-linolenic acid. Just one 30 g/1 oz portion will provide you with more than the recommended daily intake. An adequate and balanced intake of the omega fats has been linked with protection from ageing, cardiovascular disease, cancer, arthritis, skin problems and diseases of the nervous system. For people who don't eat fish and fish oils, an intake of omega-3 fats from other sources, such as walnuts, linseeds and soya, is important.

- Good source of fibre and B vitamins.
- Rich in omega-3 fats and antioxidants for health protection.
- Good source of a range of important minerals.
- Can lower 'bad' cholesterol and blood pressure and increase elasticity of the arteries.

DID YOU KNOW?

The most popular type of walnut for eating is Juglans Regia, the so-called 'English walnut'. Black and white walnuts are also edible, although their shells are difficult to crack.

PRACTICAL TIPS

The high levels of polyunsaturated fats mean that walnuts go rancid easily. Buy nuts with their shells on if possible, store in the refrigerator, and consume quickly. Avoid buying chopped walnuts – chopping speeds the oxidation of the nuts. Walnuts are best eaten raw as a snack, in muesli or sprinkled on yogurt and fruit.

CHICKPEA WALNUT PATTIES

These hearty patties are very similar to falafel, but have the
added richness and flavour of walnuts.

SERVES 4 • PREP TIME: 15 MINS, PLUS CHILLING • COOK TIME: 10 MINS

PER SERVING: | 320 kcal | 24.7g | 2.6g | 18.1g | 3.5g | 5.2g | 7g | 0.9g
---|---|---|---|---|---|---|---
 | CALORIES | FAT | SAT FAT | CARBS | SUGAR | FIBRE | PROTEIN | SALT

INGREDIENTS

2 garlic cloves
1 shallot
425 g/15 oz canned chickpeas, drained and rinsed
15 g/½ oz fresh flat-leaf parsley
1 tsp ground coriander
1 tsp ground cumin
½ tsp salt
⅛ tsp cayenne pepper
2 tbsp olive oil
2 tbsp plain flour
½ tsp baking powder
60 g/2¼ oz roasted, unsalted walnuts
2 tbsp sunflower oil, for frying
toasted hamburger buns, lettuce, tomato and
mayonnaise, to serve (optional)

1. Put the garlic and shallot into a food processor and pulse to chop. Add the chickpeas, parsley, coriander, cumin, salt, cayenne pepper, olive oil and flour and pulse to a chunky purée. Add the baking powder and pulse once to incorporate. Add the walnuts and pulse once to incorporate.

2. Shape the chickpea mixture into four equal-sized patties, about 10 cm/4 inches in diameter. Chill in the refrigerator for at least 30 minutes or overnight.

3. Heat the sunflower oil in a large frying pan over a medium–high heat. Add the patties and cook for 4–5 minutes on each side until golden brown. Serve hot on toasted hamburger buns, with lettuce, tomato and mayonnaise, if using.

HINT

Serve the patties in the same way you would falafel, stuffed in pittas with lettuce, tomato and cucumber.

ALMONDS

The very high vitamin E content of almonds offers protection against cancer, heart disease, heart attacks and strokes, arthritis, infertility and skin problems.

MAJOR NUTRIENTS PER 30 G/1 OZ ALMONDS

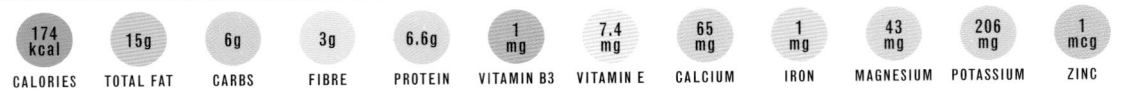

CALORIES	TOTAL FAT	CARBS	FIBRE	PROTEIN	VITAMIN B3	VITAMIN E	CALCIUM	IRON	MAGNESIUM	POTASSIUM	ZINC
174 kcal	15g	6g	3g	6.6g	1 mg	7.4 mg	65 mg	1 mg	43 mg	206 mg	1 mcg

Almonds are the seeds of a drupe fruit related to peaches and plums. They are rich in monounsaturated fats and, due to their high fat content, take a long time for the body to digest. This can help keep hunger at bay and help people watching their weight. Almonds are extremely high in vitamin E, which protects against cancer and cardiovascular diseases, helps reduce the pain of osteoarthritis and keeps skin healthy. Vitamin E can also boost male fertility. Almonds are higher in calcium than almost any other plant food and are therefore an excellent addition to vegan and dairy-free diets.

- Satisfying snack to keep hunger at bay and blood sugar levels even.
- Rich in the antioxidant vitamin E.
- Very good source of calcium.
- High in monounsaturated fat for arterial and heart health.

PRACTICAL TIPS

Buy whole almonds in their shells or, at least, still in their brown skins – these keep better than blanched, chopped or flaked almonds. Store in a cool, dark, dry place – the refrigerator is ideal. Almonds combine very well with apricots, peaches, chicken, rice and red peppers.

DID YOU KNOW?

There is a type of inedible almond, which contains a form of cyanide, known as the bitter almond. It is poisonous and is unavailable in shops.

ROASTED ALMOND GINGERSNAP BUTTER

Lightly sweetened with treacle and brown sugar, and spiced with ginger, this nutritionally loaded nut butter tastes just like ginger biscuits.

MAKES 350 G/12 OZ • PREP TIME: 10 MINS • COOK TIME: NONE

PER 350 G/12 OZ:

2204 kcal	182.3g	14.8g	110.5g	63g	31.2g	60.5g	1.5g
CALORIES	FAT	SAT FAT	CARBS	SUGAR	FIBRE	PROTEIN	SALT

INGREDIENTS

285 g/10¼ oz roasted almonds
2 tbsp soft light brown sugar
2 tbsp black treacle
1½ tsp grated fresh ginger
½ tsp ground ginger
¼ tsp salt
2–3 tbsp grapeseed oil
apple slices, to serve (optional)

1. Put the almonds into a food processor and process for 5–10 minutes, until smooth.

2. Add the sugar, treacle, fresh ginger, ground ginger, and salt and process until well combined. With the processor running, add the oil, a little at a time, until you achieve the desired consistency.

3. Serve immediately on apple slices, if using, or refrigerate until ready to use. Almond butter can be stored in the refrigerator for several weeks.

CASHEW NUTS

High in monounsaturated fats, cashew nuts protect the heart, and contain a range of minerals for strong bones, improved immunity and increased energy levels.

MAJOR NUTRIENTS PER 30 G/1 OZ CASHEW NUTS

166 kcal	13g	9g	1g	5.5g	0.1 mg	0.3 mg	0.12 mg	2 mg	88 mg	198 mg	6 mcg	1.7 mg
CALORIES	TOTAL FAT	CARBS	FIBRE	PROTEIN	VITAMIN B1	VITAMIN B3	VITAMIN B6	IRON	MAGNESIUM	POTASSIUM	SELENIUM	ZINC

Cashew nuts are considerably lower in total fat than all other nuts and could be useful as a dieter's snack. Much of their fat is monounsaturated oleic acid (the type found in olive oil), which has health benefits, including protection from heart and arterial disease. Cashew nuts are also rich in important minerals, including magnesium for strong bones and heart health, immune-boosting zinc and iron for healthy blood and energy. Like other nuts, cashew nuts are linked with protection from cardiovascular disease. People who regularly eat nuts are less likely to die from these diseases than people who never eat nuts.

- Regularly eating nuts is linked with a considerably lower risk of dying from cardiovascular diseases.
- Good source of monounsaturated fats linked to protection from disease.
- A good source of B vitamins for brain power and energy.
- Rich in zinc to boost the immune system.

DID YOU KNOW?

Commercially roasted cashew nuts will have lost the benefit of their unsaturated oils, which are oxidized at high temperatures, but you can roast raw cashew nuts at home in a low oven for 20 minutes.

PRACTICAL TIPS

You can use cashew nuts to make cashew nut butter at home just as you would peanut butter. Buy whole, shelled cashew nuts and store in the refrigerator. Combine cashew nuts with dried apricots for a healthy mineral-rich snack. Add a handful of cashew nuts to a vegetable stir-fry for a healthy meal.

AVOCADO & CASHEW NUT PASTA SAUCE

This unusual meatless pasta sauce is a good source of monunsaturated fats from the avocado and cashew nuts, and magnesium, zinc and iron from the nuts.

MAKES 400 ML/14 FL OZ • PREP TIME: 20 MINS • COOK TIME: 3–4 MINS

PER 400 ML/14 FL OZ:

1666 kcal CALORIES	142.9g FAT	28.4g SAT FAT	74.1g CARBS	9.8g SUGAR	32.6g FIBRE	45.7g PROTEIN	2g SALT

INGREDIENTS

100 g/3½ oz cashew nuts
2 garlic cloves
30 g/1 oz fresh mint, leaves picked
2 ripe avocados, peeled, stoned and roughly chopped
50 g/1¾ oz finely grated Parmesan cheese
2 tbsp olive oil
juice of 1 lime
1–2 tbsp water

1. Toast the nuts in a dry frying pan over a high heat for 3–4 minutes, moving the pan regularly to prevent the nuts burning.

2. Place the nuts and garlic in a food processor and pulse until the nuts are finely chopped. Add the mint leaves, avocados and cheese. Blend and, with the motor running, pour in the oil and lime juice. Add just enough water to make a thick sauce.

3. Use immediately or keep in the refrigerator in a covered container. The sauce will keep for up to two days. Serve mixed into pasta.

PECAN NUTS

Pecan nuts contain the highest amount of antioxidant nutrients of any nut,
making them highly protective against ageing and disease.

MAJOR NUTRIENTS PER 30 G/1 OZ PECAN NUTS

207 kcal	21.6g	12.2g	4.15g	2.8g	2.7g	0.19 mg	0.35 mg	0.25 mg
CALORIES	TOTAL FAT	MONO UN-SATURATED FAT	CARBS	FIBRE	PROTEIN	VITAMIN B1	VITAMIN B3	VITAMIN B5

295 mg	6189 mg	12178 mg	55 mcg	1.4 mg	36 mg	1.35 mg	32 mg	123 mg	1.35 mg
OMEGA-3 OILS	OMEGA-6 OILS	OMEGA-9 OILS	FOLATE	IRON	MAGNESIUM	MANGANESE	PHYTOSTEROLS	POTASSIUM	ZINC

Pecans don't get the attention they deserve: studies have shown that a handful a day can help prevent heart disease and lower cholesterol. The amount of calories in pecans, and nuts in general, often leads to assumptions about weight gain, but it's important to remember that this high energy comes from the abundance of healthy oils they contain. These oils actually help raise metabolism and stop us craving the sugary foods that pile on the pounds and contribute to ageing conditions such as diabetes, arthritis and heart disease. People who eat more than two portions of nuts a week are less prone to put on weight than those who avoid these nutrient-rich foods.

- High levels of omega-9 oils (oleic acid) keep your skin clear and smooth.
- Good levels of balanced and high-quality protein ensure the necessary repairs are made to the body to hold back ageing.
- Phytosterols work with high levels of antioxidants to discourage sensitivities and intolerances.

DID YOU KNOW?

Eighty to 95 per cent of the world's pecans come from the United States, where the trees can grow and produce nuts for 300 years.

PRACTICAL TIPS

Pecans are associated with sweet desserts, but they can be eaten on their own, or used as an interesting salad ingredient. Their rich, buttery taste gives them a luxurious quality that feels like a treat and they are a healthy alternative to sweets or confectionery.

COFFEE & PECAN
MINI BREAKFAST MUFFINS

Sometimes you feel you need a sweet hit in the morning to get you through the first few hours. These little muffins provide that with none of the sugar highs and crashes.

MAKES 9 • PREP TIME: 25 MINS • COOK TIME: 20 MINS

PER MUFFIN:	170 kcal CALORIES	16.6g FAT	3.2g SAT FAT	1.6g CARBS	1.1g SUGAR	0.5g FIBRE	3.6g PROTEIN	0.5g SALT

INGREDIENTS

50 g/1¾ oz coconut flour
¼ tsp baking powder
½ tsp bicarbonate of soda
1 tbsp stevia
30 g/1 oz pecan nuts, roughly chopped
150 ml/5 fl oz soured cream
5 tbsp vegetable oil
2 large eggs, beaten
5 tbsp prepared espresso or strong instant coffee
1 tsp rice malt syrup
sea salt (optional)

1. Preheat the oven to 170°C/325°F/Gas Mark 3. Line a mini muffin tin with paper cases.

2. Put the flour, baking powder, bicarbonate of soda, stevia, 20 g/¾ oz pecan nuts and a small pinch of salt, if using, in a large bowl and mix well. Add the soured cream, oil, eggs and 4 tablespoons of the coffee, and stir until evenly mixed. Leave to stand for a moment, then spoon the mixture into the mini muffin cases.

3. Bake in the preheated oven for 20 minutes, or until well risen and the tops spring back when pressed with a fingertip. Leave to cool for 5 minutes, then transfer to a wire rack.

4. Meanwhile, put the rice malt syrup and remaining coffee into a bowl and mix. Spoon a small drizzle over each muffin. Sprinkle over the remaining nuts and serve warm.

HINT
These muffins can be stored in an airtight container for up to two days.

HAZELNUTS

Particularly rich in potassium, hazelnuts have the ability to
reduce fluid retention and lower blood pressure.

MAJOR NUTRIENTS PER 30 G/1 OZ HAZELNUTS

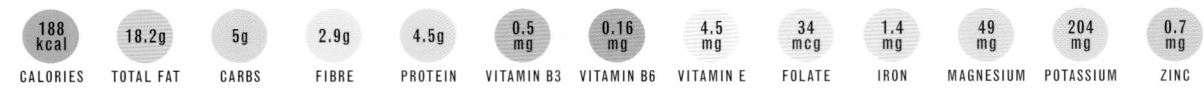

188 kcal	18.2g	5g	2.9g	4.5g	0.5 mg	0.16 mg	4.5 mg	34 mcg	1.4 mg	49 mg	204 mg	0.7 mg
CALORIES	TOTAL FAT	CARBS	FIBRE	PROTEIN	VITAMIN B3	VITAMIN B6	VITAMIN E	FOLATE	IRON	MAGNESIUM	POTASSIUM	ZINC

Hazelnuts are a good source of protein and monounsaturated fats, which have been shown to reduce 'bad' cholesterol in the blood and even slightly raise 'good' cholesterol. The nuts are high in beta-sitosterol, a plant fat that can help reduce an enlarged prostate and is also a cholesterol-lowering compound. Hazelnuts are very high in vitamin E, an antioxidant that maintains skin health and heart health and can boost the immune system. The high potassium content can help people with high blood pressure and is also a diuretic. The magnesium content helps heart health and can contribute to bone strength.

- High in beta-sitosterol, which may help prostate health.
- Rich in monounsaturates, which can help improve blood cholesterol profile.
- Very rich in antioxidant vitamin E.
- Good source of soluble fibre for lowering 'bad' cholesterol and digestive health.

DID YOU KNOW?

*Hazelnuts are also known
as filberts or cob nuts, depending
on their country of origin.*

PRACTICAL TIPS

Hazelnuts keep better than many other nuts because they contain less fat and their vitamin E acts as a preservative. Buy whole nuts rather than chopped – chopping destroys much of their nutrient content. Store in a refrigerator. Use as a snack, or add to salads, stir-fries, breakfast cereals and desserts.

BANANA, GOJI & HAZELNUT BREAD

On mornings when you don't have time to eat breakfast before you leave for work, wrap a slice or two of this superfood-packed bread in baking paper to eat on-the-go.

SERVES 10 • PREP TIME: 25 MINS, PLUS COOLING • COOK TIME: 1 HOUR

PER SERVING:

300 kcal	12.8g	5.6g	43.4g	19.3g	3.7g	5.9g	0.4g
CALORIES	FAT	SAT FAT	CARBS	SUGAR	FIBRE	PROTEIN	SALT

INGREDIENTS

10 g/¼ oz butter, for greasing
85 g/3 oz butter, softened
115 g/4 oz light muscovado sugar
2 eggs
3 bananas (500 g/1 lb 2 oz unpeeled weight), peeled and mashed
115 g/4 oz plain wholemeal flour
115 g/4 oz plain white flour
2 tsp baking powder
55 g/2 oz unblanched hazelnuts, roughly chopped
40 g/1½ oz goji berries
40 g/1½ oz dried banana chips

1. Preheat the oven to 180°C/350°F/Gas Mark 4. Grease a 900-g/2-lb loaf tin and line the base and two long sides with baking paper.

2. Cream the butter and sugar together in a large bowl. Beat in the eggs, one at a time, then the bananas.

3. Put the wholemeal flour, white flour and baking powder into a bowl and mix well. Add to the banana mixture and beat until smooth. Add the hazelnuts and goji berries and stir well.

4. Spoon the mixture into the prepared tin, smooth the top, then sprinkle with the banana chips. Bake in the preheated oven for 50–60 minutes, or until well risen, slightly cracked on top and a skewer inserted into the centre comes out clean.

5. Leave to cool in the tin for 5 minutes, then loosen the edges with a round-bladed knife and turn out onto a wire rack. Leave to cool completely, then peel away the paper and serve.

HINT

This bread can be stored in an airtight container for up to three days.

PISTACHIO NUTS

Green-tinted pistachio nuts are rich in plant sterols and soluble fibres,
which can lower 'bad' cholesterol and may protect against cancers.

MAJOR NUTRIENTS PER 30 G/1 OZ PISTACHIO NUTS

167 kcal	13.5g	8.5g	3g	6g	0.4 mg	0.5 mg	100 mcg	32 mg	1.2 mg	36 mg	308 mg	0.7 mg
CALORIES	TOTAL FAT	CARBS	FIBRE	PROTEIN	VITAMIN B3	VITAMIN B6	BETA-CAROTENE	CALCIUM	IRON	MAGNESIUM	POTASSIUM	ZINC

Pistachio nuts have become widely available in recent years and make a welcome addition to a healthy diet. They are rich in beta-sitosterols, which can help lower 'bad' blood cholesterol and may protect against cancer. Pistachio nuts are also a good source of fibre and soluble fibre, which offer benefits for the blood cholesterol profile, and may help prevent certain cancers and symptoms of digestive problems, such as constipation and irritable bowel syndrome. The nuts also contain a range of minerals and B vitamins, and are a good source of protein, being lower in fat than other types of nuts.

- High in sterols, which lower blood cholesterol and may protect against cancer.
- Rich in potassium to lower blood pressure and eliminate fluid.
- High in fibre and soluble fibre to aid the digestive system and improve blood cholesterol profile.
- Help control blood sugar levels and may be of help to diabetics and people who are insulin resistant.

DID YOU KNOW?

Pistachio nuts are one of the few nuts to contain carotenes, which cause their distinctive green-coloured flesh.

PRACTICAL TIPS

A dish of unshelled pistachio nuts makes a healthy pre-dinner snack. They are easy to shell before eating and you can eat the brown skin on the nuts, which adds extra fibre and nutrients. Add pistachio nuts to grain salads, breakfast cereals and stuffings.

PISTACHIO ICE CREAM

With no dairy and no processed sugar, this is a healthy treat. Coconut milk and almond milk are sweetened with dates, and pistachios and almond extract add extra flavour.

SERVES 6 • PREP TIME: 10 MINS • COOK TIME: NONE

PER SERVING:

195 kcal	7.5g	1.8g	31.6g	25.9g	4g	3.5g	0.1g
CALORIES	FAT	SAT FAT	CARBS	SUGAR	FIBRE	PROTEIN	SALT

INGREDIENTS

75 g/2¾ oz unsalted pistachio nuts, shelled
350 ml/12 fl oz coconut milk
350 ml/12 fl oz almond milk
8–10 Medjool dates, stoned
1 tsp vanilla extract
½ tsp almond extract

1. Put the nuts and about 125 ml/4 fl oz of the coconut milk into a food processor and process to a smooth paste.

2. Put the remaining coconut milk, the almond milk, dates, vanilla extract and almond extract into a blender. Whizz on high speed for 3–5 minutes, until puréed. Add the pistachio paste and process until well combined.

3. Transfer the mixture to the chilled container of an electric ice-cream maker and freeze according to the manufacturer's instructions. The ice cream can be served immediately, or you can transfer it to a freezer-proof container and freeze overnight for a more solid consistency.

PEANUTS

Rich in antioxidants and vitamin E, peanuts can improve blood cholesterol levels
and help prevent strokes, heart disease, cancers and cognitive decline.

MAJOR NUTRIENTS PER 30 G/1 OZ SHELLED PEANUTS

170 kcal	14.7g	4.8g	2.5g	7.7g	3.6 mg	2.5 mg	28 mg	72 mcg	1.4 mg	50 mg	212 mg	1 mg
CALORIES	TOTAL FAT	CARBS	FIBRE	PROTEIN	VITAMIN B3	VITAMIN E	CALCIUM	FOLATE	IRON	MAGNESIUM	POTASSIUM	ZINC

Research has found that peanuts rival the antioxidant content
of blackberries and strawberries. They are rich in antioxidant polyphenols,
including coumaric acid, to help thin the blood, and resveratrol, which
can protect against hardened arteries. They have high vitamin E content,
an antioxidant linked with heart and arterial health, brain power and
protection from strokes, heart attacks and cancer. Peanuts contain mostly
monounsaturated fat, which has a better effect on blood cholesterol
levels than polyunsaturates. They are a good source of the amino acids
tryptophan, which helps boost mood and encourages proper sleep
patterns, and l-tyrosine, which is linked with brain power.

- Rich in antioxidants, which protect against heart disease.
- High in amino acids to boost mood and brain function.
- Contain phytosterols, which may help prevent colon cancer.
- Rich in monounsaturated fats, which are linked with protection
  against heart disease.

DID YOU KNOW?

*Peanuts, also known as
groundnuts, are not in fact true
nuts but members of the legume
family, like peas or beans.*

PRACTICAL TIPS

Ideally, buy peanuts in their shells, or at least in their skins – they will keep
for longer. Fresh peanuts should smell fresh, not musty. Buy unsalted
peanuts and store them in the refrigerator – their high oil content means
that they don't last long in warm conditions. Make your own peanut butter by
blending with a little groundnut oil until it has a good spreading consistency.

CHICKEN & PEANUT CURRY

This rich-tasting curry will rival any takeaway curry for flavour. It is packed
with protein and antioxidants, so it will do you nothing but good.

SERVES 4 • PREP TIME: 15 MINS • COOK TIME: 20 MINS

PER SERVING:

						37.1g	2.1g
568 kcal	41.3g	21.7g	16g	8.5g	2.2g	37.1g	2.1g
CALORIES	FAT	SAT FAT	CARBS	SUGAR	FIBRE	PROTEIN	SALT

INGREDIENTS

75 g/2¾ oz roasted, unsalted peanuts
4 skinless and boneless chicken breast fillets about
140 g/5 oz each
1 tbsp vegetable oil
1 shallot, diced
2–4 tbsp Thai red curry paste
400 ml/14 fl oz canned coconut milk
1 tbsp Thai fish sauce
1 tbsp soft light brown sugar
juice of 1 lime
30 g/1 oz chopped fresh coriander leaves
chopped fresh coriander, to garnish (optional)

1. Put the peanuts into a food processor and process for 2–3 minutes until smooth.

2. Line a large steamer basket with baking paper and place the chicken fillets on the paper. Place the steamer over boiling water, cover and steam for 10–12 minutes until the chicken is tender and cooked through. Cut into the middle to check that the meat is no longer pink. Any juices that run out should be clear and piping hot with visible steam rising.

3. Meanwhile, heat the oil in a large frying pan and add the shallot. Cook, stirring frequently, for 5 minutes, or until soft. Add the curry paste and cook, stirring, for a further minute.

4. Open the can of coconut milk and scoop off the thick cream that has risen to the top. Add the cream to the pan and cook, stirring, until it begins to bubble. Add the remaining coconut milk along with the peanut butter, Thai fish sauce and sugar. Bring to the boil, then reduce the heat to low. Simmer for 5 minutes, or until the sauce thickens.

5. Stir in the lime juice and coriander. Serve the chicken fillets topped with a generous amount of the sauce and garnished with chopped coriander, if using.

BRAZIL NUTS

One of the richest food sources of the antioxidant, anti-cancer mineral selenium, Brazil nuts are also a good source of calcium and magnesium for healthy bones.

MAJOR NUTRIENTS PER 30 G/1 OZ BRAZIL NUTS

197 kcal	19.9g	3.7g	2.3g	4.3g	1.7 mcg	48 mg	113 mg	198 mg	575 mcg	1.2 mg
CALORIES	TOTAL FAT	CARBS	FIBRE	PROTEIN	VITAMIN E	CALCIUM	MAGNESIUM	POTASSIUM	SELENIUM	ZINC

Brazil nuts have a very high total fat content. Much of this is monounsaturated, but there is also a reasonable amount of polyunsaturates and a high content of omega-6 linoleic acid, one of the essential fats. When cooked at high temperatures, these fats oxidize and are no longer healthy, so Brazil nuts are best eaten raw. The nut is extraordinary in its extremely high content of the mineral selenium and, on average, just one to two nuts can provide a whole day's recommended intake. Selenium helps protect us from the diseases of ageing. The nuts are also a good source of magnesium and calcium.

- Extremely rich in selenium, a mineral often lacking in modern diets.
- Antioxidant, anti-ageing and anti-cancer.
- High magnesium content protects heart and bones.
- A good source of vitamin E for healthy skin and healing.

DID YOU KNOW?

Brazil nuts are not actually nuts, but seeds that are enclosed in a hard fruit the size of a coconut. The trees grow wild in the Amazon rainforests of Brazil and are rarely cultivated successfully.

PRACTICAL TIPS

Keep unshelled nuts in a cool, dry, dark place for up to six months. The shells of Brazil nuts are tough to crack so purchase a good quality nutcracker. Shelled nuts should be stored in the refrigerator and consumed within a few weeks because their high fat content means they go rancid quickly. They are best eaten raw as a handy snack or added to your breakfast muesli.

BERRY & BRAZIL NUT SMOOTHIE

Frozen berries are a healthy and handy storecupboard staple. Blitz with
protein-boosting cashew and Brazil nuts for a delicious shake.

SERVES 4 • PREP TIME: 10–15 MINS • COOK TIME: NONE

PER SERVING:	213 kcal	12.8g	2.4g	23.2g	11.6g	3.5g	4.7g	0.2g
	CALORIES	FAT	SAT FAT	CARBS	SUGAR	FIBRE	PROTEIN	SALT

INGREDIENTS
250 g/9 oz frozen mixed sliced
strawberries and blueberries
40 g/1½ oz Brazil nuts
40 g/1½ oz cashew nut pieces
30 g/1 oz porridge oats
450 ml/15 fl oz almond milk
2 tbsp maple syrup

1. Place the frozen berries, Brazil nuts and cashew nuts in a
blender. Sprinkle over the oats, then pour in half the almond
milk. Blend until smooth.

2. Add the remaining milk and maple syrup, and blend again
until smooth. Pour into four glasses and serve immediately with
spoons. As the drink stands, the blueberries will almost set the
liquid, but as soon as you stir it, it will turn to liquid again.

COCONUT

Coconut is an extremely dense energy source. It boosts the metabolism and satisfies hunger, helping to maintain youthful weight levels, energy and vitality.

MAJOR NUTRIENTS PER 100 G/3½ OZ DESICCATED COCONUT, UNSWEETENED

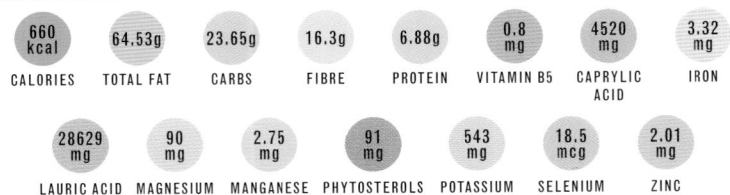

660 kcal	64.53g	23.65g	16.3g	6.88g	0.8 mg	4520 mg	3.32 mg
CALORIES	TOTAL FAT	CARBS	FIBRE	PROTEIN	VITAMIN B5	CAPRYLIC ACID	IRON

28629 mg	90 mg	2.75 mg	91 mg	543 mg	18.5 mcg	2.01 mg
LAURIC ACID	MAGNESIUM	MANGANESE	PHYTOSTEROLS	POTASSIUM	SELENIUM	ZINC

Like nuts, coconut often gets a bad press, as it is high in fat. However, this is plant fat rather than animal fat, and as such it is easy for us to burn off as energy and digest. Cultures that include coconut regularly in their diets consistently show lower incidences of obesity, high cholesterol, heart disease and diabetes. As this suggests, the anti-ageing benefits of this food are vast. It has been shown to prevent tumours, regulate cholesterol, normalize blood sugar levels and combat the ageing effects of stress by nourishing tired adrenal glands.

- Good levels of phytosterols, zinc and selenium help combat ageing elements in the environment.
- Contains lauric acid, also found in human breast milk, which protects against viruses and bacterial infections.
- Caprylic acid kills off fungal infections that can upset digestion and lower immune protection.

DID YOU KNOW?

Coconut is a native plant of the tropical Pacific, but also features in Indian writings as far back as 2,000 years ago, causing much debate as to its true origins.

PRACTICAL TIPS

The flesh that comes from inside the coconut may be eaten in its desiccated (dried) form or as milk, when the flesh has been mashed, steeped and cooked. Dried coconut is best enjoyed unsweetened and, as a snack, will satisfy a sweet craving.

COCONUT, CACAO & HAZELNUT TRUFFLES

These power-packed little balls are just bursting with a nutritious
mix of vital minerals, vitamins, protein and raw ingredients.

MAKES 20 PIECES • PREP TIME: 25 MINS • COOK TIME: NONE

PER TRUFFLE:	46 kcal	3.5g	1g	3.2g	2.1g	0.9g	1.3g	TRACE
	CALORIES	FAT	SAT FAT	CARBS	SUGAR	FIBRE	PROTEIN	SALT

INGREDIENTS

85 g/3 oz unblanched hazelnuts
55 g/2 oz cacao nibs
6 dried 'soft' figs, roughly chopped
30 g/1 oz desiccated coconut
1 tbsp maple syrup
finely grated rind and juice of ½ small orange
1 tbsp cacao nibs, for coating
2 tbsp desiccated coconut, for coating

1. Add the hazelnuts and the 55 g/2 oz cacao nibs to a food processor and process until very finely chopped.

2. Add the figs, the 30 g/1 oz coconut, maple syrup and orange rind and juice to the processor, and process until finely chopped and the mixture has come together in a ball.

3. Scoop the mixture out of the food processor, then cut into 20 even-sized pieces. Roll into small balls in your hands.

4. Finely chop the extra cacao nibs, then mix with the extra coconut on a sheet of non-stick baking paper or a plate. Roll the truffles, one at a time, in the cacao and coconut mixture, then arrange in a small plastic container. Store in the refrigerator for up to three days.

HINT

*Although desiccated coconut has quite a long shelf life, it is best
stored in an airtight container in the refrigerator.*

PINE NUTS

A source of omega-3 fats for a variety of health benefits, pine nuts are also rich in vitamin E, zinc and cholesterol-lowering plant sterols.

MAJOR NUTRIENTS PER 15 G/½ OZ PINE NUTS

101 kcal	10g	2g	0.6g	2g	1.4 mcg	0.8 mg	38 mg	90 mg	1 mg
CALORIES	TOTAL FAT	CARBS	FIBRE	PROTEIN	VITAMIN E	IRON	MAGNESIUM	POTASSIUM	ZINC

Pine nuts come from several species of pine tree. All have similar nutritional benefits, although the longer Asian types contain more oil. They are rich in polyunsaturated omega-6 fats, but also contain some of the less widely available omega-3 fats that are important for heart health as well as brain power. Pine nuts are very rich in vitamin E and zinc, two antioxidants that help the heart, boost the immune system and increase fertility. They also contain sterols and stanols, compounds that help lower blood cholesterol.

- High in omega-6 fats and contain omega-3s.
- Contain plant sterols for lowering cholesterol and promoting a healthy immune system.
- Rich in zinc and vitamin E.
- Good source of a range of minerals and fibre.

PRACTICAL TIPS

Pine nuts have a rich yet delicate flavour with a hint of resin. They tend to go rancid quickly, so buy in small quantities, store in the refrigerator, and use within a few weeks. Pine nuts go well with spinach, strong cheeses, sultanas and oily fish. You can make a basil pesto with fresh basil, pine nuts, Parmesan and olive oil. Lightly dry-fry the nuts to toast, but do not overcook as they can burn easily and oxidize. Pine nuts are best eaten raw.

DID YOU KNOW?

Research shows that pine nuts have been used for food since the Paleolithic period, which ended around 40,000 years ago.

SPICED COD WITH HARISSA & PINE NUT CRUST

This dish takes minutes to prepare and makes a delicious, easy and nutritious midweek meal. The spicy, crunchy topping contrasts beautifully with the soft fish flakes.

SERVES 2 • PREP TIME: 10 MINS • COOK TIME: 15 MINS

PER SERVING:

334 kcal	15.1g	1.4g	10.2g	3.7g	3.1g	39.6g	1.2g
CALORIES	FAT	SAT FAT	CARBS	SUGAR	FIBRE	PROTEIN	SALT

INGREDIENTS
30 g/1 oz pine nuts
15 g/½ oz fresh or dried white breadcrumbs
grated zest of 1 unwaxed lemon
2 tbsp roughly chopped fresh coriander
pinch of sea salt
1 tsp olive oil
200 g/7 oz cherry tomatoes on the vine
2 cod fillets, about 200 g/7 oz each
2 tsp rose harissa

1. Preheat the oven to 200°C/400°F/Gas Mark 6. Crush the pine nuts in a pestle and mortar. Tip them into a bowl, add the breadcrumbs, lemon zest, coriander, salt and oil and mix well.

2. Put the cherry tomatoes on a large baking tray and add the cod fillets skin side down, arranging everything in a single layer. Spread a teaspoon of rose harissa over each cod fillet, then top with the breadcrumb mixture, pressing down gently.

3. Bake in the top of the preheated oven for 15 minutes, or until the topping is crisp and golden and the fish flakes easily when pressed with a knife. Serve the cod hot with the tomatoes.

CHIA SEEDS

Mild-tasting chia seeds have become one of the most popular ingredients in superfood recipes in the past few years and even a small portion provides several health benefits.

MAJOR NUTRIENTS PER 15G/1 TBSP DRY WEIGHT CHIA SEEDS

73 kcal	4.6g	6.3g	5.2g	2.5g	1.3 mg	95 mg	1.2 mg	50 mg	0.7 mg
CALORIES	TOTAL FAT	CARBS	FIBRE	PROTEIN	VITAMIN B3	CALCIUM	IRON	MAGNESIUM	ZINC

Chia seeds are a really excellent source of omega-3 fats – just 1 tbsp contains around 2.6g which is comparable with the amount found in 25g walnuts or 250g salmon. They are also a very good source of fibre, a quarter of which is the soluble type that can help improve health in several ways. For example, it can improve the blood cholesterol profile, reducing total cholesterol and increasing beneficial HDL cholesterol, and helps to regulate insulin levels in the blood. Chia seeds are a useful tool for weight control as their high fibre level and ability to absorb liquid helps prolong a feeling of fullness and prevent hunger. The seeds are one of our best plant sources of calcium as well as being a good source of iron, and they contain a range of other important minerals and antioxidants.

- Rich in omega-3 fats which make up over half of their total fat content.
- Good plant source of calcium and iron.
- Can improve blood cholesterol profile.
- Helps regulate insulin levels in the blood.
- Useful to prevent hunger and as a weight loss tool.

DID YOU KNOW?

The first known use of chia seeds as a food was in the Mayan civilization of central America around 3,000 years ago, where the seeds were thought to be an aid to strength and stamina. The chia plant is related to sage, with pretty, long purple flowering spikes.

PRACTICAL TIPS

The seeds can be eaten either whole or finely ground. Try adding ground seeds to your porridge or yogurt, salads or smoothies, but first soak them, usually in a ratio of one part dry seeds to three parts liquid. You can stir whole seeds directly into your recipe, where they will absorb its liquid and produce a good set. Chia seeds can take from 15 minutes up to an hour or two (depending on the age of the seeds) to form a gelatinous mix with their soaking liquid. You can even make healthy jam by adding seeds to pureed berries!

CHIA SEED & BANANA ICE LOLLIES

Chia seeds are combined with bananas, honey and yogurt, to create
these sensational full-of-goodness ice lollies.

SERVES 6 • PREP TIME: 20 MINS, PLUS FREEZING • COOK TIME: NONE

PER SERVING:

84 kcal	**1.2g**	**0.5g**	**18.5g**	**10.6g**	**2.3g**	**1.9g**	**0.0g**
CALORIES	FAT	SAT FAT	CARBS	SUGAR	FIBRE	PROTEIN	SALT

INGREDIENTS

3 large ripe bananas
3 tbsp Greek-style natural yogurt
2 tsp clear honey
2 tsp chia seeds

YOU WILL ALSO NEED

6 x 50-ml/2-fl oz ice lolly moulds
6 ice lolly sticks

1. Blend the bananas, Greek yogurt and honey in a blender or food processor until you have a thick, smooth consistency. Stir in the chia seeds. Transfer the mixture to a jug and pour the mixture evenly into the six ice lolly moulds.

2. Place a lolly stick in the centre of each mould. Place in the freezer and freeze for 6 hours before serving.

3. To unmould the lollies, dip the frozen moulds in warm water for a few seconds and gently release the lollies while holding the sticks.

PUMPKIN SEEDS

Rich in zinc, pumpkin seeds help boost the immune system and fertility. They also contain sterols linked with protection against hormone-based cancers.

MAJOR NUTRIENTS PER 15 G/½ OZ PUMPKIN SEEDS

81 kcal	6.9g	2.7g	0.6g	3.7g	0.3 mg	2.2 mg	80 mg	121 mg	1.1 mg
CALORIES	TOTAL FAT	CARBS	FIBRE	PROTEIN	VITAMIN B3	IRON	MAGNESIUM	POTASSIUM	ZINC

Pumpkin seeds are a nutritious snack and, even in small servings, they provide a significant amount of minerals, especially zinc and iron. Zinc is an antioxidant mineral, which boosts the immune system and, for men, improves fertility and protects against prostate enlargement and cancer. Iron is important for healthy blood cells and energy levels. High iron and zinc content make pumpkin seeds a particularly significant food for vegetarians. The seeds contain sterols, which can help remove 'bad' cholesterol from the body as well as helping to inhibit the development of breast, colon and prostate cancer cells. In addition, pumpkin seeds contain some omega-3 fats, vitamin E, folate and magnesium that can help maintain heart health.

- Rich in zinc for fertility, immune boosting and cancer protection.
- Rich in iron for healthy blood and to fight fatigue.
- Can help improve blood cholesterol profile.
- Good source of heart-healthy and anti-inflammatory nutrients.

DID YOU KNOW?

If you grow or buy pumpkins and squashes, don't discard the seeds – make your own roasted pumpkin seeds. Wash and dry the seeds and toss in a little groundnut or light olive oil. Spread on a baking sheet and lightly roast on a low heat for 20 minutes.

PRACTICAL TIPS

Pumpkin seeds are not edible when raw and those for sale are almost always roasted. Chew the seeds well to ensure maximum absorption of nutrients. Add to salads and muesli, or sprinkle on breakfast cereal or yogurt. The seeds can be ground and added to vegetable, nut and bean burgers to provide extra nutrients.

GREEK-STYLE YOGURT WITH ORANGE ZEST & SEEDS

Toasting the seeds in this recipe enhances their flavour, so they contrast wonderfully with the smooth, creamy yogurt.

SERVES 2 • PREP TIME: 5 MINS • COOK TIME: 3 MINS

PER SERVING:

172 kcal	10.6g	4.3g	8.1g	4.3g	3.3g	12g	TRACE
CALORIES	FAT	SAT FAT	CARBS	SUGAR	FIBRE	PROTEIN	SALT

INGREDIENTS

2 tsp linseeds
2 tsp pumpkin seeds
2 tsp chia seeds
200 g/7 oz Greek-style natural yogurt
grated zest of 1 small orange
1 tsp orange juice

1. Place a small frying pan over a medium heat. When it is hot, tip in the seeds. Toast, stirring constantly with a wooden spoon, until they start to turn brown and release a nutty aroma. Tip them onto a plate and leave to cool.

2. Spoon the yogurt into two glass pots or serving bowls, then scatter the seeds on top, followed by the orange zest. Sprinkle over the orange juice and serve immediately.

SESAME SEEDS

The lignan fibres in sesame seeds help lower 'bad' cholesterol, and the seeds may also have an anti-inflammatory action, reducing the pain of arthritis.

MAJOR NUTRIENTS PER 15 G/½ OZ SESAME SEEDS

85 kcal	7.2g	3.9g	2.5g	2.5g	0.8 mg	14 mcg	20 mg	1.2 mg	52 mg	61 mg	1.5 mg
CALORIES	TOTAL FAT	CARBS	FIBRE	PROTEIN	VITAMIN B3	FOLATE	CALCIUM	IRON	MAGNESIUM	POTASSIUM	ZINC

Sesame seeds contain two special types of fibre – sesamin and sesamolin – which are members of the lignans group. They can lower 'bad' cholesterol and help prevent high blood pressure which helps to protect against cardiovascular disease. Sesamin is a powerful antioxidant in its own right and has been shown to protect the liver from damage. Plant sterols contained in the seeds also have a cholesterol-lowering action. The seeds are particularly rich in copper, which may be of use to arthritis sufferers because it is thought to have an anti-inflammatory action, reducing pain and swelling. Sesame seeds also contain the minerals iron, zinc, calcium and potassium in varying quantities.

- Good source of plant fibres and sterols to help lower cholesterol.
- Source of the antioxidant lignan sesamin.
- High in iron and zinc.
- Contain large amounts of calcium, useful for non-dairy eaters.

DID YOU KNOW?

Sesame seeds can be found in a range of colours that include pale cream, brown, red and black; the darker the colour, the stronger the flavour tends to be.

PRACTICAL TIPS

Store in a cool, dry, dark place in an airtight tin. Sesame seeds can be eaten raw or lightly toasted in a low oven, but do not overcook – this destroys some healthy fats. Sprinkle the seeds on vegetables such as broccoli or spinach before serving, or add to grain salads. Sesame seed oil is good for stir-fries, while tahini, a sesame seed paste, can be added to hummus and other dips.

STEAK & SESAME STIR-FRY

Vibrant green sprouting broccoli and juicy beef are the stars of this hearty vitamin- and mineral-rich stir-fry, and the sesame oil introduces a nutty depth and richness.

SERVES 2 • PREP TIME: 15 MINS, PLUS MARINATING • COOK TIME: 10 MINS

PER SERVING:

366 kcal	24.5g	4.8g	10.5g	2.2g	4.1g	28.6g	1.4g
CALORIES	FAT	SAT FAT	CARBS	SUGAR	FIBRE	PROTEIN	SALT

INGREDIENTS

1 tbsp soy sauce
1 tbsp sesame oil
200 g/7 oz sirloin beef steak, cut into strips
2 tsp sesame seeds
1 tbsp groundnut oil
1 large garlic clove, thinly sliced
250 g/9 oz sprouting broccoli
3 tbsp water

1. Mix the soy sauce and sesame oil in a large bowl, add the steak and toss. Cover and leave to marinate for 10 minutes.

2. Toast the sesame seeds in a large dry wok over a high heat until they are just beginning to brown, then tip them into the bowl with the steak and set aside.

3. Remove the wok from the heat and wipe it clean with kitchen paper. Return to the heat and pour in the oil. Remove the steak from the marinade and quickly cook, turning occasionally, until brown all over and cooked to your liking. Transfer to a plate and set aside.

4. If the pan is dry, add a splash more oil, then add the garlic and fry for 1 minute. Add the sprouting broccoli, steak marinade and water, stir and cook for 1 minute, until the broccoli is bright green and just beginning to soften.

5. Return the steak to the wok and stir well. Divide the stir-fry between two plates and serve immediately.

HINT

If you're on a reduced-salt diet, use low-sodium soy sauce, as regular soy sauce is very salty.

SUNFLOWER SEEDS

Rich in a range of minerals and vitamin E, sunflower seeds also offer
protection from inflammation and cardiovascular disease.

MAJOR NUTRIENTS PER 15 G/½ OZ SUNFLOWER SEEDS

86 kcal	7.4g	1.6g	3.4g	0.7 mg	5mg	34 mcg	17 mg	1 mg	53 mg	103 mg	9 mcg	0.8 mg
CALORIES	TOTAL FAT	FIBRE	PROTEIN	VITAMIN B3	VITAMIN E	FOLATE	CALCIUM	IRON	MAGNESIUM	POTASSIUM	SELENIUM	ZINC

Sunflower seeds, usually sold shelled, are one of the world's major sources of vegetable oil and are rich in polyunsaturated fats. The seeds are also very rich in vitamin E, and can help protect from inflammatory conditions, such as asthma and rheumatoid arthritis. Vitamin E is also an antioxidant, neutralizing the free radicals that can damage the body cells and speed up the ageing process. It is also linked with a lower risk of cardiovascular disease and with protection from colon cancer. Sunflower seeds are rich in plant sterols, which have a cholesterol-lowering effect, and various minerals including iron, magnesium and selenium.

- Rich in the omega-6 linoleic acid, which is an essential fat.
- Very high in antioxidant vitamin E, which has a range of health benefits.
- High in plant sterols for cholesterol-lowering effect.
- Nutrient and mineral rich.

DID YOU KNOW?

Native to Central and South America, sunflower seeds have been eaten in North America for around 5,000 years, but are now grown all across the world for their high oil content.

PRACTICAL TIPS

The high polyunsaturated content of sunflower seeds means that they spoil quickly and can go rancid if kept in warm conditions. Shelled nuts and seeds can be frozen and thawed at room temperature. The seeds make a good addition to salads, muesli and porridge, or can be eaten as a snack.

COURGETTE SPAGHETTI

Courgettes are cut into thin strips, which are then lightly cooked and tossed with pesto. Toasted sunflower seeds add crunch and some vital vitamin E too.

SERVES 2 • PREP TIME: 30 MINS • COOK TIME: 25–27 MINS

PER SERVING:

 464 kcal CALORIES
 37.8g FAT
 9.7g SAT FAT
 19.9g CARBS
 10.9g SUGAR
 6g FIBRE
 16.7g PROTEIN
1.5g SALT

INGREDIENTS

150 g/5½ oz cherry tomatoes
4 garlic cloves, sliced
1 tbsp olive oil
50 g/1¾ oz sunflower seeds
2 large courgettes
2 tbsp fresh pesto
70 g/2½ oz feta cheese, crumbled
salt and pepper (optional)
30 g/1 oz fresh basil, roughly chopped, to garnish

1. Preheat the oven to 200°C/400°F/Gas Mark 6. Cut half of the cherry tomatoes in half horizontally and leave the remainder whole. Place all the tomatoes and garlic in a small roasting tin and drizzle over the oil. Shake well to coat and place in the preheated oven for 20 minutes.

2. Meanwhile, place a dry frying pan over a medium heat. Add the sunflower seeds and fry for 3–4 minutes, or until the seeds are just toasted. Set aside.

3. Lay a box grater on its side and grate the length of the courgette into long strands. Try not to be firm – a loose grip makes this easier.

4. Bring a saucepan of water to the boil and add the courgette strips. Cook for 1–2 minutes before draining thoroughly in a colander, gently squeezing any excess water away with the back of a spoon. Return the spaghetti to the pan and stir through the pesto. Season with salt and pepper, if using.

5. Stir two thirds of the roasted tomato mixture, half the sunflower seeds and half the cheese into the spaghetti and divide the mixture between two plates. Top with the remaining tomatoes, sunflower seeds and cheese. Garnish with the basil and a sprinkling of pepper, if using. Serve immediately.

LINSEEDS

Golden linseeds are one of nature's true superfoods. Soaking them bulks up the therapeutic fibres and helps you access their age-defying nutrients.

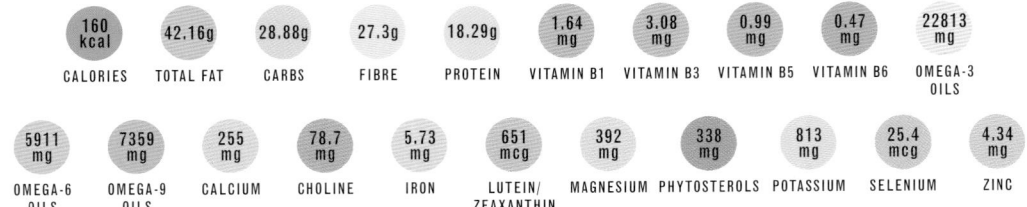

160 kcal	42.16g	28.88g	27.3g	18.29g	1.64 mg	3.08 mg	0.99 mg	0.47 mg	22813 mg
CALORIES	TOTAL FAT	CARBS	FIBRE	PROTEIN	VITAMIN B1	VITAMIN B3	VITAMIN B5	VITAMIN B6	OMEGA-3 OILS

5911 mg	7359 mg	255 mg	78.7 mg	5.73 mg	651 mcg	392 mg	338 mg	813 mg	25.4 mcg	4.34 mg
OMEGA-6 OILS	OMEGA-9 OILS	CALCIUM	CHOLINE	IRON	LUTEIN/ ZEAXANTHIN	MAGNESIUM	PHYTOSTEROLS	POTASSIUM	SELENIUM	ZINC

Linseeds, soaked to open up the tough outer covering and puff out the fibre inside, is an age-old way of keeping the bowels regular. They combat constipation and diarrhoea and ensure the rapid removal of ageing toxins before they can cause the body any damage. The seed also binds to excess cholesterol in the body, which is then removed in support of heart and brain health. Regular consumption exercises the bowel muscle, improving digestive function in the long term. The soaking process also produces a mucilage that coats the gut wall, offering protection and healing, helping reduce food intolerances, and supporting the immune system to prevent premature ageing.

- High levels of omega-3 oils prevent ageing inflammation and keep the skin supple and smooth.
- Contain lignans, which are a type of phytoestrogen. Phytoestrogen regulates hormones to assist both male and female sexual health and potency.
- High in antioxidants due to the lignans, phytosterols, lutein and selenium, which give this food an excellent anti-ageing profile.

DID YOU KNOW?

The Holy Roman Emperor Charlemagne (AD 742–814) popularized the use of flax as food, in medicine and cloth by making it the law to grow and eat it.

PRACTICAL TIPS

Linseeds are either brown or golden, but the golden variety is easier to absorb. Soak for 10 minutes in warm water, then add a dessertspoon – including the water – to porridge, cereal, a smoothie or yogurt in order to take on their therapeutic benefits.

WALNUT & LINSEED CRACKERS

These crisp, nutty crackers contain milled linseeds as well as whole. Milling releases the nutrients – whole, unsoaked, unmilled linseeds simply provide fibre.

MAKES 20 • PREP TIME: 20 MINS, PLUS CHILLING • COOK TIME: 20–22 MINS

PER CRACKER:

68 kcal CALORIES	4g FAT	1.4g SAT FAT	7.6g CARBS	3.1g SUGAR	1.4g FIBRE	1.5g PROTEIN	0.1g SALT

INGREDIENTS

70 g/2½ oz milled linseeds
150 g/5½ oz wholemeal flour
½ tsp salt
2 tbsp soft light brown sugar
85 g/3 oz unsalted butter, at room temperature
145 g/5¼ oz raisins
125 ml/4 fl oz milk
60 g/2¼ oz walnuts, chopped
35 g/1¼ oz whole linseeds
10 g/¼ oz wholemeal flour, for dusting

1. Preheat the oven to 180°C/350°F/Gas Mark 4. Put the milled linseeds, flour, salt and sugar into a large mixing bowl and mix with a hand-held electric mixer. Add the butter and mix on medium speed for 2–3 minutes until coarse crumbs form.

2. Add the raisins, milk, walnuts and whole linseeds and mix until the dough comes together. Turn out the dough onto a piece of clingfilm and shape it into a round. Wrap and chill in the refrigerator for about 10 minutes.

3. Lay a large sheet of baking paper on a work surface. Turn out the dough onto the paper and flatten it into a large rectangle with the palms of your hands. Sprinkle with a little flour, then roll out as thinly as possible (to the thickness of the chopped nuts).

4. Using a sharp knife, score the dough into 5-cm/2-inch squares. Slide the paper onto a large baking sheet and bake in the preheated oven for 20–22 minutes, until the crackers are lightly browned. Remove from the oven, break apart and leave to cool before serving.

HINT

These crackers make a great healthy snack that can be packed up and eaten on-the-go.

TAHINI

Tahini is a delicious way to eat large quantities of the highly beneficial and therapeutic sesame seed.

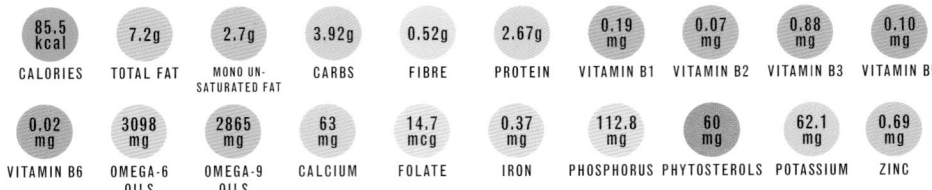

85.5 kcal	7.2g	2.7g	3.92g	0.52g	2.67g	0.19 mg	0.07 mg	0.88 mg	0.10 mg
CALORIES	TOTAL FAT	MONO UN-SATURATED FAT	CARBS	FIBRE	PROTEIN	VITAMIN B1	VITAMIN B2	VITAMIN B3	VITAMIN B5
0.02 mg	3098 mg	2865 mg	63 mg	14.7 mcg	0.37 mg	112.8 mg	60 mg	62.1 mg	0.69 mg
VITAMIN B6	OMEGA-6 OILS	OMEGA-9 OILS	CALCIUM	FOLATE	IRON	PHOSPHORUS	PHYTOSTEROLS	POTASSIUM	ZINC

Sesame seeds contain two exclusive compounds: sesamin and sesamolin, types of lignans that offer potent heart protection by regulating cholesterol and high blood pressure. They also revitalize vitamin E in your body to increase antioxidant activity, particularly in the skin, where it helps heal scars and blemishes, and prevent age spots. Sesame seeds have the highest levels of phytosterols of any food, vital for immune function and lowering cholesterol. Sesame seeds also contain the fat-soluble nutrients beta-carotene and vitamin E, which are important antioxidants.

- High levels of vitamin B3, phosphorus and calcium keep bones strong and young.
- Sesamin helps prevent damage in the liver from the toxins it is exposed to, supporting the organ's elimination of harmful, ageing waste.
- High levels of omega-6 oils and zinc promote a healthy hormone balance in women, which encourages positive mood and good bone health.

DID YOU KNOW?

Tahini is mentioned as an ingredient in hummus in a thirteenth-century Arabic cookbook, and has become popular in recent years as an alternative to butter.

PRACTICAL TIPS

Tahini, or sesame seed paste, makes a versatile addition to the kitchen cupboard. It may be mixed with olive oil to make a dressing, used as a spread or to make hummus, or added to falafel, as is traditional in the Middle East. The darker version is preferable as the seeds don't have the nutritious outer hull removed, but it can be a little rich for some tastes.

BANANA FLATBREAD BITES WITH TAHINI & DATE SYRUP

Sometimes the best things are the simplest. Assembled in minutes, this speedy snack is perfect for combating the 4 p.m. energy slump.

SERVES 4 • PREP TIME: 15–20 MINS • COOK TIME: 5–6 MINS

PER SERVING:	354 kcal	11.3g	2.5g	60g	25.4g	4.1g	9.4g	0.5g
	CALORIES	FAT	SAT FAT	CARBS	SUGAR	FIBRE	PROTEIN	SALT

INGREDIENTS
4 x 20-cm/8-inch pieces wholemeal tortillas
4 tbsp tahini
3 tbsp date syrup
4 bananas, peeled

1. Preheat a dry frying pan, then add the tortillas, one by one, and warm for 30 seconds on each side.

2. Arrange the tortillas on a chopping board, thinly spread each one with tahini, then drizzle with the date syrup. Add a whole banana to each tortilla, just a little off centre, then roll up tightly.

3. Cut each tortilla into thick slices, secure the bites with a cocktail stick and arrange on a plate. Serve warm.

HERBS, SPICES,
FLAVOURINGS & OILS

MINT

Popular as a garden herb, mint is a remedy to calm and relax the stomach,
and can relieve travel sickness and the congestion of colds.

MAJOR NUTRIENTS PER 15 G/½ OZ MINT

7 kcal	TRACE	1.2g	1g	0.5g	30 mg	16 mcg	1.8 mg	9 mg	69 mg
CALORIES	TOTAL FAT	CARBS	FIBRE	PROTEIN	CALCIUM	FOLATE	IRON	MAGNESIUM	POTASSIUM

For thousands of years, mint has been used for its flavour as well as its
medicinal purposes. The three main types of mint commonly used are
peppermint, spearmint and apple mint. The menthol oils that they contain,
particularly peppermint, are a natural remedy for indigestion, which is
why mint tea is traditionally consumed after a rich meal. Menthol can also
clear head and chest congestion during colds and flu, and for people who
suffer from allergic rhinitis. The oils are antibacterial and may help prevent
Helicobacter pylori, which causes stomach ulcers, and food poisoning
bugs salmonella and E.coli, from multiplying.

- Relieves indigestion and calms the stomach.
- Relieves nasal and chest congestion.
- Contains antibacterial properties.

DID YOU KNOW?

*If you put a few stalks of freshly
picked mint in a jar of water,
within a few days they will grow
roots, which can be planted indoors
for a year-round supply.*

PRACTICAL TIPS

Mint is best enjoyed fresh as the dried leaves lose much of their potency.
A simple way to enjoy fresh mint is to chop it finely and mix with plain
yogurt to serve with lamb or aubergine. Make an easy mint sauce by
combining fresh chopped mint with balsamic vinegar. You can also steep
a handful of fresh leaves in boiling water for 5 minutes to make mint tea –
strain before drinking.

ORZO WITH MINT & FRESH TOMATOES

Orzo pasta, which resembles fat grains of rice, pairs up with baby spinach, mint and cherry tomatoes for a palate-pleasing, digestion-calming and fresh-tasting meat-free side.

SERVES 4 • PREP TIME: 20 MINS • COOK TIME: 20 MINS

PER SERVING:	443 kcal	11.4g	7.1g	70.9g	5.1g	5g	14g	0.1g
	CALORIES	FAT	SAT FAT	CARBS	SUGAR	FIBRE	PROTEIN	SALT

INGREDIENTS

350 g/12 oz orzo
125 g/4½ oz crème fraîche
150 g/5½ oz baby spinach
30 g/1 oz fresh mint, roughly chopped
300 g/10½ oz cherry tomatoes, roughly chopped
salt and pepper (optional)
1 tbsp roughly chopped fresh mint, to garnish

1. Bring a large saucepan of water to the boil and drop the orzo into the water. Stir vigorously to prevent the little grains sticking and then stir occasionally during cooking. Simmer for 8 minutes, or until the orzo is tender but still firm to the bite. Scoop out 100 ml/3½ fl oz of the cooking water and set aside.

2. Drain the orzo and return to the pan with the reserved cooking water. Place over a very gentle heat and add the crème fraîche and spinach. Stir until the spinach has wilted and the crème fraîche has coated the grains. Remove from the heat.

3. Stir in the mint and cherry tomatoes. Season with salt and pepper, if using. Garnish with mint and serve immediately.

ROSEMARY

Pungent fresh rosemary has strong medicinal benefits, can fight the symptoms of colds and flu and help prevent diseases of ageing.

MAJOR NUTRIENTS PER 15 G/½ OZ ROSEMARY

20 kcal	0.9g	3.1g	2g	0.5g	48 mg	16 mcg	1 mg	14 mg	100 mg
CALORIES	TOTAL FAT	CARBS	FIBRE	PROTEIN	CALCIUM	FOLATE	IRON	MAGNESIUM	POTASSIUM

Traditionally, rosemary has been used as a mental stimulant, memory booster, general tonic and to aid circulation. An infusion of rosemary tea has long been recommended by herbalists to treat colds, flu and rheumatism. Like several other herbs, rosemary has been shown to fight bacteria that can cause throat infections such as E.coli and staphylococcus, so an infusion of rosemary makes a good gargle. In addition, recent research has found that rosemary is one of the leading herbs for its antioxidant activity, helping to reduce the risk of diseases and ageing effects.

- Strong antioxidant activity.
- Memory and brain booster.
- Contains antibacterial properties.
- Used as a general tonic and may lift depression.

DID YOU KNOW?

In tests, rosemary extract (rather than fresh or dried leaves) has been found to act as a detoxifier for the liver, to help boost skin condition, and to block oestrogens in the body in a similar way to anti-breast cancer drugs.

PRACTICAL TIPS

Rosemary dries well and retains some of its antioxidant effects. Hang sprigs up to dry in a warm kitchen, then remove the leaves and store in an airtight container. Fresh rosemary leaves can be chopped and mixed with thyme, sage and oregano and added to Mediterranean casseroles or omelette fillings. Use fresh sprigs with garlic to season roast chicken, lamb and pork. When making bread, add chopped fresh leaves to the mix.

ROSEMARY, SEA SALT & SESAME POPCORN

Forget about fat- and additive-laden potato crisps – popcorn can be cooked in a fraction of the oil for a healthier alternative.

SERVES 4 • PREP TIME: 10–15 MINS • COOK TIME: 6–8 MINS

PER SERVING:

79 kcal	25.2g	3.2g	30g	1.6g	6.6g	6.4g	1.5g
CALORIES	FAT	SAT FAT	CARBS	SUGAR	FIBRE	PROTEIN	SALT

INGREDIENTS

40 g/1½ oz sesame seeds
2 tbsp olive oil
2 fresh rosemary sprigs, torn into large pieces
200 g/7 oz popping corn
1 tsp sea salt
2 tbsp balsamic vinegar, or to taste

1. Add the sesame seeds to a large frying pan with 1 teaspoon of the oil, cover and cook over a medium heat for 2–3 minutes, shaking the pan from time to time, until the seeds are toasted golden brown and beginning to pop. Scoop out of the pan into a bowl and wipe out the pan with a piece of kitchen paper.

2. Add the remaining oil and the rosemary to the pan and heat gently, shaking the pan to release the rosemary's oil. Add the corn, cover with the lid and cook over a medium heat for 3–4 minutes, shaking the pan, until all the popcorn has popped. Remove from the heat and sprinkle with the toasted sesame seeds and season with the salt and vinegar, then tip into a serving bowl, discarding the rosemary just before eating.

BASIL

The highly fragrant, bright green leaves of basil are mildly sedative and
pain relieving, and can help beat indigestion.

MAJOR NUTRIENTS PER 15 G/½ OZ BASIL

222 kcal	1.8g	46g	3.6g	5g	0.2 mg	3 mg
CALORIES	TOTAL FAT	CARBS	FIBRE	PROTEIN	VITAMIN B1	VITAMIN B3

0.3mg	20 mg	0.8 mg	848 mcg	19.6 mcg	86 mg	1.3g
VITAMIN B6	CALCIUM	IRON	LUTEIN/ ZEAXANTHIN	SELENIUM	MAGNESIUM	ZINC

Basil is perhaps best known as the major ingredient in the Italian sauce
pesto. Yet the herb has been used for thousands of years in India and
the Mediterranean, has several health benefits, and has long been used
in traditional herbal medicine as a remedy for indigestion, nausea and
stomach ache. It is mildly sedative and an infusion of basil oil can even be
used as an insect repellent and to offer sting relief. Basil contains strongly
antioxidant flavonoid compounds. The leaves contain volatile oils that have
chemicals to fight food-poisoning bacteria. The chemical eugenol, also
present, is an anti-inflammatory similar to aspirin that can help relieve the
pain of arthritis and may ease irritable bowel syndrome.

- Traditionally used in remedies for indigestion, nausea and
  stomach ache.
- Acts as an insect repellent and has antibacterial action.
- Anti-inflammatory.
- High in lutein and zeaxanthin for eye health.

DID YOU KNOW?

*The chemical estragole, found
in basil, has been linked with
cancer in animals, but there is
no risk to humans even if huge
amounts are eaten.*

PRACTICAL TIPS

Basil is best added at the end of cooking to preserve its flavour, aroma and
oils. Basil leaves, if large, should be torn rather than cut with a knife. To
make a quick pesto, crush basil with pine nuts, olive oil, salt and pepper
and use to dress pasta. Sprinkle basil over a tomato and mozzarella salad.

BASIL & RAW GARLIC HUMMUS

Stomach-soothing basil makes an interesting addition to this garlicky hummus
and is a worthy replacement for the more usual cumin seeds.

SERVES 4 • PREP TIME: 15–20 MINS • COOK TIME: NONE

PER SERVING:

 152 kcal CALORIES 7.3g FAT 1g SAT FAT 15g CARBS 3.4g SUGAR 5.3g FIBRE 6.4g PROTEIN TRACE SALT

INGREDIENTS

400 g/14 oz canned chickpeas,
drained and rinsed
3 tbsp tahini
30 g/1 oz fresh basil, roughly chopped
pinch of paprika
2 garlic cloves
finely grated zest and juice of 1 lemon
4-5 tbsp cold water
salt and pepper (optional)
30 g/1 oz fresh basil sprigs, to garnish

1. Place the chickpeas, tahini, basil, paprika, garlic and lemon zest and juice in a food processor. Process to a coarse paste.

2. With the food processor still running, slowly add the cold water until a smooth, thick paste forms, adding a little more if needed. Season with salt and pepper, if using.

3. Garnish with basil and serve immediately or place in a covered container and keep in the refrigerator. This hummus will keep in the refrigerator for up to three days.

THYME

This herb may be tiny but, with an antioxidant action in the top ten of all herbs, it packs a huge health punch.

MAJOR NUTRIENTS PER 15 G/½ OZ THYME

15 kcal	0.2g	3.6g	2.1g	0.8g	24 mg	428 mcg	61 mg	2.6 mg	91 mg	0.3 mg
CALORIES	TOTAL FAT	CARBS	FIBRE	PROTEIN	VITAMIN C	BETA-CAROTENE	CALCIUM	IRON	POTASSIUM	ZINC

The evergreen leaves of thyme have a powerful, aromatic flavour and strong antioxidant action because of the volatile oils and plant compounds they contain. The most important of these is thymol. Research on this oil has found it can boost the effects of healthy omega-3 fats on the body, for example the omega-3 DHA found in fish oils, which has been shown to be important for healthy brain function. The oils in thyme are strongly antibacterial and can protect against food poisoning bugs such as E.coli, bacillus and staphylococcus. Lastly they are rich in flavonoids, which protect us against the diseases of ageing, and they are a good source of vitamin C and iron.

- Boosts omega-3 fats' actions in the body.
- May boost brain power.
- Strongly antiseptic and antibiotic.
- Rich in flavonoid antioxidants, vitamin C and iron.

DID YOU KNOW?

Thyme oil has been used since the Middle Ages for its antiseptic properties, and is often recommended by herbalists today as a treatment for bronchitis or a mouthwash.

PRACTICAL TIPS

Fresh stalks can be tied with bay leaves and parsley to make a simple bouquet garni for fish soups and stews. Add chopped fresh thyme leaves, mint and parsley to an omelette for wonderful flavour and aroma. Stuff a roasting chicken with plenty of thyme or lemon thyme. If necessary, the easiest way to remove leaves from stalks is with a fork.

ROAST FIGS WITH HONEY & THYME

You don't need to do much with fresh figs, but roasting them brings out their flavour beautifully. You can use Greek-style natural yogurt instead of labneh.

SERVES 4 • PREP TIME: 10 MINS • COOK TIME: 20 MINS

PER SERVING:

220 kcal	4.8g	2.8g	46.1g	42.9g	3g	2.4g	0.2g
CALORIES	FAT	SAT FAT	CARBS	SUGAR	FIBRE	PROTEIN	SALT

INGREDIENTS

8 figs
10 fresh thyme sprigs, broken into pieces
125 ml/4 fl oz clear honey
100 g/3½ oz labneh, to serve

1. Preheat the oven to 180°C/350°F/Gas Mark 4. Using a very sharp knife, cut a deep X-shape through each fig, stopping just before the base, and stuff it with two pieces of thyme.

2. Line a small roasting tin with crumpled baking paper, allowing it to come up the sides. Put the figs on the paper, drizzle a tablespoon of honey onto each one, then scatter over the remaining thyme.

3. Roast the figs for 20 minutes. Serve hot with the syrup in the baking paper and a generous spoonful of labneh, if using.

CORIANDER LEAF

The leaves of coriander are antibacterial and anti-inflammatory, and can significantly improve the blood cholesterol profile.

MAJOR NUTRIENTS PER 15 G/½ OZ CORIANDER LEAF

3 kcal	TRACE	0.5g	0.4g	0.3g	590 mcg	10 mg	9 mcg	0.3 mg	130 mcg	78 mg
CALORIES	TOTAL FAT	CARBS	FIBRE	PROTEIN	BETA-CAROTENE	CALCIUM	FOLATE	IRON	LUTEIN/ ZEAXANTHIN	POTASSIUM

Coriander leaf has a reputation for being high on the list of the healing herbs. Research has shown that when coriander leaf was added to the diet of diabetic mice, it helped stimulate their secretion of insulin and lowered their blood sugar. The leaves contain the compound dodecenal, which tests show is twice as effective at killing salmonella bacteria as some antibiotics. In addition, eight other antibiotic compounds were isolated from the plant. Coriander leaf has also been shown to lower 'bad' cholesterol and increase 'good' cholesterol. It is a good source of several nutrients, including potassium and calcium, and contains high levels of lutein and zeaxanthin, which help protect our eyes and eyesight.

- Regulates blood sugars and therefore may help diabetics and people who are insulin-resistant.
- Anti-inflammatory and antibacterial.
- Has a positive impact on blood cholesterol levels.
- May contribute to improved eye health.

DID YOU KNOW?

Leaves of fresh coriander bear a strong resemblance to Italian flat-leaf parsley – they both belong to the same plant family, Umbelliferae.

PRACTICAL TIPS

Use fresh coriander as it loses most of its aroma and flavour when dried. The leaves are very delicate so store carefully, well wrapped, or use leaves from a growing plant. Fresh coriander should be added to cooked dishes at the last minute, as it loses aroma and flavour when cooked.

TURKEY WITH CORIANDER PESTO & SOBA NOODLES

Lean, low-fat turkey and health-promoting fresh coriander leaf combine
in a delicious and well-flavoured dish that is full of goodness.

SERVES 6 • PREP TIME: 20 MINS, PLUS MARINATING & RESTING • COOK TIME: 1 HOUR

PER SERVING:

 771 kcal CALORIES
 25.2g FAT
 2.5g SAT FAT
 67.9g CARBS
 15.8g SUGAR
 4.4g FIBRE
 71.4g PROTEIN
4.6g SALT

INGREDIENTS

4 tbsp reduced-salt soy sauce
2 tsp chilli paste
3 garlic cloves, sliced
1 boneless, skinless turkey breast
about 1.3–1.8 kg/3–4 lb
450 g/1 lb dried soba noodles

PESTO

85 g/3 oz fresh coriander, chopped
125 ml/4 fl oz vegetable oil
50 g/1¾ oz sugar
4 garlic cloves
2 tbsp finely chopped fresh ginger
2 tsp chilli paste
juice of 1 lime
2 tsp salt

1. Combine the soy sauce, chilli paste and garlic in a bowl large enough to hold the turkey breast. Add the turkey breast and turn to coat. Cover and marinate in the refrigerator for at least 2 hours or overnight.

2. To cook the turkey, allow it to come to room temperature and preheat the grill to medium. Grill for about 30 minutes on each side, until a meat thermometer inserted into the thickest part registers 75°C/165°F.

3. Meanwhile, cook the noodles according to the packet instructions. Drain and set aside.

4. To make the pesto, combine the coriander, oil, sugar, garlic, ginger, chilli paste, lime juice and salt in a food processor and process until well combined.

5. Remove the cooked turkey from the grill, loosely cover with foil and leave to rest for at least 5 minutes before slicing.

6. Toss the noodles with the pesto and slice the turkey into 5-mm/¼-inch slices. Serve immediately with the noodles.

SAGE

Rich in beneficial compounds, sage helps to slow down the ageing process
and reduce symptoms of arthritis and asthma.

MAJOR NUTRIENTS PER 15 G/½ OZ SAGE

								1.9 mg	30 mg	75 mg
22 kcal	0.9g	4.2g	2.8g	0.7g	244 mcg	116 mg	19 mcg	1.9 mg	30 mg	75 mg
CALORIES	TOTAL FAT	CARBS	FIBRE	PROTEIN	BETA-CAROTENE	CALCIUM	FOLATE	IRON	MAGNESIUM	POTASSIUM

Native to the Mediterranean, sage has been used for thousands of years and has one of the longest histories of use of any medicinal herb. It contains a variety of volatile oils, flavonoids and phenolic acids. Sage is in the top ten of herbs that have the most powerful antioxidant effect, neutralizing the cell-damaging free radicals that are thought to be linked with the ageing process. Herbalists have long believed that sage is an outstanding memory enhancer and in trials, even small amounts significantly improved short-term recall. Sage is also antibacterial and can help reduce the number of hot flushes in menopausal women, and is recommended for people with inflammatory conditions such as rheumatoid arthritis and asthma.

- Strongly antioxidant, antibacterial and preservative.
- Boosts memory.
- Reduces hot flushes in many menopausal women.
- Has anti-inflammatory properties.

DID YOU KNOW?

For a long time herbalists have recognized sage's antioxidant qualities. The Ancient Greeks used it to help preserve meat, while tenth-century physicians in Arabia believed it helped promote immortality.

PRACTICAL TIPS

Sage is an easy-to-grow, perennial hardy shrub available throughout the year. The leaves can be dried on a rack in a warm, dry place and then stored in an airtight tin. Add sage to other chopped herbs for a herb omelette or stuffing. Sprinkle chopped fresh sage on pizzas and pasta.

BUTTERNUT WEDGES WITH SAGE & PUMPKIN SEEDS

Packed full of nutrition, butternut squash is one of the all-round good things about autumn and winter, and roasting brings out its nutty sweetness.

SERVES 3 • PREP TIME: 20 MINS • COOK TIME: 35 MINS

PER SERVING:

259 kcal	13.3g	2.1g	33.9g	6.1g	7.2g	7.8g	TRACE
CALORIES	FAT	SAT FAT	CARBS	SUGAR	FIBRE	PROTEIN	SALT

INGREDIENTS

1 large butternut squash
1 tbsp olive oil
½ tsp chilli powder
12 fresh sage leaves, finely chopped
50 g/1¾ oz pumpkin seeds
salt and pepper (optional)

1. Preheat the oven to 200°C/400°F/Gas Mark 6. Prepare the butternut squash by washing any excess dirt from the skin and slicing off the top and bottom. Using a sharp knife cut the squash into six long wedges. Scoop out any seeds and discard. Place the wedges on a baking tray. Brush with half the oil and sprinkle with the chilli powder. Roast in the preheated oven for 25 minutes.

2. Remove from the oven and brush with the remaining oil. Sprinkle over the sage and pumpkin seeds. Season with salt and pepper, if using, and return the wedges to the oven for a further 10 minutes. Serve immediately, garnished with extra pepper, if using.

PARSLEY

A traditional herbal remedy, parsley is strongly antioxidant and anticoagulant, and is also rich in vitamin C and iron.

MAJOR NUTRIENTS PER 15 G/½ OZ PARSLEY

5 kcal	TRACE	1g	0.5g	0.5g	20 mg	758 mcg	21 mg	23 mcg	0.9 mg	834 mcg	8 mg	83 mg
CALORIES	TOTAL FAT	CARBS	FIBRE	PROTEIN	VITAMIN C	BETA-CAROTENE	CALCIUM	FOLATE	IRON	LUTEIN/ ZEAXANTHIN	MAGNESIUM	POTASSIUM

Flat-leaf and curly-leaf parsley both have a similar nutritional profile. Parsley sprigs are often simply used as a garnish and then discarded, which is a pity, as the leaves are a good source of several nutrients including vitamin C and iron. Myristicin, a compound found in parsley has a strong antioxidant action, neutralizing carcinogens in the body, such as the dangerous compounds in tobacco smoke and barbecue smoke. Parsley is also an anticoagulant, and contains compounds of oils that are linked with relief from menstrual problems such as pain, fluid retention and cramps.

- A good source of vitamin C and iron, potassium and folate.
- Source of lutein and zeaxanthin to prevent macular degeneration.
- A breath purifier.
- Antioxidant and anti-cancer action.
- Contains the essential oil apiol, used as a traditional remedy for fluid retention and menstrual disorders.

DID YOU KNOW?

Parsley is a member of the Umbelliferae family of plants and is closely related to parsnip. There is a 'root parsley' that can be used in a similar way and is popular in European cooking.

PRACTICAL TIPS

Picked parsley keeps well for several days in the refrigerator in a polythene bag. Combine plenty of chopped parsley with mint, lemon juice and oil and toss with cooked bulgar wheat to make tabbouleh. Make a flat-leaf parsley pesto with ground walnuts and olive oil to serve with pasta.

PARSLEY PURIFIER JUICE

The strong flavours of the herbs and garlic are balanced by the natural sweetness of the sugar snap peas and the delicate flavour of the cucumber.

SERVES 1 • PREP TIME: 10–15 MINS • COOK TIME: NONE

PER SERVING:	152 kcal	2.5g	0.2g	22.1g	9.7g	1.9g	7g	0.3g
	CALORIES	FAT	SAT FAT	CARBS	SUGAR	FIBRE	PROTEIN	SALT

INGREDIENTS

115 g/4 oz sugar snap peas
small handful of fresh flat-leaf parsley
2 fresh rosemary sprigs
1 garlic clove
55 g/2 oz young spinach
½ cucumber
2 celery sticks, halved
1 tsp hempseed oil
chilled water, to taste
ice cubes, to serve (optional)

1. Feed the peas, parsley (reserving 1 sprig to garnish), rosemary and garlic through a juicer, followed by the spinach, cucumber and celery.

2. Pour into a glass and stir in the oil with water to taste.

3. Garnish with the reserved parsley. Serve with ice, if using.

OREGANO

Pungent oregano is the herb highest in antioxidant activity, helping to combat food-poisoning bacteria and boost the immune system.

MAJOR NUTRIENTS PER 15 G/½ OZ OREGANO

21 kcal	0.8g	4.5g	3g	0.7g	0.4 mg	288 mcg	110 mg	3 mg	19 mcg	19 mg	117 mg
CALORIES	TOTAL FAT	CARBS	FIBRE	PROTEIN	VITAMIN B3	BETA-CAROTENE	CALCIUM	IRON	FOLATE	MAGNESIUM	POTASSIUM

According to tests carried out by the United States Department of Agriculture, oregano has more antioxidant activity than any other herb. The herb has demonstrated 42 times more antioxidant activity than apples, 12 times more than oranges, and four times more than blueberries. The volatile oils in this spice include thymol and carvacrol, which have both been shown to strongly inhibit the growth of bacteria, including Staphylococcus aureus. Oregano is also a good source of several nutrients, including calcium, potassium, iron and magnesium. It is also high in dietary fibre and may help lower 'bad' cholesterol.

- One of the most powerful antioxidant plants.
- Antibacterial and may relieve the symptoms of colds.
- Rich in minerals.
- High in fibre and may aid digestion.

DID YOU KNOW?

When replacing fresh oregano with dried leaves in a recipe, reduce the amount you use by about half.

PRACTICAL TIPS

Oregano is an easy-to-grow herb and can be kept in a pot on the windowsill. The leaves dry well and can be stored in an airtight container. Replace dried oregano at least every three months as it loses its aroma and flavour over time. Oregano is one of the traditional herbs to include in mixed herbs and herbes de Provence. Oregano marries particularly well with eggs, tomatoes, lamb and chicken.

CAPER & OREGANO VINAIGRETTE

Extra virgin olive oil, which is naturally high in healthy monounsaturated fat and
low in saturated fat, is the best oil to use for this herb-packed vinaigrette.

MAKES 125 ML/4 FL OZ • PREP TIME: 15 MINS • COOK TIME: NONE

PER 125 ML/4 FL OZ:	519 kcal	54.4g	7.5g	11.6g	3.8g	1.5g	1.1g	0.6g
	CALORIES	FAT	SAT FAT	CARBS	SUGAR	FIBRE	PROTEIN	SALT

INGREDIENTS

juice of 2 lemons
1 tbsp finely chopped capers
2 tbsp finely chopped fresh oregano
2 garlic cloves, crushed
4 tbsp extra virgin olive oil
pinch of soft brown sugar
salt and pepper (optional)

1. Simply squeeze the lemon juice into a small jug and stir in the capers, oregano, garlic, oil and brown sugar. Whisk well and season with salt and pepper, if using.

2. Serve immediately or place in a covered container and keep in the refrigerator for up to 1 month. This vinaigrette goes well with any salad or drizzled over mozzarella cheese.

CHILLIES

Fiery chillies pack a nutritional and flavourful punch and research shows that they are one of the healthiest spices available.

MAJOR NUTRIENTS PER 30 G/1 OZ CHILLI

12 kcal	TRACE	2.6g	0.4g	0.5g	0.4 mg	43 mg	160 mcg	0.4g	0.3 mg	213 mcg	97 mg
CALORIES	TOTAL FAT	CARBS	FIBRE	PROTEIN	VITAMIN B3	VITAMIN C	BETA-CAROTENE	FOLATE	IRON	LUTEIN/ZEAXANTHIN	POTASSIUM

The heat that chillies add to a dish comes from a compound called capsaicin, which is known to relieve the pain and inflammation associated with arthritis. Capsaicin also appears to block production of cancerous cells in prostate cancer, and to act as an anticoagulant to help protect against blood clots, which can cause heart attacks or strokes. Red chillies also contain high levels of carotenes. Chilli consumption helps reduce the amount of insulin required to lower blood sugar after a meal and thus could be of help to diabetics and people with insulin resistance. Chillies may also increase the metabolic rate slightly, which could help with weight loss.

- Contain capsaicin, which can relieve pain and inflammation associated with arthritis.
- Strongly antioxidant to help beat the effects of ageing diseases.
- Help lower 'bad' cholesterol and reduce risk of blood clots.
- Rich in vitamin C and carotenes to boost the immune system.

DID YOU KNOW?

Chillies are said to improve psoriasis and shingles when topically applied in a cream.

PRACTICAL TIPS

There are hundreds of types of chillies in various shapes, colours and degrees of heat. Don't rub your eyes when preparing chillies – you can wear thin disposable gloves when handling. Dried peppers and chilli powders should be kept in a dark, airtight jar.

TABBOULEH-STUFFED JALAPEÑOS

Jalapeño chillies are small in size but are loaded with flavour and nutrition. These little chillies derive their heat from a natural compound called capsicum.

SERVES 4 • PREP TIME: 22 MINS • COOK TIME: 10–12 MINS

PER SERVING:	331 kcal	18.4g	2.5g	40.3g	9.5g	15.5g	8.6g	0.5g
	CALORIES	FAT	SAT FAT	CARBS	SUGAR	FIBRE	PROTEIN	SALT

INGREDIENTS

75 g/2½ oz quinoa
100 g/3½ oz fresh parsley, chopped
100 g/3½ oz fresh mint, chopped
100 g/3½ oz fresh coriander, chopped
1 preserved lemon, chopped
1 tbsp walnuts, chopped
seeds from 1 pomegranate
24 jalapeño chillies, halved and deseeded
2 avocados, peeled, stoned and sliced
juice of 1 lemon
salt and pepper (optional)

1. Cook the quinoa according to the packet instructions. Drain and refresh under cold water, then drain again and place in a large bowl.

2. Add the parsley, mint, coriander, preserved lemon, walnuts and pomegranate seeds and mix thoroughly. Season to taste with salt and pepper, if using.

3. Spoon the tabbouleh into the chillies. Top each one with a couple of slices of avocado, then squeeze over the lemon juice to serve.

HINT
If you really like to turn up the heat, don't deseed the chillies, as the seeds are where most of the heat resides.

GINGER

The plant compounds in fresh ginger have a powerful cancer-destroying action, are anti-inflammatory, and can calm nausea and aid digestion.

MAJOR NUTRIENTS PER 15 G/½ OZ GINGER

19 kcal	0.3g	3.8g	0.7g	0.5g	0.4 mg	0.6 mg	10 mg	73 mg
CALORIES	TOTAL FAT	CARBS	FIBRE	PROTEIN	VITAMIN B1	IRON	MAGNESIUM	POTASSIUM

For thousands of years, ginger has been considered a healthy food and recent research has borne this out. The main active compounds are terpenes and gingerols, which have anti-cancer properties and have been shown to destroy colon, ovarian and rectal cancer cells. Gingerols also have a powerful anti-inflammatory action and ginger has been shown to improve pain and swelling in up to 75 per cent of people with arthritis – it also improves mobility. It may also ease migraine tension. Ginger has long been used as a remedy for nausea and to aid digestion, relaxing the intestines and helping to eliminate flatulence.

- As effective as prescription medicine in beating motion sickness without drowsiness.
- Proven relief from the pain of arthritis.
- Digestive aid.

DID YOU KNOW?

Ginger is a type of root known as a rhizome and grows underground in tropical climates.

PRACTICAL TIPS

Try to buy fresh ginger rather than other forms of ginger, such as ground or preserved, because this contains the highest levels of beneficial compounds. Fresh ginger can be stored in the refrigerator and peeled, chopped or grated as required. Make a soothing ginger drink by combining freshly grated ginger, lemon juice, honey and hot water.

GINGER, GARLIC & SOY DRESSING

Widely regarded for its anti-inflammatory properties, fresh ginger adds a
lovely aromatic, spicy flavour to this Chinese-style dressing.

MAKES 150 ML/5 FL OZ • PREP TIME: 10 MINS • COOK TIME: NONE

PER 150 ML/5 FL OZ:	400 kcal	40.5g	5.6g	8.6g	4.8g	0.4g	2.4g	4.5g
	CALORIES	FAT	SAT FAT	CARBS	SUGAR	FIBRE	PROTEIN	SALT

INGREDIENTS

6-cm/2¼-inch piece fresh ginger, grated,
juices reserved
2 garlic cloves, crushed
2 tbsp rice vinegar
2 tbsp dark soy sauce
1 tsp caster sugar
3 tbsp olive oil
2 tbsp water

1. Place the ginger in a screwtop jar with any juices. Add the garlic, vinegar, soy sauce, sugar, oil and water. Shake well until thoroughly combined.

2. Chill and store in the refrigerator until ready to use. This dressing improves with age so prepare the day before it is needed, if possible. It goes well with a Chinese noodle salad or chopped Chinese leaves.

CINNAMON

Sweet cinnamon is an anti-inflammatory, antibacterial spice that can help relieve bloating and heartburn, and offers protection against strokes.

MAJOR NUTRIENTS PER 15 G/½ OZ CINNAMON

18 kcal	TRACE	5.5g	3.7g	TRACE	84 mg	2.6 mg	287 mcg	34 mg
CALORIES	TOTAL FAT	CARBS	FIBRE	PROTEIN	CALCIUM	IRON	FOLATE	POTASSIUM

Cinnamon contains several volatile oils and compounds, including cinnamaldehyde, cinnamyl acetate and cinnamyl alcohol, which have a variety of beneficial actions. Cinnamaldehyde has an anticoagulant action, meaning that it can help to protect against strokes, and is also anti-inflammatory, relieving the symptoms of arthritis and asthma. The spice is a digestive aid, relieving bloating and flatulence, and it can reduce the discomfort of heartburn. Cinnamon has antibacterial action that can block the yeast fungus, candida, and bugs that can cause food poisoning. In one study, cinnamon was shown to lower blood sugars and blood cholesterol.

- Helps to beat indigestion and bloating.
- Antibacterial and antifungal.
- Helps prevent blood clots.
- May lower 'bad' cholesterol and blood sugars.

DID YOU KNOW?

True cinnamon is the inner bark of an evergreen tree of the Laurel family native to Sri Lanka, and cassia is another variety native to China. Both are widely available, but it is not always possible to know which one you are buying.

PRACTICAL TIPS

Whole bark cinnamon sticks will retain their flavour and aroma for a year, while the ground dried spice will last for about six months. You can tell if ground cinnamon is still fresh by sniffing it – if it has lost its aroma then you need to discard it. Whole or part sticks can be added to apple or pear fruit compotes and mulled wine. Ground cinnamon is a good addition to a curry.

APPLE & CINNAMON CRISPS

Crisp and crunchy, without the fat, salt and strong flavours of potato crisps,
these make a much healthier alternative for all the family.

SERVES 4 • PREP TIME: 20–25 MINS • COOK TIME: 1 HOUR 30 MINS–2 HOURS

PER SERVING: 72 kcal	0.2g	TRACE	19.1g	14.2g	3.4g	0.3g	0.7g
CALORIES	FAT	SAT FAT	CARBS	SUGAR	FIBRE	PROTEIN	SALT

INGREDIENTS
1 litre/1¾ pints water
1 tbsp sea salt
3 dessert apples, such as Braeburn or Gala
pinch of ground cinnamon

1. Preheat the oven to 110°C/225°F/Gas Mark ¼. Put the water and salt into a large mixing bowl and stir until the salt has dissolved.

2. Very thinly slice the apples, one at a time, with a sharp knife or mandolin, leaving the skin on and the core still in place, but removing any pips. Add each apple slice to the water. Turn to coat in the salt water, which will help prevent discoloration.

3. Drain the apple slices in a colander, then lightly pat dry with a clean tea towel. Arrange in a thin layer on a large roasting rack. Place in the preheated oven so that the heat can circulate under the slices as well as over the tops.

4. Bake for 1½–2 hours, until the apple slices are dry and crisp. Loosen with a palette knife and transfer to a large plate or chopping board, then sprinkle with cinnamon. Leave to cool completely, then serve.

HINT
To store, pack into a plastic container, seal and keep in the refrigerator for up to two days.

BLACK PEPPER

Black pepper kick-starts our enjoyment of the foods it garnishes, and stimulates revitalizing beta-endorphins, with a positive effect on mood and immunity.

MAJOR NUTRIENTS PER 15 G/½ OZ BLACK PEPPERCORNS

38 kcal	0.48g	9.72g	3.98g	1.64g	3.15 mg	85.2 mg	TRACE	29.1 mg	0.84 mg	189 mg
CALORIES	TOTAL FAT	CARBS	FIBRE	PROTEIN	VITAMIN C	CALCIUM	CHROMIUM	MAGNESIUM	MANGANESE	POTASSIUM

The spicy taste of black pepper comes from piperine, which has recently been understood to assist in the absorption of nutrients, such as energizing B-vitamins and the immune-supporting antioxidants selenium and beta-carotene. It also supplements the anti-inflammatory and anti-cancer actions of the chemical curcumin, found in turmeric, by making it easier to absorb. The essential oils in black pepper are made of terpenes, such as limonene, also found in citrus fruits, and pinene, found in pine trees, that help prevent cancer, regulate heartbeat and are antibacterial.

- Source of the mineral chromium, which promotes blood sugar balance and good weight management.
- Strengthens membranes to help prevent varicose veins and keep skin firm and young.
- Believed to have antidepressant qualities, so encouraging a youthful, positive and motivated attitude.

DID YOU KNOW?

Black peppercorns are not in the same family as sweet peppers or chilli, but the explorer Christopher Columbus assumed that this was the case when he came across them in Haiti.

PRACTICAL TIPS

Black peppercorns have more nutrients than white peppercorns. Both are prepared from unripe pepper berries, but the white peppercorns have their skins removed. Buy the whole corns and invest in a good grinder for fresh ground and best-tasting pepper. Keep in a sealed glass container in a cool, dark place.

T-BONE STEAK WITH PEPPERCORN SAUCE

It's the peppercorns that make this classic dish so mouth-watering – and they have the added advantage of being really beneficial for your health.

SERVES 4 • PREP TIME: 10 MINS • COOK TIME: 20 MINS

PER SERVING:

870 kcal	56.1g	26.4g	4.9g	1.3g	0.9g	68.8g	3.5g
CALORIES	FAT	SAT FAT	CARBS	SUGAR	FIBRE	PROTEIN	SALT

INGREDIENTS

4 T-bone steaks, each weighing 300 g/10½ oz
1 tsp salt
1 tsp pepper
2 tbsp olive oil

PEPPERCORN SAUCE

1 tbsp olive oil
1 tbsp butter
2 shallots, finely chopped
2 garlic cloves, crushed
100 ml/3½ fl oz brandy
200 ml/7 fl oz double cream
1 tbsp Dijon mustard
1 tsp salt
1 tbsp mixed cracked peppercorns

1. To make the peppercorn sauce, heat a saucepan over a medium–low heat, add the oil and butter and then cook the shallots and garlic for 5–10 minutes, or until translucent.

2. Add the brandy and flambé. Add the cream and cook until reduced by half. Then add the mustard, salt and cracked peppercorns. Set aside and keep warm.

3. Season the steaks with the salt and pepper, and rub with the oil.

4. Preheat a griddle pan over a high heat and cook the steaks for 5 minutes on each side for medium-rare, or until cooked to your liking. Cook the steaks in batches if necessary.

5. Set aside to rest for 5 minutes before serving with the peppercorn sauce.

VARIATION

This peppercorn sauce would work well with other cuts of steak, choose your favourite or ask your butcher for advice.

NUTMEG

Compounds in nutmeg are sedative, anaesthetic and antibacterial. The fruit also contains monoterpenes, which can help prevent cardiovascular disease.

MAJOR NUTRIENTS PER 15 G/½ OZ NUTMEG

12 kcal	0.8g	1g	0.5g	TRACE	4mg	4mg	8mg
CALORIES	TOTAL FAT	CARBS	FIBRE	PROTEIN	CALCIUM	MAGNESIUM	POTASSIUM

Nutmeg is the fruit of an evergreen native to Indonesia, now grown in several countries. The spice is made from the seed of this fruit. The fruit contains the compounds myristicin and elemicin, which are mildly sedative and anaesthetic. It also contains monoterpenes, which are believed to have anti-coagulant action and may help prevent cardiovascular disease. Like many other spices, nutmeg has antibacterial action and can help to protect us from food poisoning bacteria, such as E.coli. Nutmeg has also been used to treat Crohn's disease, an inflammatory condition of the bowel, and it is said that the essential oil of the fruit can help painful gums.

- Mildly sedative.
- Helps prevent blood clots and cardiovascular disease.
- Antibacterial.
- May be anti-inflammatory.

DID YOU KNOW?

Nutmeg is a hallucinogenic and is toxic in large quantities, so use it sparingly. A teaspoonful or less in a recipe will be sufficient.

PRACTICAL TIPS

Nutmeg is best used freshly grated from a whole dried fruit – ground nutmeg quickly loses its aroma and flavour. Nutmeg goes well with cooked fruits, such as apples, and with milk desserts, such as rice pudding. Nutmeg can also be used in savoury dishes, such as game casseroles, meat sauces and curries. A little nutmeg can be stirred into spinach and carrots toward the end of cooking time.

SPINACH & NUTMEG BAKED EGGS

Nutrient-rich fresh spinach adds delicious flavour and colour to this popular egg dish, lightly seasoned with ground nutmeg.

SERVES 4 • PREP TIME: 20 MINS • COOK TIME: 20–30 MINS

PER SERVING:

235 kcal	16.5g	4.2g	7.5g	1.6g	1.1g	14.2g	0.4g
CALORIES	FAT	SAT FAT	CARBS	SUGAR	FIBRE	PROTEIN	SALT

INGREDIENTS

1 tbsp olive oil, for brushing
1 tbsp olive oil, for frying
4 shallots, finely chopped
3 garlic cloves, sliced
100 g/3½ oz baby spinach
8 eggs
½ tsp ground nutmeg
salt and pepper (optional)

1. Preheat the oven to 180°C/350°F/Gas Mark 4. Lightly brush the insides of four 200-ml/7-fl oz ramekins with oil.

2. Heat the oil in a frying pan. Once hot, add the shallots and garlic and fry over a medium heat for 3–4 minutes, or until soft. Add the baby spinach and stir for 2–3 minutes, or until just wilted. Season with salt and pepper, if using.

3. Spoon the spinach mixture into the bases of the prepared ramekins and crack 2 eggs into each. Sprinkle over the nutmeg and place the ramekins in a roasting tin. Fill the roasting tin with boiling water until the water reaches halfway up the ramekins – this creates a steamy environment for the eggs so there is no chance of them drying out.

4. Carefully transfer the roasting tin to the preheated oven for 15–20 minutes. Leave the ramekins to cool slightly, then serve.

VARIATION
Serve with your favourite kind of toasted bread for a wholesome breakfast or brunch.

PAPRIKA

Paprika is dried and powdered capsicum (sweet pepper). It offers the same circulation-enhancing action as chilli, helping your skin to stay looking young.

MAJOR NUTRIENTS PER 15 G/½ OZ GROUND PAPRIKA

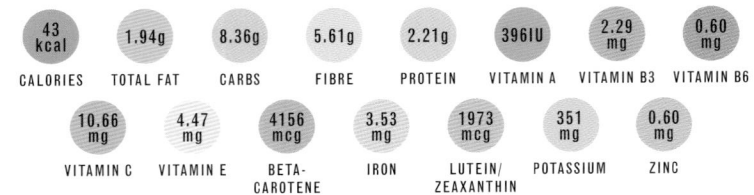

43 kcal	1.94g	8.36g	5.61g	2.21g	396IU	2.29 mg	0.60 mg
CALORIES	TOTAL FAT	CARBS	FIBRE	PROTEIN	VITAMIN A	VITAMIN B3	VITAMIN B6

10.66 mg	4.47 mg	4156 mcg	3.53 mg	1973 mcg	351 mg	0.60 mg
VITAMIN C	VITAMIN E	BETA-CAROTENE	IRON	LUTEIN/ZEAXANTHIN	POTASSIUM	ZINC

Paprika has been used traditionally to promote heart health, and has been shown to reduce 'bad' cholesterol/LDL. It is said to create heat in the body without burning or irritating, which improves circulation and ensures that invigorating oxygen and nutrients are distributed effectively around the whole body, including the heart. Like turmeric and cumin, paprika is high in salicylic acid, which forms the basis of aspirin. A single highly spiced curry can actually provide more than is contained within an aspirin tablet. This explains the anti-inflammatory actions of these spices, which help keep joints mobile and the skin clear.

- Contains more protective vitamin C than lemon juice by weight, which is retained during drying and cooking.
- Increases saliva production, so promoting good digestion and the absorption of nutrients that fight ageing.
- Helps reduce the bacterial infections that put stress on the body and age us prematurely.

DID YOU KNOW?

Paprika has been used as a colouring in cosmetics for centuries, and some zoos have been known to add it to the flamingo food to enhance their pink colour.

PRACTICAL TIPS

Store paprika away from light and only get it out of the cupboard when you need to use it, as it loses colour and flavour quickly when exposed. This also applies to the cooking process, so add it as close to the end of cooking as possible (unless you are making goulash). Don't be fooled by its mild taste in the packet: paprika increases in strength and flavour when heated.

PAPRIKA TURKEY STRIPS

Turkey has the reputation of being a bit bland and uninteresting, although it is high in nutrition. The addition of paprika to this dish really adds that vital zing!

SERVES 4 • PREP TIME: 10 MINS • COOK TIME: 7–10 MINS

PER SERVING:

 454 kcal — CALORIES

 10.5g — FAT

1.4g — SAT FAT

 54.7g — CARBS

1.4g — SUGAR

 2.1g — FIBRE

 34.7g — PROTEIN

 0.8g — SALT

INGREDIENTS

500 g/1 lb 2 oz turkey breast steaks
1 tbsp paprika
1 tsp crushed coriander seeds
½ tsp garlic salt
¼ tsp pepper
2 tbsp olive oil
1 red onion, sliced
3 tbsp chopped fresh coriander
720 g/1 lb 9½ oz cooked rice, to serve

1. Cut the turkey into long strips, about 1 cm/½ inch thick.

2. Put the paprika, coriander seeds, garlic salt and pepper into a large bowl and mix together. Stir in 1 tablespoon of the oil. Add the turkey strips and turn to coat evenly in the mixture.

3. Heat the remaining oil in a large frying pan or wok, add the onion and stir-fry for 1 minute. Add the turkey strips and stir-fry over a fairly high heat for 6–8 minutes, until cooked through.

4. Sprinkle over the fresh coriander and serve with the rice.

CARDAMOM

Like ginger, cardamom has a strong, soothing effect on the digestive tract. It helps you to digest a meal fully and receive all of its rejuvenating nutrients.

MAJOR NUTRIENTS PER 15 G/½ OZ CARDAMOM SEEDS

47 kcal	1g	10.27g	4.2g	1.614g	3.15 mg	57.45 mg	2.09 mg	34.35 mg	4.2 mg	167. 85mg
CALORIES	TOTAL FAT	CARBS	FIBRE	PROTEIN	VITAMIN C	CALCIUM	IRON	MAGNESIUM	MANGANESE	POTASSIUM

The strong aromas of herbs and spices are testament to the medical strength of their volatile oils. Many cultures have long relied on their inclusion in the diet to ward away illness and promote longevity. Generally speaking, they achieve this by helping circulation, cleansing and digestion and contributing to blood sugar balance. Cardamom has a particularly cleansing effect on the digestive tract, and is traditionally used to treat stomach gripes and pains, dysentery and the constipation that can lead to toxic build-up, and high cholesterol and hormonal problems.

- The oils help clear mucus from the throat, nose and chest that can lead to ageing inflammation.
- Helps clear out the kidneys to reduce fluid retention and maintain a clear, youthful-looking complexion.
- Chewing cardamom helps prevent the infections of teeth and gums that are linked to heart disease.

DID YOU KNOW?

Cardamom has been used as an antidote for scorpion and snake bites in South Asia, where it is a common flavouring. It is also used frequently in Nordic cuisine and in Middle Eastern sweets, coffee and tea.

PRACTICAL TIPS

Cardamom pods can be added to sweet and pungent dishes, but use only a few as their strength can be overwhelming. Tea made from the crushed seeds (you can reuse ones that you have cooked with) is a traditional remedy for depression, and can be combined with cinnamon to help alleviate a sore throat or hoarseness. The oil of cardamom is recommended for massaging away muscle tension.

CARDAMOM, FENNEL & GINGER TEA

Get your day off to a great start with this fragrant and
soothing low-sugar tea, infused with spices.

MAKES 1 LITRE/1¾ PINTS • PREP TIME: 10 MINS • COOK TIME: NONE

PER 1 L/1¾ PINTS:

2 kcal CALORIES	0g FAT	0g SAT FAT	0.5g CARBS	0g SUGAR	0.1g FIBRE	0.1g PROTEIN	0g SALT

INGREDIENTS

10 green cardamom pods
1 tsp fennel seeds
8-cm/3¼-inch piece fresh ginger, sliced
1 litre/1¾ pints boiling water

1. Place the cardamom pods on a heavy chopping board and gently bruise each pod with a rolling pin.

2. Place the crushed pods in a teapot. Add the fennel seeds and fresh ginger. Pour over the boiling water and infuse the tea for 5–6 minutes, or to taste.

3. Pour the tea into mugs through a tea strainer and serve immediately.

TURMERIC

The warm spice turmeric contains healing properties as powerful as modern drugs in the fight against inflammatory diseases such as arthritis.

MAJOR NUTRIENTS PER 15 G/½ OZ TURMERIC

24 kcal	0.7g	4.4g	1.4g	0.5g	225 mcg	2.8 mg	13 mg	172 mg
CALORIES	TOTAL FAT	CARBS	FIBRE	PROTEIN	FOLATE	IRON	MAGNESIUM	POTASSIUM

Turmeric comes from the orange-fleshed root of a plant native to Indonesia and southern India. Its volatile oils and curcumin, the yellow/orange pigment, have been proved to offer protection comparable to that of modern drugs against inflammatory diseases. Curcumin is thought to be the main health-promoting compound in turmeric, and studies have shown that it is also a powerful antioxidant. Turmeric can help prevent colon cancer and inhibit the growth of certain types of cancer cells, such as breast and prostate cancers. The compound is also able to lower 'bad' cholesterol, and increase 'good' cholesterol.

- Powerful anti-inflammatory.
- Contains anti-cancer properties.
- Improves blood cholesterol profile.
- May slow progression of Alzheimer's disease and multiple sclerosis.

DID YOU KNOW?

Turmeric was traditionally called Indian saffron because of its deep yellow colour, and has been used throughout history as a textile dye as well as a spice. For this reason it is hard to remove turmeric stains from clothing.

PRACTICAL TIPS

You can usually find only ground turmeric in shops. Store it in an airtight container. Make your own curry blend with four parts turmeric, one part chilli powder, one part cumin seed and one part coriander seed. Add a little turmeric to lentils when cooking them, or to yogurt for a healthy dip. Stir-fry vegetables, such as cauliflower or green beans, in oil with turmeric added.

ROAST CAULIFLOWER, KALE & CHICKPEA BOWL

This bowl is packed with goodness and, as well as having numerous health benefits, the spices help to make it feel really nourishing.

SERVES 4 • PREP TIME: 20 MINS • COOK TIME: 40 MINS

PER SERVING:

 406 kcal CALORIES
 19.5g FAT
 4.2g SAT FAT
 41.4g CARBS
 10.7g SUGAR
 12.2g FIBRE
19.5g PROTEIN
0.9g SALT

INGREDIENTS

1 tsp turmeric
1 tsp mustard seeds
½ tsp cumin seeds
½ tsp ground ginger
½ tsp ground coriander
½ tsp ground cinnamon
1 head of cauliflower, broken into florets
400 g/14 oz canned chickpeas, drained
2 red onions, thickly sliced
2 tbsp olive oil
200 g/7 oz kale, shredded
100 g/3½ oz fresh wholemeal breadcrumbs
3 tbsp walnuts, chopped
2 tbsp flaked almonds
55 g/2 oz freshly grated Parmesan cheese

1. Preheat the oven to 200°C/400°F/Gas Mark 6.

2. Dry-fry the turmeric, mustard seeds, cumin seeds, ginger, coriander and cinnamon in a small frying pan for 2 minutes, or until the mustard seeds start to 'pop'.

3. Place the cauliflower florets, chickpeas and onion slices in a large roasting tin. Sprinkle with the spices and toss well together. Drizzle over the oil and toss again.

4. Roast in the preheated oven for 20 minutes.

5. Stir the kale into the roast vegetables, and roast for a further 10 minutes until the vegetables are tender and slightly charred.

6. Mix the breadcrumbs, walnuts, almonds and cheese together and sprinkle over the vegetables. Roast for a further 5–8 minutes until golden.

7. Divide between four bowls and serve immediately.

CLOVES

Cloves are associated with infusing the cold winter with warmth. Their warming property is the key to their ability to relieve aches and pains in the muscles and joints.

MAJOR NUTRIENTS PER 15 G/½ OZ CLOVES

									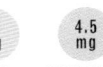	
48.5 kcal	3.04g	9.18g	5.13g	0.89g	12.12 mg	22.27 mcg	96.9 mg	13 mg	4.5 mg	165 mg
CALORIES	TOTAL FAT	CARBS	FIBRE	PROTEIN	VITAMIN C	VITAMIN K	CALCIUM	IRON	MANGANESE	POTASSIUM

Cloves contain the active compound eugenol in sufficient quantities to be effective in detoxifying the harmful and ageing pollutants that we take on from the environment. This is the substance used in dental preparations, such as mouthwashes, throat sprays and toothpastes, as it both reduces bacteria in the mouth and has a mildly anaesthetic effect on the sensitivities that cause pain. As mouth infections are associated with heart disease, this is an important anti-ageing consideration. Studies have also shown that eugenol can reduce inflammation. If you eat cloves as part of an existing healthy diet, you will be helping to combat inflammatory symptoms like joint pain, skin flare-ups and headaches, and reducing the level of 'bad' cholesterol/LDL in your body.

- The flavonoids kaempferol and rhamnetin offer youth-retaining antioxidant properties.
- Clove oil is used traditionally to treat acne and rashes, and to heal scars after burns and injuries, keeping skin looking young.

DID YOU KNOW?

Cloves are pressed into oranges at Christmas to make fragrant pomanders, and have also been used in incense.

PRACTICAL TIPS

Cloves are included in the curry spice mix garam masala and in the spiced tea chai. They are often mixed with cinnamon and cumin to provide warmth and comfort, especially in winter. Cloves can be added to hot water, honey and lemon to make a delicious drink that is also an effective remedy for colds or flu. To further spice this up, add ginger and cinnamon.

FRESH PHO WITH BEEF

Transport your taste buds across the world and enjoy the enticing fresh and clean flavours of this popular Vietnamese beef and noodle dish.

SERVES 4 • PREP TIME: 20–25 MINS • COOK TIME: 40 MINS

PER SERVING:

 411 kcal CALORIES   **3.7g** FAT   **1.3g** SAT FAT   **47.1g** CARBS   **4.4g** SUGAR   **2.5g** FIBRE **46.1g** PROTEIN **4.6g** SALT

INGREDIENTS

1.6 litres/2¾ pints beef stock
4-cm/1½-inch piece fresh ginger, sliced
1 star anise
2 cinnamon sticks
5 cloves
50 ml/1¾ fl oz Thai fish sauce
1 red chilli, finely sliced
200 g/7 oz vermicelli rice noodles
350 g/12 oz rump steak, very finely sliced
100 g/3½ oz mangetout, finely sliced
40 g/1½ oz beansprouts
30 g/1 oz fresh coriander, roughly chopped, to garnish
30 g/1 oz fresh Thai basil, roughly chopped, to garnish
1 tbsp finely sliced red chilli, to garnish

1. Pour the stock into a large saucepan. Add the ginger, star anise, cinnamon sticks, cloves, fish sauce and chilli to the pan and place over a high heat. Bring to the boil, then reduce the heat and simmer over a low heat, covered, for 30 minutes.

2. Meanwhile, place the dry noodles in a large bowl and pour boiling water over the top. Leave to stand for 3–4 minutes, or until they are completely softened. Drain, return to the bowl, cover and set aside.

3. Add the steak strips to the beef broth and poach for 2–3 minutes. Remove the ginger slices, star anise, cinnamon sticks and cloves from the broth with a slotted spoon.

4. Divide the noodles between four deep bowls. Add a handful of raw mangetout and beansprouts, then ladle over the hot broth mixture. Garnish with the coriander, Thai basil and sliced red chilli and serve immediately.

VARIATION

Sprinkle some toasted sesame seeds over the top of the soup for some extra crunch.

MACA

Maca is a herbaceous plant of the broccoli family, native to the mountains of Peru, and is commonly used there as a root vegetable.

MAJOR NUTRIENTS PER 3G DRIED MACA POWDER

12 kcal	TRACE	2.4g	0.6g	0.6g	0.4g
CALORIES	TOTAL FAT	CARBS	FIBRE	PROTEIN	IRON

The turnip-like maca root has been used as a herbal health tonic for many years in Peru. Scientific trials have found that the root may help ease anxiety and depression and may also help to improve libido and sexual function. The plant has also traditionally been used to treat fatigue, loss of energy, lack of stamina, high blood pressure, osteoarthritis and stress and also to boost the immune system. The plant contains glucosinolates and isothiocyanates, compounds known to help prevent cancers. Maca has been shown to improve prostate health, and some studies find the plant can help improve brain power and bone density too. The root is a good source of some minerals, especially iron.

- May ease anxiety and depression.
- May help beat fatigue, lack of stamina and act as a general body tonic.
- High in a range of minerals and in cancer-fighting plant chemicals.

DID YOU KNOW?

Maca is sometimes known as 'Peruvian Ginseng', and in Peru the fresh plant is often eaten baked or roasted, made into a soup or into a fermented drink maca chicha. Maca is a relative of radish and turnip and some people think it has a sweet odour similar to butterscotch.

PRACTICAL TIPS

Maca is hard to find outside Peru as a fresh vegetable so is usually bought as a supplement – in tablet or powder form. Powdered maca can be added to smoothies, juices, yogurt or soups. A typical daily dose of the dried root is up to 3g.

GRAPEFRUIT CRUSH JUICE

This fresh and cooling juice is mixed with coconut water, which is packed
with electrolytes and minerals to help counter dehydration.

SERVES 1 • PREP TIME: 10–15 MINS • COOK TIME: NONE

PER SERVING: 185 kcal CALORIES 1.2g FAT 0.1g SAT FAT 43.5g CARBS 28.7g SUGAR 3g FIBRE 4.7g PROTEIN 0.4g SALT

INGREDIENTS

150 g/5½ oz cucumber, roughly chopped
½ pink grapefruit, zest and a little pith removed,
deseeded and roughly chopped
2 kiwi fruit, peeled and roughly chopped
2 celery sticks, roughly chopped
1 tsp maca powder
4 tbsp coconut water
1 pink grapefruit segment, to garnish
crushed ice, to serve (optional)

1. Feed the cucumber, grapefruit, kiwi fruit and celery through a juicer.

2. Stir through the maca powder and coconut water until combined.

3. Pour over crushed ice, if using, garnish with a grapefruit segment and serve immediately.

GREEN TEA

The Chinese and Japanese have long understood the health attributes of green tea, and view it as an important part of their heart, energy and skin regimes.

MAJOR NUTRIENTS PER 225 ML/8 FL OZ GREEN TEA

approx* 2kcal	0g	Negligible	0g	0g	3.75g
CALORIES	TOTAL FAT	CARBS	FIBRE	PROTEIN	CATECHINS

*CAN VARY GREATLY BETWEEN VARIETIES AND STRENGTH OF BREW

The leaves of the tea plant Camellia sinensis are loaded with catechins, which have been found to have natural antioxidant, antibacterial and antiviral properties, thereby protecting against cancer and helping to lower cholesterol and regulate blood clotting. One such compound, epigallocatechin gallate (EGCG), is able to penetrate the cells and protect the crucial DNA that the body relies on to replicate cells and combat the damage caused by ageing. EGCG also prevents cancer cells forming and can help reduce the severity of allergies by blocking the body's response.

- Green tea may also act as a weight loss aid by helping to burn fat and regulate blood sugar and insulin levels.
- Contains quercetin, a bioflavonoid (plant chemical) that reduces inflammation and helps control food allergies.
- Catechins promote liver detoxification, so assisting in the removal of ageing toxins and promoting glowing skin.

DID YOU KNOW?

Green tea leaves are the dried leaves of the tea plant, while black, 'normal' tea is fermented. The fermentation process makes black tea much higher in caffeine: roughly 50 mg a cup compared to 5 mg for green tea.

PRACTICAL TIPS

Changing from black tea or coffee to green tea, which will still give you a boost, will lower your total intake of caffeine with its ageing effects. Different varieties have different strengths and flavour. Genmaicha is a particularly palatable Japanese blend, with a nutty taste from the toasted brown rice that has been added to it.

GREEN TEA FRUIT SALAD

Bursting with beneficial vitamins and antioxidants, this multi-coloured fruit salad makes a light and delicious dessert. Pistachios and pomegranate seeds add a final flourish of goodness.

SERVES 4 • PREP TIME: 25 MINS, PLUS BREWING, COOLING AND CHILLING • COOK TIME: NONE

PER SERVING:

 258 kcal CALORIES

 3.5g FAT

 0.4g SAT FAT

 59.5g CARBS

 45.3g SUGAR

 8.4g FIBRE

 4.1g PROTEIN

TRACE SALT

INGREDIENTS

2 tsp green tea
225 ml/8 fl oz boiling water
1 tbsp clear honey
½ small watermelon, cut into cubes
1 large mango, cut into cubes
1 papaya, deseeded and cut into cubes
2 pears, cut into cubes
2 kiwi fruit, cut into cubes
2 tbsp roughly chopped fresh mint
seeds of ½ pomegranate
2 tbsp roughly chopped pistachio nuts

1. Place the tea in a jug or teapot, pour over the boiling water and leave to brew for 3–4 minutes. Strain into a small bowl, stir in the honey and leave to cool.

2. Put the watermelon, mango and papaya in a large serving bowl, then add the pears, kiwi fruit and mint. Pour over the cooled green tea and gently stir everything together.

3. Cover with clingfilm and chill in the refrigerator for 1 hour. Stir gently to mix the tea through the fruit.

4. Spoon the fruit salad into four bowls. Serve immediately, sprinkled with the pomegranate seeds and pistachio nuts.

HONEY

Raw honey is one of nature's oldest known antibacterial products. It destroys harmful invaders, keeping you young both inside and out.

MAJOR NUTRIENTS PER 15 ML/1 TBSP HONEY

 45.5 kcal CALORIES   **0g** TOTAL FAT   **12.36g** CARBS   **0.03g** FIBRE   **0.04g** PROTEIN

Honey is created when the saliva of bees meets the pollen they collect from flowers, so the properties of a particular honey will reflect those of the flowers the bees have visited. In its raw state, it contains an array of antioxidants like chrysin and vitamin C to help you stay young, but these properties are destroyed when it is excessively heated or processed. Manuka honey from New Zealand is the only honey that has been tested for its ability to destroy harmful bacteria, and batches of this are given a Unique Manuka Factor (UMF), according to strength. Manuka has been shown to be twice as effective as other honeys against the E. coli and Staphylococcus bacteria, which commonly infect wounds.

- Raw honey contains propolis, which helps reduce inflammation and premature ageing.
- Good-quality honey contains probiotic beneficial bacteria lactobacilli and bifidobacteria to support youth-protecting immunity.
- When applied to the skin, it helps heal spots, burns, cuts and sores that can age your appearance.

DID YOU KNOW?

When mixed with water, honey creates antiseptic hydrogen peroxide, which can be applied directly to wounds to dry them out and keep them free from infection while they heal.

PRACTICAL TIPS

Choose good-quality honey: look out for local, raw and unprocessed varieties from farm shops. Darker kinds, like buckwheat and sage, contain the most antioxidants, and the honey produced by flower-fed bees in the summer contains more beneficial bacteria. Use in place of sugar, but sparingly, or you will set off sugar cravings.

HONEY SALMON WITH COUSCOUS

Loaded with beneficial nutrients, this light yet substantial meal
makes a great quick-and-easy mid-week meal for two.

SERVES 2 • PREP TIME: 15 MINS • COOK TIME: 15 MINS

PER SERVING:							
711 kcal	27.4g	5.7g	83g	35g	4.3g	35.2g	2.2g
CALORIES	FAT	SAT FAT	CARBS	SUGAR	FIBRE	PROTEIN	SALT

INGREDIENTS

2 salmon fillets,
about 125 g/4½ oz each
115 g/4 oz couscous
200 ml/7 fl oz vegetable stock
2 spring onions, chopped
1 tbsp vegetable oil,
for drizzling
salt and pepper (optional)
4 steamed baby courgettes, to serve

SAUCE

4 tbsp clear honey
2 tbsp Dijon mustard
2 tbsp lukewarm water
2 tsp soy sauce
1 tsp olive oil

1. To make the sauce, heat the honey, mustard, water, soy sauce and oil in a saucepan over a low heat for 5 minutes, stirring occasionally. Place the salmon fillets on a sheet of foil and season with salt and pepper, if using. Brush generously with some of the sauce. Preheat the grill to high.

2. Put the couscous in a heatproof bowl. Pour the stock over the couscous, cover and leave to stand for 10 minutes. Meanwhile, cook the salmon fillets under the preheated grill for 4 minutes, then turn them over, brush with more of the sauce and cook for a further 4 minutes, or until cooked through.

3. Drizzle the couscous with a little oil and run a fork through it. Brush the salmon with the remaining sauce and sprinkle with the chopped spring onions. Serve the salmon with the couscous and steamed baby courgettes.

VARIATION

The honey and mustard sauce could also be served with grilled or baked chicken or pork.

CHIVES

Chives belong to the allium family and provide the same protective sulphur compounds as garlic and onion. These foods work hard to keep you detoxified.

MAJOR NUTRIENTS PER 15 G/½ OZ CHIVES

30 kcal	0.73g	4.35g	2.5g	3.27g	4353 IU	58.1 mg	212.7 mcg	2612 mcg	323 mcg
CALORIES	TOTAL FAT	CARBS	FIBRE	PROTEIN	VITAMIN A	VITAMIN C	VITAMIN K	BETA-CAROTENE	LUTEIN/ ZEAXANTHIN

Chives have the same health benefits as garlic, but are slightly weaker. They contain the same potent sulphur substance sulfoquinovosyl diacylglycerol, which is also found in spinach, parsley, green tea and carrots, and which has been shown to stop the action that makes cancer cells proliferate. These foods also have antifungal and antibacterial properties, which help keep your digestive tract free from the elements affecting health and digestion, so preventing debilitating gas, bloating and constipation. Because they are antiviral, too, they reduce the viral load that threatens the body's stocks of youthful energy and vitality.

- Contain the energy-producing nutrients vitamin C, citric acid, malic acid and glutamic acid.
- Immune-supporting antioxidant power comes from vitamin C, beta-carotene, quercetin and ferulic acid.
- Aid circulation in support of heart health so that it can pump revitalizing nutrients to all parts of the body.

DID YOU KNOW?

Chives are grown in gardens to repel unwanted insects that feed off plants, and also to attract the bees that pollinate them.

PRACTICAL TIPS

Chives are easy to grow. Keep a plant handy on a kitchen windowsill so you can add them to fish, potatoes and soups. As they have a mild flavour, they can be easier to include in the diet than their cousin, garlic. They are particularly tasty with soft cheeses and herring, or other cured fish.

THREE HERB & RICOTTA OMELETTE

Vibrant green mixed garden herbs add lots of lovely natural flavour and colour to this appetizing omelette. Served with fresh bread, it's a satisfying breakfast or lunch for two.

SERVES 2 • PREP TIME: 15 MINS • COOK TIME: 8 MINS

PER SERVING:	390 kcal	32g	10g	2.8g	0.7g	0.2g	21.7g	0.6g
	CALORIES	FAT	SAT FAT	CARBS	SUGAR	FIBRE	PROTEIN	SALT

INGREDIENTS

4 large eggs
2 tbsp finely snipped fresh chives
2 tbsp finely chopped fresh basil
2 tbsp finely chopped fresh parsley
100 g/3½ oz ricotta cheese, crumbled
2 tbsp olive oil
salt and pepper (optional)

1. Crack the eggs into a small mixing bowl and lightly beat with a fork. Stir the herbs and cheese into the bowl and season with salt and pepper, if using.

2. Heat the oil in a non-stick frying pan over a high heat until hot. Pour in the egg mixture and, using a spatula, draw the outside edges (which will cook more quickly) towards the gooey centre. Allow any liquid mixture to move into the gaps. Continue with this action for about 4–5 minutes. The omelette will continue to cook once the pan is removed from the heat.

3. Cut the omelette in half and divide between two plates. Serve immediately.

COCONUT WATER

Refreshing and with a sweet taste, coconut water makes an ideal drink for rehydration at any time of day as it is isotonic, meaning it is readily utilised by the body.

MAJOR NUTRIENTS PER 225ML/8 FL OZ COCONUT WATER

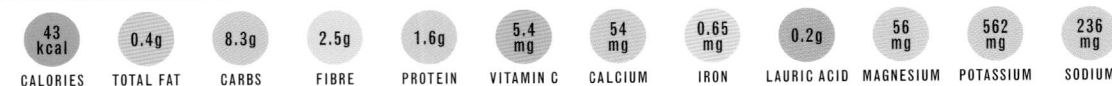

43 kcal	0.4g	8.3g	2.5g	1.6g	5.4 mg	54 mg	0.65 mg	0.2g	56 mg	562 mg	236 mg
CALORIES	TOTAL FAT	CARBS	FIBRE	PROTEIN	VITAMIN C	CALCIUM	IRON	LAURIC ACID	MAGNESIUM	POTASSIUM	SODIUM

Not to be confused with coconut milk, coconut water is the clear liquid that is extracted from the centre of the coconut when it is young and green. This liquid contains easily digested sugars, and electrolytes – the minerals calcium, magnesium, potassium and sodium which are essential to health because they govern electrical impulses and the balance of fluid in our bodies. Coconut water is a useful tool for those wanting to lose weight as it is low in calories and naturally fat and cholesterol free. It also contains some protein, vitamin C, fibre and iron, and plant chemicals called cytokinins which appear to have anti-ageing and anti-cancer properties.

- An isotonic drink ideally suited to rehydrating the body after exercise.
- Low in calories and ideal as part of a weight loss plan.
- Contains cytokinins which may help prevent the signs of ageing.
- A source of protein, vitamin C, fibre and iron.

DID YOU KNOW?

Coconut water is often called 'Mother nature's sports drink' because of its rehydrating ability and favourable electrolyte profile. Coconut water contains a small amount of lauric acid, a saturated fat that may help to reduce calorie consumption in dieters, some research has found.

PRACTICAL TIPS

While coconut water can be syphoned from young green coconuts, it is widely available to purchase in bottles and cartons. It is best drunk chilled and is an ideal addition to smoothies, frozen tropical fruit sorbets and granitas.

MELON BREEZE SOUP

Unlike winter soups, which warm your insides, this soup will cool you down – perfect for a summer starter or as part of your lunch.

SERVES 1 • PREP TIME: 10 MINS • COOK TIME: NONE

PER SERVING:	134 kcal	1.1g	0.4g	27.9g	20.6g	6.6g	4.8g	0.7g
	CALORIES	FAT	SAT FAT	CARBS	SUGAR	FIBRE	PROTEIN	SALT

INGREDIENTS

300 g/10 ½ oz green melon, peeled and deseeded
250 g/9 oz cucumber
4 tbsp chopped fresh mint, plus a sprig to garnish
200 ml/7 fl oz chilled coconut water

1. Chop the melon and cucumber and place in a blender.

2. Add the mint, pour over the coconut water and blend until smooth and creamy.

3. Serve immediately or chill in the refrigerator and stir just before serving. Garnish with a sprig of mint.

CHOCOLATE & COCOA POWDER

Not just an indulgent treat, the cocoa bean contains
flavonoids, magnesium and iron for protection from heart disease.

MAJOR NUTRIENTS PER 15 G/½ OZ COCOA POWDER

34 kcal	2g	8g	5g	3g	19mg	2mg	22mg	229mg	1mg
CALORIES	TOTAL FAT	CARBS	FIBRE	PROTEIN	CALCIUM	IRON	MAGNESIUM	POTASSIUM	ZINC

Chocolate is made from cocoa beans, which are rich in antioxidant flavonoids, fibre and minerals. The chocolate-making process also provides procyanidins, which have an anti-inflammatory action. For better or worse, chocolate contains caffeine, and a 100 g/3½ oz bar of plain chocolate has about as much as a cup of coffee. Cocoa powder is a relatively low-fat, high-fibre source of minerals and antioxidants, and for chocolate lovers watching their fat intake, a cocoa drink made with skimmed milk is a good option.

- Antioxidant content can have an anticoagulant action and protect against the oxidation of cholesterol in our bodies.
- Magnesium content protects the heart.
- Iron content can keep blood healthy and maintain energy levels.
- Contains the stimulant theobromine, which is a diuretic.

DID YOU KNOW?

Cocoa beans grow on cocoa trees, which are now mainly grown in South America and Africa. They were first imported to Europe by Christopher Columbus in the early sixteenth century.

PRACTICAL TIPS

Generally, the more cocoa solids chocolate contains, the more antioxidants and minerals it has. This means that plain chocolate with 70 per cent cocoa solids is a good source, while standard milk chocolate is not. Cocoa butter is high in total fat and saturated fat, so even plain chocolate should be consumed in moderate amounts. White chocolate is a mix of cocoa butter and milk solids and has negligible amounts of healthy nutrients.

SUPERFOOD CHOCOLATE BARK

This pretty chocolate bark is a delicious way to eat healthy nuts and berries. It comes together really quickly and makes a useful, nutritious snack.

SERVES 6 • PREP TIME: 15 MINS, PLUS COOLING • COOK TIME: 5 MINS

PER SERVING:

 227 kcal CALORIES 15.7g FAT 5.3g SAT FAT 17.7g CARBS  10.2g SUGAR 5.1g FIBRE 5.1g PROTEIN 0.0g SALT

INGREDIENTS

100 g/3½ oz plain chocolate, 70% cocoa solids, broken into pieces
85 g/3 oz mixed Brazil nuts, unblanched almonds and pistachio nuts, roughly chopped
2 tbsp dried goji berries, roughly chopped
2 tbsp dried cranberries, roughly chopped
1 tbsp chia seeds

1. Place the chocolate in a heatproof bowl set over a saucepan of gently simmering water and heat for 5 minutes until melted.

2. Line a large baking sheet with non-stick baking paper. Stir the chocolate, then pour it onto the paper and spread to a 20 x 30-cm/8 x 12-inch rectangle.

3. Sprinkle the nuts, berries and chia seeds over the top, then leave to set in a cool place or the refrigerator.

4. To serve, lift the chocolate off the paper and break into rough-shaped shards. Store in a plastic container in the refrigerator for up to three days.

CUMIN SEEDS

With its antiseptic action, cumin offers sore throat relief. It also helps the digestive system to work efficiently.

MAJOR NUTRIENTS PER 15 G/½ OZ CUMIN SEEDS

23 kcal	1g	2.6g	0.6g	1g	 56 mg	4 mg	22 mg	107 mg
CALORIES	TOTAL FAT	CARBS	FIBRE	PROTEIN	CALCIUM	IRON	MAGNESIUM	POTASSIUM

Small, brown cumin seeds are harvested from a herb belonging to the parsley family. Its flavour is warm and spicy but not too hot. The spice has been used since ancient times – the Romans used it as an appetizer and digestive. Research has shown that cumin stimulates the secretion of pancreatic enzymes necessary for efficient digestion and nutrient absorption. Currently, cumin is being investigated for its antioxidant powers and it may help to block cancer growth. The seeds are rich in iron. Cumin is an antiseptic, so an infusion of cumin seeds with honey makes an ideal drink for people with a sore throat.

- Aid digestion.
- May help prevent cancers.
- Contain antiseptic properties.
- Rich in iron for healthy blood.

DID YOU KNOW?

Cumin seeds are native to the Middle East but have been cultivated in India and China for thousands of years, and are one of the key ingredients in curry blends.

PRACTICAL TIPS

Buy whole seeds as these retain their aroma longer than ground cumin. All dried spices are best kept in airtight containers in cool, dry, dark conditions. Use opaque containers to store spices as they deteriorate rapidly in light. Add lightly ground cumin seeds to brown rice and chopped dried fruits and nuts for a delicious salad. Cumin also goes well with pulses, such as lentils and chickpeas.

FEEL-THE-HEAT
HARISSA SAUCE

Depending on the chillies used, the colour of this hot sauce will range from red to brownish-red. After several days, the covering oil will have absorbed some of the heat and can be used in salad dressings.

MAKES 175 ML/6 FL OZ • PREP TIME: 5 MINS, PLUS SOAKING AND STANDING • COOK TIME: 1–2 MINS

PER 175 ML/6 FL OZ:

1422 kcal	139.3g	17.3g	47.4g	29.3g	24.8g	11.7g	0.2g
CALORIES	FAT	SAT FAT	CARBS	SUGAR	FIBRE	PROTEIN	SALT

INGREDIENTS

12 hot dried red chillies,
such as aji, guajillo, New Mexican or pasilla, or a
combination
1 tbsp Aleppo chilli flakes
125 ml/4 fl oz olive oil,
plus extra if needed
1 tsp caraway seeds
1 tsp cumin seeds
½ tsp fennel seeds
2 red jalapeño chillies, finely chopped
salt and pepper(optional)

1. Put the dried chillies into a heatproof bowl, pour over boiling water to cover and leave to stand for 15 minutes. Drain well and pat dry. When cool enough to handle, remove the stems and finely chop the chillies.

2. Transfer to a bowl and add the chilli flakes and oil. Set aside for 1 hour.

3. Meanwhile, heat a dry frying pan over a medium–high heat. Add the caraway seeds, cumin seeds and fennel seeds and dry-fry for 1–2 minutes, or until aromatic. Tip the seeds out of the pan, then finely grind in a mortar with a pestle.

4. Transfer the soaked chilli mixture, seeds and chopped chillies to a small food processor or blender. Season with salt and pepper, if using, then purée. Adjust the seasoning, if necessary. Slowly add more oil, if necessary, to make a thick sauce and serve.

HINT

Store with a layer of olive oil poured over the surface in an airtight container in the refrigerator for up to two weeks.

WASABI

Wasabi is a strong natural antiparasitic, which helps us to enjoy omega-3-rich oily fish without the damaging consequences of a parasite infection.

MAJOR NUTRIENTS PER 5 ML/1 TSP WASABI PASTE

5.5 kcal	TRACE	1.18g	0.39g	0.24g	2.09 mg	28.4 mg
CALORIES	TOTAL FAT	CARBS	FIBRE	PROTEIN	VITAMIN C	POTASSIUM

Wasabi is a hotter, Asian version of horseradish. The hot vapours come from the isothiocyanates it contains. Its pungency is the secret weapon that can kill off a whole host of microbes, which we ingest perfectly naturally along with the various foods that we eat. As these micro-organisms can compromise our digestion, immune system and nervous system – potentially affecting all the systems of the body – to stay youthful and vibrant we need to employ continual defences from nature's clever chemical larder, such as wasabi.

- Related to broccoli, cabbage and horseradish, with the same power to help the liver eliminate ageing toxins.
- The isothiocyanates support youthful heart health, helping to reduce the risk of stroke and heart attack.
- Anti-inflammatory action boosts the youthful functioning of the joints and lungs.

DID YOU KNOW?

Wasabi and its pungent vapours are at the centre of research into the development of a sensory fire alarm for the deaf.

PRACTICAL TIPS

Dyed horseradish is sometimes served in Japanese restaurants in place of wasabi. It will contain the beneficial properties of horseradish, but also the potentially unhealthy chemicals of the green dye. Check that you are being served the real thing, and buy good-quality wasabi for use when cooking at home. Always use fresh wasabi and store it carefully as it will lose colour and pungency quickly when exposed to air.

RAINBOW SALAD WITH WASABI DRESSING

A salad doesn't need to be complicated to be good. This bright, healthy
salad is an easy and exciting way to eat more vegetables.

SERVES 4 • PREP TIME: 10–15 MINS • COOK TIME: 5 MINS

PER SERVING:	119 kcal	8.3g	0.8g	8.2g	3.7g	1.8g	3.4g	1.5g
	CALORIES	FAT	SAT FAT	CARBS	SUGAR	FIBRE	PROTEIN	SALT

INGREDIENTS

1 tbsp sunflower oil
4 tbsp sunflower seeds
2 tbsp soy sauce
*200 g/7 oz rainbow chard leaves, shredded and
cut into strips*

DRESSING

1 tsp wasabi paste
1 tbsp mirin
juice of 1 small orange
pepper (optional)

1. Heat the oil in a covered frying pan over a medium heat. Add the sunflower seeds, cover and fry for 2–3 minutes, shaking the pan so they don't stick, until you hear them begin to pop. Remove the pan from the heat, add the soy sauce, cover and leave to cool.

2. To make the dressing, put the wasabi paste, mirin and orange juice in a jam jar, season with a little pepper, if using, screw on the lid and shake well.

3. Put the chard leaves in a salad bowl. Drizzle over the dressing, then toss gently together. Sprinkle with the toasted sunflower seeds and serve.

HINT

*Any type of leaves would work well in this recipe, try adding a
mixture such as mizuna, radicchio or chicory.*

COCONUT OIL

Cooking with coconut oil is a sure way to reduce your exposure to the ageing free radicals that are produced when roasting, frying and baking.

MAJOR NUTRIENTS PER 15 ML/1 TBSP COCONUT OIL

129 kcal	15g	0g	0g	0g	270 mg	870 mg	1.125g	6.69g	2.5g
CALORIES	TOTAL FAT	CARBS	FIBRE	PROTEIN	OMEGA-6 OILS	OMEGA-9 OILS	CAPRYLIC ACID	LAURIC ACID	MYRISTIC ACID

Whenever we cook with oil, the heat causes some damage to the oil's fat molecules, which has a knock-on effect in our bodies. The free radicals produced can damage our body tissues and make us more susceptible to cancer, heart disease and osteoporosis. Of all the saturated fats, coconut oil is the least prone to damage by heat, light and oxygen, and can be heated to temperatures as high as 190°C/375°F. Because it is so stable, it keeps for a very long time. Coconut oil contains about 60 per cent medium-chain triglycerides (MCTs), plant-based oils that raise metabolism and cannot be stored as fat in our bodies. Researchers have found that in countries where breast milk is high in MCTs, the population as a whole demonstrates a better quality of ageing.

- The fats in coconut oil help feed the lining of the gut, ensuring good digestion and the elimination of ageing toxins.
- Has been shown to assist thyroid function and regulate metabolism and mood, keeping us both trim and happy.

DID YOU KNOW?

Many Pacific Island countries use coconut oil as fuel for cars, trucks, buses and generators, and also as engine lubricant.

PRACTICAL TIPS

Coconut oil, which becomes a clear liquid when heated, can be used in all kinds of cooking and doesn't retain any of the coconut flavour from the flesh. It does behave differently from other oils, however, so a little experimentation may be necessary. Choose an unprocessed variety, and avoid any that have been hydrogenated or contain preservatives.

COCONUT QUINOA BOWL

This high-protein, low-sugar quinoa granola is served on a creamy coconut-and-banana 'porridge', with lots of omega-3 fats from walnuts and pecans.

SERVES 4 • PREP TIME: 20 MINS • COOK TIME: 15 MINS

PER SERVING:

 746 kcal CALORIES

 43.1g FAT

26g SAT FAT

 84.7g CARBS

31.3g SUGAR

 11.3g FIBRE

 11.8g PROTEIN

0.1g SALT

INGREDIENTS

100 g/3½ oz coconut oil
1 tbsp honey
2 tbsp dark muscovado sugar
100 g/3½ oz quinoa flakes
150 g/5½ oz rolled oats
3 tbsp desiccated coconut
½ tsp ground cinnamon
1 tbsp dried cranberries
1 tbsp chopped pecan nuts
2 bananas, peeled and chopped
55 g/2 oz walnuts
200 ml/7 fl oz coconut milk
1 tsp ground cinnamon, to sprinkle
100 g/3½ oz raspberries
small handful of mint leaves
2 tbsp maple syrup

1. Preheat the oven to 180°C/350°F/Gas Mark 4. Put the coconut oil, honey and sugar into a saucepan over a low heat and heat, stirring, until the sugar has dissolved.

2. Remove from the heat and stir in the quinoa flakes, 55 g/2 oz of the oats, 2 tablespoons of the coconut, the cinnamon, cranberries and pecan nuts. Mix well to combine.

3. Spread the mixture over a baking sheet and bake in the preheated oven for 15 minutes, stirring halfway through the cooking time.

4. Remove from the oven, spoon into a bowl and leave to cool.

5. Meanwhile, place the bananas, the remaining oats, the walnuts and coconut milk in a food processor and process until almost smooth.

6. Pour into four bowls and add the granola. Top with the cinnamon, raspberries, mint, the remaining desiccated coconut, and a drizzle of maple syrup.

OLIVE OIL

Well known for being high in heart-protective monounsaturates, virgin olive oils also contain a range of antioxidant plant compounds and vitamin E.

MAJOR NUTRIENTS PER 15 ML/1 TBSP OLIVE OIL

130 kcal CALORIES   **15g** TOTAL FAT   **2.1g** VITAMIN E

The main type of fat in olive oil is monounsaturated, which helps prevent cholesterol being deposited on artery walls and therefore helps protect us from cardiovascular disease and strokes. In addition, early pressings of the olives (as in extra virgin olive oil, particularly 'cold pressed') produce an oil that is rich in beneficial plant compounds. These can protect against cancer and high blood pressure and lower cholesterol. The compound oleocanthal is an anti-inflammatory with similar action to ibuprofen. Finally, olive oil is a good source of vitamin E.

- Helps improve blood cholesterol profile and protect us from cardiovascular disease.
- Rich in polyphenols to protect against colon and other cancers.
- Can help prevent helicobacter pylori, which can lead to stomach ulcers.
- Antibacterial and antioxidant.

DID YOU KNOW?

Researchers in Italy have found that light destroys many of the disease-fighting compounds in olive oil. Studies showed that after a year, oils stored in clear bottles under store lighting showed at least a 30 per cent decrease in antioxidants.

PRACTICAL TIPS

Olive oil should be stored in the dark and used within one to two months. Buy olive oil from a source with a high turnover where the oil is kept in dimly lit conditions. For its full benefit, eat it cold in salad dressings or drizzled on bread or vegetables. Don't use extra virgin olive oil for cooking at high temperatures or the beneficial chemicals will be destroyed.

BEEF CARPACCIO

Loaded with essential protein, minerals and beneficial plant compounds, this traditional Italian starter would also make a good light lunch or supper, served with lots of crusty bread.

SERVES 2 • PREP TIME: 5 MINS, PLUS FREEZING AND CHILLING • COOK TIME: NONE

PER SERVING: **766 kcal** CALORIES   **70g** FAT   **11.5g** SAT FAT   **3.9g** CARBS   **1.6g** SUGAR   **1.3g** FIBRE   **32.8g** PROTEIN   **0.3g** SALT

INGREDIENTS

250 g/9 oz excellent quality beef fillet (cut from the thin end of the fillet)
100 ml/3½ fl oz extra virgin olive oil
30 g/1 oz pine nuts
100 g/3½ oz rocket
10 g/¼ oz Parmesan cheese
salt and pepper(optional)

1. Put the beef in the freezer for 1 hour before use to firm it up before slicing. Trim any fat or sinew from the beef, then cut the fillet into slices as thinly as possible.

2. Lay a slice of beef on a chopping board and, using a flat, broad knife, press against the meat, pushing down hard and pulling across the beef in a spreading motion. Repeat with all the beef slices.

3. Pour a little pool of oil into a wide dish. Place a layer of beef on the oil, lightly season with salt and pepper, if using, and pour over some more oil. Repeat until all the beef has been seasoned in this way.

4. Chill in the refrigerator for at least 30 minutes, or for up to 2 hours. Meanwhile, toast the pine nuts in a dry frying pan over a medium heat until lightly browned, then set aside.

5. Pile a bed of rocket onto two serving plates, remove the beef slices from the marinade and divide evenly between the plates.

6. Scatter with the pine nuts and shave the Parmesan cheese over, using a vegetable peeler, and serve.

RAPESEED OIL

This is one of the healthiest oils, rich in monounsaturates and omega-3 fats to protect against cancers, heart disease and other ailments.

MAJOR NUTRIENTS PER 15 ML/ 1 TBSP RAPESEED OIL

 130 kcal CALORIES   **15g** TOTAL FAT   **2.6 mg** VITAMIN E

Rapeseed oil had been neglected as a health-giving oil until recently, when more European farmers began producing it as a competitively priced alternative to olive oil. In fact, rapeseed oil in many ways has an even better 'health profile' than its rival does. It has nearly as high a content of monounsaturated fat as olive oil and contains higher amounts of the essential omega-3 fat alpha-linolenic acid than any other oil used in quantity for culinary purposes. Rapeseed oil also has a perfect balance between omega-6 and omega-3 fats and is lower in saturated fat than all the other commonly used oils. It is also a good source of vitamin E.

- Excellent balance of essential fats in line with recommended guidelines.
- Low in saturated fat.
- Good source of the antioxidant vitamin E.
- High in omega-3 fats, which have a variety of health benefits when eaten regularly.

DID YOU KNOW?

Rapeseed oil is an annual plant and a member of the Brassica family. It has bright yellow flowers in summer and turns many fields golden.

PRACTICAL TIPS

Refined rapeseed oil is a good choice for cooking because it doesn't degrade when heated. Cold pressed or extra virgin rapeseed oil is a great choice for salad dressings and drizzling. Its nutty flavour is particularly good drizzled over artichoke hearts or asparagus. It is ideal for mayonnaise because it has a milder flavour than olive oil.

GARLIC & CHILLI DIPPING OIL

This golden flavoured oil will add life and heat to your favourite dipping ingredients –
it is very quick and easy to make and is a great standby to have in the refrigerator.

MAKES ABOUT 225 ML/8 FL OZ • PREP TIME: 15 MINS, PLUS COOLING • COOK TIME: 1½–2 HOURS

PER 225 ML/8 FL OZ:	1989 kcal	225g	16.6g	0g	0g	0g	0g	TRACE
	CALORIES	FAT	SAT FAT	CARBS	SUGAR	FIBRE	PROTEIN	SALT

INGREDIENTS

5 garlic cloves, halved lengthways
2 tbsp deseeded and chopped jalapeño chilli
1 tsp dried oregano
225 ml/8 fl oz rapeseed oil

1. Preheat the oven to 150°C/300°F/Gas Mark 2. Combine the garlic, chilli and oregano with the oil in an ovenproof glass measuring jug.

2. Place on a glass pie plate in the centre of the oven and heat for 1½–2 hours. The temperature of the oil should reach 120°C/250°F.

3. Using thick oven gloves, carefully remove the jug from the oven, leave to cool, then strain through muslin into a clean jar. Store in an airtight container in the refrigerator for up to 1 month. You can also leave the garlic and chilli pieces in the oil and strain before using.

FLAXSEED OIL

Flaxseed oil is one of the best plant sources of anti-inflammatory omega-3 oils. These balance with the omega-6 oil content to create a superior anti-ageing ingredient.

MAJOR NUTRIENTS PER 15 ML/1 TBSP FLAXSEED OIL

132 kcal	0.43g	4.63g	11.58g	0.5g	1.19g	0.05 mg	0.04 mg	0.64 mg	0.21 mg	0.06 mg	0.05 mg
CALORIES	TOTAL FAT	MONO UN-SATURATED FAT	CARBS	FIBRE	PROTEIN	VITAMIN B1	VITAMIN B2	VITAMIN B3	VITAMIN B5	VITAMIN B6	VITAMIN C

7995 mg	1905 mg	3029 mg	9.9 mg	27.6 mcg	0.74 mg	31.5 mcg	24 mg	0.9 mg	69 mg	2.7 mcg	0.75 mg
OMEGA-3 OILS	OMEGA-6 OILS	OMEGA-9 OILS	CALCIUM	FOLATE	IRON	LUTEIN/ ZEAXANTHIN	MAGNESIUM	MANGANESE	POTASSIUM	SELENIUM	ZINC

Most modern diets are much higher in omega-6 oils than omega-3. This can cause health problems and the dry skin and poor concentration associated with omega-3 oil deficiency. The omega oil ratio in flaxseed oil provides the optimum support for heart, joint and brain function. Flaxseed oil is also rich in lignans, renowned for their antioxidant, antiviral, antibacterial and anti-cancer actions. Lignans help regulate sex hormones and combat premenstrual syndrome, menopausal symptoms, prostate problems and hormone-sensitive cancers such as breast and prostate. Flaxseeds contain by far the highest amount of these valuable substances – ten times more than any other seed, grain or vegetable.

- Important rejuvenating food for people who do not get their essential omega-3 oils from oily fish.
- Excellent gut-healing action that stops harmful elements entering the bloodstream and prevents inflammatory food intolerances.
- High in heart-revitalizing oleic acid (omega-9 oil), the same as is found in olive oil.

DID YOU KNOW?

Also known as linseed oil, flaxseed oil hardens on exposure to air. This is why it is used to mix oil paints and to create a hard, glossy surface.

PRACTICAL TIPS

Flaxseed oil is easily damaged by heat, light and oxygen. To preserve its benefits, it needs to be stored in dark glass bottles and cannot be used for any type of cooking. It makes a healthy base for salad dressings, and can also be added to juices or smoothies, slowing the release of sugars into the bloodstream.

RUBY COUSCOUS SALAD WITH GRIDDLED CHICKEN

This salad looks good and does you good too! The beetroot turns everything a deep vibrant red and the whole plate glistens, jewel-like, with the pomegranate seeds.

SERVES 4 • PREP TIME: 10–15 MINS • COOK TIME: 20–30 MINS

PER SERVING:

517 kcal	18.6g	2.4g	53.8g	16g	8.1g	36.2g	0.2g
CALORIES	FAT	SAT FAT	CARBS	SUGAR	FIBRE	PROTEIN	SALT

INGREDIENTS

175 g/6 oz giant wholewheat couscous
175 g/6 oz cooked beetroot in natural juices(drained weight), diced
1 small red onion, finely chopped
125 g/4½ oz cherry tomatoes, halved
1 pomegranate, halved, seeds reserved
juice of 2 lemons
2 tbsp flaxseed oil
2 tbsp olive oil
4 tsp tomato purée
2 tbsp roughly chopped fresh mint
1 tsp black peppercorns, roughly crushed
500 g/1 lb 2 oz chicken breast mini fillets, sliced
salt and pepper (optional)

1. Bring a saucepan of water to the boil. Add the couscous, bring back to the boil, then simmer for 6–8 minutes, or until just tender. Drain through a sieve, rinse with cold water, then transfer to a salad bowl. Add the beetroot, onion, tomatoes and pomegranate seeds.

2. To make the dressing, put the juice of 1 lemon, the flaxseed oil, half the olive oil and half the tomato purée into a screwtop jar, season to taste with salt and pepper, if using, screw on the lid and shake well. Drizzle over the salad, then sprinkle over the chopped mint and toss together.

3. Put the remaining lemon juice, olive oil and tomato purée and the crushed peppercorns in a clean polythene bag, twist and shake well. Add the chicken, seal the bag, then shake until the chicken is evenly coated.

4. Preheat a ridged griddle pan over a high heat. Cook the chicken (in batches if necessary) in the hot pan for 10 minutes, turning once or twice, until cooked through. Cut through the middle of a slice to check that the meat is no longer pink and that any juices run clear and are piping hot. Arrange over the salad and serve.

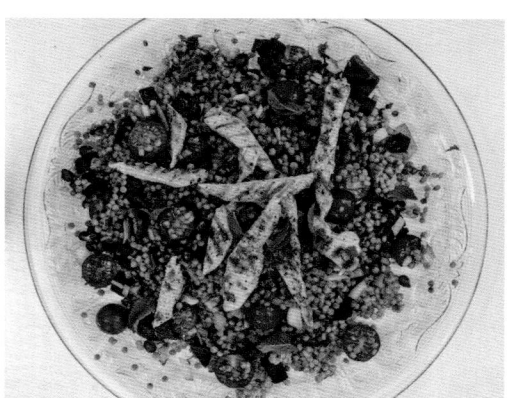

GLOSSARY

ALLERGIES Immune system reactions that set off inflammation and can be triggered by foods or environmental factors.

ALPHA-LINOLENIC ACID A polyunsaturated fat; one of the omega-3 group of essential fats which we need to consume for health as our bodies can't manufacture it. Can be converted into EPA and DHA within the body.

AMINO ACIDS The 'building blocks' of protein contained in many foods in varying combinations and amounts. Only nine are indispensable (essential) for adults and when a food contains all nine in good proportion that food is often described as a 'complete protein'.

ANTHOCYANIN An antioxidant – see bioflavonoids.

ANTI-INFLAMMATORY DIET Inflammation is the body's natural immune reaction to stress and illness and is thought to be linked to health problems such as heart disease and arthritis. An anti-inflammatory diet is said to reduce inflammation.

ANTIOXIDANT Antioxidants are phytochemicals, vitamins and other nutrients that protect our cells from damage and ageing caused by free radicals. Antioxidants should be consumed in foods rather than taken as dietary supplements.

'BAD' LDL CHOLESTEROL Low density lipoproteins transport cholesterol from the liver to the heart. If LDL is higher than 'good' HDL cholesterol then the risk of heart disease increases.

BIOFLAVONOID/FLAVONOID A group of several thousand antioxidant compounds found in fruits, vegetables and other plant foods, and including rutin, anthocyanins, catechins and quercetin.

CARBOHYDRATE Carbohydrate can be in the form of sugars, starches or fibre and is usually the main source of energy in the human diet. It is present in most foods and in largest quantity in cereals, root vegetables, beans, fruits, vegetables as well as in milk and most dairy produce.

CAROTENES Yellow, red or orange pigments found in foods such as carrots with several health benefits including protection from cancers. Carotenes include alpha and beta, lutein, lycopene, zeaxanthin, cryptozanthin and betacryptoxanthin – these are some of the most researched and beneficial.

CHOLESTEROL A fatty substance present in many foods of animal origin and manufactured in humans in the liver, it is essential in the body but under certain circumstances can also encourage the development of coronary artery disease. See HDL and 'Bad' LDL.

CIRCULATION The system by which blood is pumped by the heart around the body, delivering oxygen and nutrients to all cells.

DETOXIFICATION The process in the liver and all individual cells by which harmful and ageing toxins are broken down and eliminated.

DHA FATS Docosahexaenoic acid – a 'long chain' omega-3 fatty acid found only in fish, particularly oily fish, with several health benefits.

DIGESTION The process by which we break down, absorb and assimilate the food we eat to derive the nutrients we need.

EPA FATS Eicosapentaenoic acid – a 'long chain' omega-3 fatty acid found only in fish, particularly oily fish, with several health benefits.

ENZYMES Proteins which act as catalysts to bring about biochemical reactions. The human body contains thousands of different enzymes vital for digestion and metabolism of food, for example.

ESSENTIAL FATTY ACIDS/EFAS Essential fats – linoleic acid and alpha-linolenic acid – which must be provided in the diet in balanced and adequate amounts for good health.

FATS One of the major sources of calories in the human diet as well as providing vitamins and some also provide phytochemicals including antioxidants.

FREE RADICALS Highly reactive, unstable atoms or molecules in the body which are a normal by-product of metabolism but are believed, in excess, to be a factor in onset or disease and the ageing process.

GLUCOSINOLATES A group of sulphur-based plant compounds, including indoles and isothiocyanates, found in brassicas such as cabbage and kale, which support immune function and can help prevent cancers.

GLYCAEMIC INDEX A system of ranking carbohydrate foods according to their effect on blood sugar levels.

'GOOD' CHOLESTEROL/HDL High-density lipoproteins that bind to cholesterol and carry it through the blood to help keep arteries clear and protect against cardiovascular disease.

HOMOCYSTEINE An amino acid which can build up in the blood. High levels are a strong risk factor for cardio-vascular disease.

HYPOALLERGENIC Relating to food, an item unlikely to cause an allergic reaction.

IMMUNE SYSTEM Body system responsible for protection against bacteria, viruses, disease and other potentially harmful pathogens.

INDOLES see Glucosinolates.

INSOLUBLE FIBRE The indigestible portion of plant foods which moves all the way through the digestive system, absorbing water, increasing stool bulk and helping satiety. It can help prevent disorders of the bowel.

INSULIN A hormone produced by the pancreas which regulates blood sugar levels. In insulin resistance, the insulin doesn't work effectively and can lead to type 2 diabetes.

INTOLERANCES Food intolerances are non-allergic food hypersensitivity. They are an adverse reaction to a food (or component of food) or drink that produces unwanted symptoms in the body without being an allergy.

LIGNAN One of a range of plant chemicals with oestrogen-like effects, thought to be of benefit in hormone-related health issues including breast cancer, prostate cancer, menopause symptoms and heart disease. Other oestrogenic plant chemicals include coumestrol and daidzein.

L-TYROSINE An amino acid which can help improve brain function and energy levels and is found in a variety of high-protein foods.

METABOLISM The chemical reactions that occur in the body to maintain life, during which food and drink are broken down and their nutrients used for body repair, maintenance and energy.

MINERALS Natural inorganic chemicals around 20 of which are vital for the body's health and which cannot be made in the body so are needed via food and drink.

MONOUNSATURATED FAT A type of fat found in most foods but in high quantities in a few such as olive oil, avocados and some nuts which has a beneficial effect on cholesterol levels, cardio-vascular disease and other health problems.

OLEIC ACID A type of omega-9 monounsaturated fat found in high amounts in olive oil, avocado and rapeseed oil for example. Thought to be helpful in diabetes and insulin resistance as it can improve blood glucose levels, insulin sensitivity and blood circulation.

OMEGA-3 Polyunsaturated fats that help prevent and minimise inflammation and disease; necessary for strong immune and heart function.

OMEGA-6 Polyunsaturated fats found in a wide variety of plant foods, the most common of which is linoleic acid, one of the essential fatty acids.

OMEGA-9 A group of monounsaturated fats, of which oleic acid is the most common.

ORAC Stands for Oxygen Radical Absorbance Capacity and is an international scale of measurement of antioxidant capacity of foods.

PLANT COMPOUNDS Natural chemicals or compounds found in plants thought to be largely responsible for the health protective effects plants offer when consumed.

PHYTOCHEMICALS/PHYTONUTRIENTS see plant compounds

PHYTOSTEROLS A group of plant compounds, including beta-sitosterol, that have a cholesterol-lowering effect when eaten regularly.

POLYPHENOL/PHENOLS/PHENOLIC COMPOUNDS A large category of anti-oxidant plant compounds, including anthocyanins, ellagic acid, resveratrol and tannins, strongly linked with the prevention of heart disease.

POLYUNSATURATED FAT Type of fat high in omega-6 and which also includes the omega-3 fatty acids.

PREBIOTICS Types of fibre, including inulin, oligofructose and oligosaccharides, found in plant foods, that act as food for beneficial bacteria (probiotics) in the intestines.

PROBIOTICS Beneficial bacteria, such as lactobacilli and bifidobacteria, which are present in the digestive system and help to support digestion, immunity and detoxification, as well as helping to reduce allergies, intolerances and inflammation.

PROTEIN A macronutrient that the body needs in order to make and maintain lean tissue (muscle) and for a variety of other functions. See also amino acids.

SAPONINS Plant compounds found for example in oats, soya beans and yams, with a unique foaming ability that can help prevent colon cancer and can block the body's absorption of cholesterol.

SATURATED FAT Fats that are found in largest quantities in foods of animal origin and remain solid at room temperature. High consumption has long been associated with increased risk of heart disease and other health problems but further research needs to be done. One type of saturated fat – lauric acid, found mainly in coconuts, is thought to have positive health benefits, being easy to digest and of possible help in cholesterol-lowering and weight loss.

SOLUBLE FIBRE Various types of soluble fibre include pectin, oligosaccharides and beta-glucans which not only have a beneficial effect on digestive health but can also help reduce cholesterol as well as controlling blood sugar levels by slowing sugar absorption.

STEROLS see phytosterols

SULPHIDES Antioxidant and immune-stimulating plant compounds found for example in onions, garlic and leeks.

SULPHORAPHANE Found in cruciferous vegetables such as cauliflower, broccoli and Brussels sprouts, this compound, a member of the glucosinolate family, has anti-cancer and anti-diabetic properties.

TRYPTOPHAN An amino acid that enables relaxation and improves mood and sleep by promoting the secretion of the brain chemical serotonin.

VITAMIN A group of organic substances essential to metabolism in small quantities and found in minute amounts in food. A deficiency can lead to a variety of health problems and diseases.

INDEX

PEPPERS 114
Mexican Beef & Bean Bowl 215
Stuffed Peppers with Chickpeas & Bulgar Wheat 115

PINE NUTS 242
Grilled Sardines Stuffed with Feta & Pine Nuts 167
Roasted Broccoli with Pine Nuts & Parmesan 89
Spiced Cod with Harissa & Pine Nut Crust 243

PINEAPPLES 36
Pineapple & Mint Iced Tea 37

PISTACHIO NUTS 234
Green Tea Fruit Salad 295
Pistachio Ice Cream 235
Pistachio-crusted Lamb Chops 149
Superfood Chocolate Bark 303
Watermelon Sundaes 15

PLUMS 58
Rice Pudding with Cinnamon-poached Plums 59

POMEGRANATES 62
Gingered Carrot & Pomegranate Salad 63
Watermelon Sundaes 15

PORK 152
Layered Pork & Spiced Sauerkraut Soup 123
Pork Fillet with Roasted Rhubarb 49
Pork-stuffed Cabbage Leaves 153

POT BARLEY 196
Hearty Barley Vegetable Soup 197

POTATOES 138
New Potatoes with Garlic & Chilli Butter 139

PRUNES 66
Compote of Dried Fruits 67

PUMPKIN 108
Pumpkin, Feta & Aduki Bean Parcels 109

PUMPKIN SEEDS 246
Butternut Wedges with Sage & Pumpkin Seeds 269
Crunchy Greek Yogurt Melon Pots 33
Greek-style Yogurt with Orange Zest & Seeds 247

PURPLE SPROUTING BROCCOLI 124
Purple Sprouting Broccoli Salad 125

QUAIL EGGS 188
Tuna & Asparagus Salad with Quail Eggs 189

QUINOA 192
Coconut Quinoa Bowl 309
Red Cabbage, Turkey & Quinoa Pilaf 145
Smashed Avocado & Quinoa Wrap 193
Tuna & Asparagus Salad with Quail Eggs 189

RADICCHIO 130
Radicchio Caesar Salad 131

RADISHES 134
Pan-cooked Tuna with Radish Relish 135

RAPESEED OIL 312
Garlic & Chilli Dipping Oil 313

RASPBERRIES 28
Açai Power Bowl 9
Buckwheat Breakfast Bowl 203
Coconut Quinoa Bowl 309
Raspberry & Mascarpone Ice Cream 29
Roasted Fruit Crumble 41

RED CABBAGE 74
Pak Choi with Red Onions & Cashew Nuts 121
Purple Sprouting Broccoli Salad 125
Red Cabbage, Turkey & Quinoa Pilaf 145
Turkey Goujons with Red Cabbage & Kale Slaw 75

RHUBARB 48
Pork Fillet with Roasted Rhubarb 49

ROCKET 140
Cool Watermelon, Goat's Cheese & Rocket Salad 185
Rocket Fuel Soup 141

ROSEMARY 260
Rosemary, Sea Salt & Sesame Popcorn 261

RYE 194
Pancakes with Creamy Citrus Filling 195

SAGE 268
Butternut Wedges with Sage & Pumpkin Seeds 269

SALMON 154
Grilled Salmon with Citrus Salsa 155
Honey Salmon with Couscous 297
Mixed Seafood Chowder 173
Pesto Salmon with Spring Veg 99
Salmon Parcels with Millet & Spinach 205
Smoked Salmon & Pink Grapefruit Salad 43
Sushi Roll Bowl 117

SARDINES 166
Grilled Sardines Stuffed with Feta & Pine Nuts 167

SAUERKRAUT 122
Layered Pork & Spiced Sauerkraut Soup 123

SAVOY CABBAGE 136
Grape & Cabbage Booster 137
Pork-stuffed Cabbage Leaves 153

SCALLOPS 170
Chilli Orange Noodles with Seared Scallops 171

SEAWEED 116
Sushi Roll Bowl 117

SESAME SEEDS 248
Ginger & Sesame Trout with Braised Pak Choi 169
Rosemary, Sea Salt & Sesame Popcorn 261
Steak & Sesame Stir-fry 249

SOYA BEANS 212
Green Bean Protein Burst 213
Tuna with Pak Choi & Soba Noodles 159

SPELT 206
Spelt & Carrot Salad 207

SPINACH 100
Beetroot, Lobster & Spinach Risotto 179
Prawns with Spinach 101
Salmon Parcels with Millet & Spinach 205
Spinach & Nutmeg Baked Eggs 283

SQUASH 126
Butternut Wedges with Sage & Pumpkin Seeds 269
Squash, Kale & Farro Stew 127

STRAWBERRIES 12
Berry & Brazil Nut Smoothie 239
Layered Avocado & Strawberry Soup 13
Strawberry & Passion Fruit Yogurts 45

SUNFLOWER SEEDS 250
Açai Power Bowl 9
Courgette Spaghetti 251
Crunchy Greek Yogurt Melon Pots 33

SWEET POTATOES 76
Smoky Paprika Sweet Potato Chips 77
Sweet Roots Bowl 79

TAHINI 254
Banana Flatbread Bites with Tahini & Date Syrup 255
Sweet Roots Bowl 79

THYME 264
Roast Figs with Honey & Thyme 265

TOFU 220
Green Bean Protein Burst 213
Tofu Parcels 221

TOMATOES 80
Orzo with Mint & Fresh Tomatoes 259
Slow-cooked Tomato Pasta Sauce 81
Stuffed Tomatoes 163
Vegetable Cocido 219

TROUT 168
Ginger & Sesame Trout with Braised Pak Choi 169

TUNA 158
Pan-cooked Tuna with Radish Relish 135
Sushi Roll Bowl 117
Tuna & Asparagus Salad with Quail Eggs 189
Tuna with Pak Choi & Soba Noodles 159

TURKEY 144
Paprika Turkey Strips 285
Red Cabbage, Turkey & Quinoa Pilaf 145
Turkey with Coriander Pesto & Soba Noodles 267
Turkey Goujons with Red Cabbage & Kale Slaw 75
Turkey Miso Soup 209

TURMERIC 288
Roast Cauliflower, Kale & Chickpea Bowl 289

WALNUTS 224
Carrot Cake Muffins 95
Chickpea Walnut Patties 225
Coconut Quinoa Bowl 309
Walnut & Linseed Crackers 253

WASABI 306
Rainbow Salad with Wasabi Dressing 307

WATERCRESS 128
Fig, Goat's Cheese & Watercress Salad 129

WATERMELON 14
Cool Watermelon, Goat's Cheese & Rocket Salad 185
Crunchy Greek Yogurt Melon Pots 33
Green Tea Fruit Salad 295
Layered Powerbowl Smoothie 31
Watermelon Sundaes 15

YOGURT 180
Crunchy Greek Yogurt Melon Pots 33
Greek-style Yogurt with Orange Zest & Seeds 247
Healthy Caesar Dressing 181
Strawberry & Passion Fruit Yogurts 45